D1571439

BOAT PLANS

AT

MYSTIC SEAPORT

Anne and Maynard Bray

BOAT PLANS

AT
MYSTIC SEAPORT

Anne and Maynard Bray

MYSTIC SEAPORT
MYSTIC, CONNECICUT

Dedicated

to the memory of

Joel White

1930 – 1997

———————

Mystic Seaport, Mystic, CT 06355-0990
© 2000 by Mystic Seaport Museum, Inc.
All rights reserved
First edition

Printed in the United States of America

Cataloging in Publication data:

Bray, Anne.
Boat plans at Mystic Seaport / Anne and Maynard Bray. —
Mystic, Conn. : Mystic Seaport, c2000.
p. : ill., plans, ports. ; cm.

1. G. W. Blunt White Library. Ships Plans Division - Catalogs.
2. Naval architecture - Designs and plans - Catalogs. I. Bray,
Maynard.

VM297.8.B7

ISBN 0-913372-86-2

Designed by Sherry Streeter
Illustrations by Michael Gellatly

FOREWORD

Yacht design as a profession began with half-hull models carved from wood, from which the full-sized yacht would be scaled up by the builder. The last great American designer to create his yachts exclusively by carving half-hulls was Nathanael G. Herreshoff (1848-1938), the Wizard of Bristol. The profession then turned to faired lines drawn by the designer with pencil on paper, for subsequent tracing in ink on linen (and replication by blueprint). The first important American designer to create yachts exclusively from drawn lines was A. Cary Smith (1837-1911). Such are the ironies of history that Herreshoff with his traditional methods of shaping hulls proved to be the greater innovator, while his near contemporary Archie Smith is best remembered today as a gifted marine painter of traditional gaff-rigged yachts.

Meanwhile, the computer has rendered hand-drawn plans on paper as quaintly obsolete as carved pine half-hulls ever were. Not one yacht designer in one hundred will develop a set of lines with splines and ducks in Y2K. As for the task of tracing lines in India ink on linen, who has the time or skill, who has the linen?

And so, generation after generation, the conflicting imperatives of tradition and innovation do their work. In the process yacht design and yacht designing evolve.

N. G. Herreshoff's protégé W. Starling Burgess and Burgess's protégé L. Francis Herreshoff were two of the outstanding yacht designers of the twentieth century. In the work of both men the opposing forces of old and new express themselves in dazzling ways. Winthrop L. Warner, Frederick Geiger, and Louis Kromholz were perhaps less brilliant in their work. But what they lacked in genius, they amply made up for in balance and integrity. You couldn't ask for a better all-around cruising sailboat than Warner's famous Cadet Class sloop or his trio of sisters *Alarm*, *Astral*, and *Mary Loring*. Or a more perfect round-bottomed sport fisherman than Fred Geiger's elegant *Paranda* of 1951, a particular favorite of mine for more than forty-five years. Or a more appealing motorsailer than Louis Kromholz's *Yarra*, which will never go out of style or date. As for Albert Condon, a fine designer of fishing vessels who occasionally turned his hand to yachts, his Eastern-rigged dragger *Roann*, now on permanent exhibit at Mystic Seaport, is a triumph of functional design that has stood the test of time.

Thanks in good part to the efforts and vision of Maynard Bray, a dominant figure in the wooden boat revival and America's leading contemporary historian of yacht design, the work of these six twentieth-century masters of the drawn line and of others, as well, is now part of Mystic Seaport's unrivalled collection of ship's plans. And thanks to Maynard and his wife, Anne, we now have, in *Boat Plans at Mystic Seaport*, a readable, authoritative, and absolutely fascinating guide to some of the treasures that make up Mystic's Ships Plans Division.

One day soon, by computer and modem, you will be able to browse these treasures at will. As for me, I don't own a computer. And as long as books keep being published of the quality of Maynard and Anne Bray's *Boat Plans at Mystic Seaport*, I never will.

—*Llewellyn Howland III*

AUTHORS' INTRODUCTION

The information era in which we currently find ourselves allows access and understanding never before possible, and is creating exciting new possibilities for the vast and intriguing collections held by museums and libraries. Whereas institutional holdings have long been organized by means of index cards with two or three laboriously prepared and sorted cross-indexes, computers now make it fast and easy for outsiders to browse, sort, and print lists in response to wide-ranging queries. Virtually at the touch of a button you can have before you whatever information you seek, be it a search for an individual item or a custom-tailored summary of many—provided the computer you're asking has been fed consistent and reliable raw data beforehand.

In preparing this catalog, we have worked to publish succinct lists of seven of the many collections of boat, yacht, and vessel drawings contained in Mystic Seaport's "Ships Plans Division." So organized, one can obtain both an overview of what has been cataloged and, with little more than a glance, can locate the particular design being sought. In general, Mystic Seaport groups plans by the designer who drew them, although some collections (mostly ones consisting of copies such as blueprints amassed by non-designers) get grouped and named after the person who donated them. For a more specific overview on how things are organized, we refer you to the *Guide to the Ships Plans Collection at Mystic Seaport Museum* prepared by the collection manager, Ellen C. Stone.

By contrast, our catalog's scope is narrower and deeper. Specific designs and the resulting watercraft built from them are listed and sorted by type and by overall length and beam—characteristics that aren't likely ever to change. Thus, if you were searching for a sailboat of, say, 28' that you knew had been designed by Winthrop Warner, you'd be able to locate it and find its catalog number, after which you could order a set of plans or, during a visit to the Museum, arrange to view the original drawings.

In the not-too-distant future, you'll be able to call up the images themselves at home on your own personal computer, just as you're able to do now for paintings in the Louvre or objects in the National Air and Space Museum. For now, however, while this colossal transition from index cards and big storage drawers to electronic sorting and digital imaging takes place, reasonably lucid descriptions and organized listings such as are contained herein will provide access that, while not ultimate and forever, is nevertheless a resource never before possible. (For now, the most convenient way to view a drawing whose description you find compelling is by visiting Mystic and looking at the microfilm that has been made of each drawing herein listed.)

The uses for drawings of watercraft can, and we feel should, vary widely, ranging from attractive wall hangings to their original application in building boats. Although the museum cares not about their end use, a few of Francis Herreshoff's designs being the single exception, and sells them on a fixed price-per-sheet basis, it cannot assure that information shown on them is complete or reliable or that, if used for building, the finished boat will perform as hoped. On each purchased copy of each drawing, there's a disclaimer to this effect.

A word about the conventions used in the plan lists that follow: "Length" is the overall length of the hull and doesn't include appendages such as bowsprits and overhanging booms. "Beam" is the width outside the hull at its widest point. "Date" is generally the year the design was created, although for boats known to have been built, "date" may mean the year of the launching. "Design No.," if listed, is the number assigned by the designer. "Cat. No." is the unique number assigned by Mystic Seaport at the time the plans were cataloged, and is the proper number to use for inquiries and for ordering copies.

Although this catalog required considerable work to produce, we the authors benefited greatly from the works of others. Mystic Seaport president and director Revell Carr sanctioned the idea of this catalog which, in effect, brought us the assistance of other museum staff members when needed. Ben Fuller, Curator at the start of Mystic Seaport's electronic cataloging endeavors, and under whose direction the Ships Plans Division fell, gave the project his enthusiastic support.

The important and recently-donated Warner and Geiger plan collections—two that we felt should definitely be included—were cataloged by volunteers recruited by Trustee Bill Ames and coordinated by us. To this wonderful group we say thanks, and to the Ships Plans staff whose normal routine this ambitious project disrupted, we sincerely apologize. Helping out at some very critical points along the way were two friends and colleagues in boatbuilding and publishing, Jon Wilson

and the late Joel White, who shared our interest in enhancing access to Mystic Seaport's Ships Plans drawings. We deeply appreciate the work of Sherry Streeter, who designed this book; Jane Crosen, who did the editing; and Blythe Heepe, who dealt with arranging text on the pages. We also are very grateful indeed to Orin Edson and Joel White for timely and generous financial support.

Anne & Maynard Bray
Brooklin, Maine
Winter, 1998

ACCESS TO BOAT PLANS

The Ships Plans Division of the G.W. Blunt White Library is one of the special library collections that are part of the American Maritime Education and Research Center, located across the street from the Seamen's Inne restaurant. The Ships Plans office is open weekdays, 9:00 A.M. to 5:00 P.M., and closed on Mystic Seaport staff holidays. Research inquiries may be made by phone (860) 572-5360, by mail, e-mail, or personal visit.

Ready reference queries are answered at no charge. Research fees may be assessed for inquiries that require a written response, with additional charges for complex research and inquiries from commercial clients. Researchers are encouraged to visit and conduct their own research at no charge. It is suggested that you call ahead so that staff may prepare in advance for your visit.

OBTAINING COPIES
Copies of most plans can be purchased. Some are restricted, however, as to use. Full-scale blueline prints are the method of reproduction, and microfilm reader-printer copies are available for those images preserved on film. Prices for copies vary depending upon a number of factors, including production charges and postage. We suggest that you inquire before placing an order.

Copies obtained from the Ships Plans Division are provided for personal use only. Permission from our Museum Rights and Reproductions office in contract form is required for any project involving copying, distribution, or publication of plans. Details

of project proposals should be submitted in writing. Any publication-quality prints will be provided by Mystic Seaport's Photographic Division. Use fees are levied, above and beyond the cost of production, at the completion of any project or publication. Please note that all reproduction fees go into a special museum fund for the preservation of existing collections and acquisition of new collections.

Specially selected plans of watercraft and maritime objects now or formerly owned by the museum appear on a printed list available at no cost entitled "The Guide to Plans for Watercraft in the Collection of Mystic Seaport Museum, Inc." This list also appears on the Ships Plans web page, found within the museum's web site. Visit the museum's web site at www.mysticseaport.org.

Division of Ships Plans
G.W. Blunt White Library
Mystic Seaport
75 Greenmanville Avenue
P.O. Box 6000
Mystic, CT 06355-0990
Phone: (860) 572-5360
e-mail: shipsplans@mysticseaport.org

DONATION OF ADDITIONAL PLAN COLLECTIONS
One of Mystic Seaport's very important goals is to continue collecting and preserving plans and drawings of watercraft and maritime-industry subjects. Additional offerings of plans would be greatly appreciated, as would donations in support of their cataloging and preservation.

CONTENTS

BOAT PLANS

AT

MYSTIC SEAPORT

Anne and Maynard Bray

W. STARLING BURGESS
1878–1947

Possessed of a mind for math and engineering, an eye for things beautiful, and an ear for poetry, William Starling Burgess was born to wealth and social prominence, but orphaned with only modest means at the age of 12. He inherited his passion for boats and the sea from his father, Edward, who in the eight years before his untimely death in 1891 had risen from sudden financial ruin to a stunningly successful career in yacht design. The elder Burgess was creator of three *America*'s Cup defenders, *Puritan*, *Mayflower*, and *Volunteer*, in 1885, 1886, 1887, and many other celebrated yachts, both sail and steam.

Edward Burgess's example was so powerful that Starling felt compelled to leave Harvard College before graduation in 1901 to pursue his own career in yacht design. At age 22, W. Starling Burgess (WSB) set up shop as a yacht designer in Boston. Two years later in 1903, he joined forces with MIT and Herreshoff Mfg. Co. alumnus A.A. Packard—an alliance that lasted until about 1908. Packard had special expertise in the structural aspects of yacht design, and the Burgess & Packard firm (later renamed W. Starling Burgess Co., Ltd.) went on to build boats (sailing racer/cruisers, gasoline-powered autoboats, and sailing canoes, among others), as well as design them. WSB's great natural talent was further

honed in his early years by close ties with N.G. Herreshoff, George Lawley, and Edward Burgess's business successor, Arthur Binney. WSB claimed to have designed 223 yachts and commercial vessels during his first decade of practice (1901–11), including "small steamers, motoryachts, trading and fishing schooners, racing yachts, cruisers, and racing launches; also five one-design classes."

Matters of the heart (love and poetry) and an eventful and demanding seven-year foray into the aviation business diverted WSB's attention from yacht designing until after World War I when, in 1919, he settled in Provincetown, Massachusetts, to draw boats once again, this time with the help of Frank C. Paine and L. Francis Herreshoff, both of an age and some dozen years WSB's juniors.

In 1921, the operation moved to Boston and became Burgess & Paine; in 1923, when A. Loring Swasey joined the fold, Burgess, Swasey, and Paine was formed. In 1925, WSB's third marriage failed and he relocated to New York and set up yet another design office with yacht broker Jasper Morgan (and later Linton Rigg). Although the business changed names with each new alliance— from Burgess & Morgan, to Burgess, Rigg, & Morgan, to Burgess & Donaldson, to W. Starling Burgess, Ltd.—the designs produced in New York from about 1926 to 1935 all had the clear mark of WSB's genius. It is from this period that the bulk of Mystic Seaport's Burgess & Donaldson collection comes. It was also during these New York-based years that WSB designed *Enterprise* in 1930 and *Rainbow* in 1934 for the successful defense of the *America*'s Cup.

In 1933–34, WSB joined forces with Buckminster Fuller to design and produce the streamlined, three-wheeled Dymaxion automobile, but these were Depression years and the endeavor folded after only three of these revolutionary vehicles were built. WSB came away bankrupt but with a new wife (his fourth), with whom he moved to Wiscasset, Maine. There he took up a joint venture with Alcoa and Bath Iron Works having to do with aluminum-hulled, high-speed torpedo boats and destroyers for the U.S. Navy. Within a couple of years, WSB (along with co-designers Sparkman & Stephens) took on the task of designing his third *America*'s Cup defender, *Ranger*. That Bath Iron Works (the location of WSB's office) was chosen as builder seemed a natural outcome.

In Bath/Wiscasset, and later in New York and Washington, D.C., WSB had various associations with Alcoa, Bath Iron Works, and the U.S. Navy involving the use of aluminum for hull construction, the manufacture of special high-strength yacht hardware, and a wide variety of naval weaponry and anti-submarine devices. This continued throughout the war and right up until his death in 1947. Yacht designing became more of an avocation during those final years, often carried out vicariously through his protégé and fifth wife, Marjorie, who, with WSB's tutoring, became skilled at drafting and design.

THE BURGESS & DONALDSON COLLECTION

The drawings in this collection number about 905 and consist mostly of inked originals, some of which are truly works of art for their draftsmanship alone.* For the most part, the work spans the decade from 1926 to 1935 when Burgess was based in New York, at the height of his career when his office was especially prolific. Most designs are for sailing yachts: Atlantic-class sloops, Eight-Meters, 10-Meters, 12-Meters, R-boats, a Q-boat, M-boats, and J-boats are included. There are complete drawings for two of the three Burgess-designed *America*'s Cup defenders, *Enterprise* and *Rainbow*. (Drawings for the third, *Ranger*, are at Maine Maritime Museum.) Several schooners are here, including the famous and beautiful staysail schooner *Niña*. Power craft are in far shorter supply, with fewer than a half-dozen complete designs. Likewise, there is only scanty information on five small craft. Various details (having to do with existing boats, etc.) are part of this collection as well and are itemized on the following pages.

Besides the Burgess creations, one should be aware of the original inked masterpieces by Henry Gruber, surely one of the greatest draftsmen of all time, which exist within this collection under the Megargle & Gruber banner.

The Burgess & Donaldson Collection of drawings was donated to Mystic Seaport in 1952 by Boyd Donaldson, who in the early 1930s was a WSB partner in the New York firm of Burgess & Donaldson.

It is a sad fact that W. Starling Burgess's early drawings done before 1917 were wiped out in a Marblehead fire of that year. Some of his subsequent work from Provincetown and Boston days exists as part of the Frank C. Paine collection at the Hart Nautical Collections at MIT. Numerous Burgess designs have also been published in magazines such as *The Rudder*, *Yachting*, and *Forest and Stream* from 1901 when Burgess began designing up to 1944—three years prior to his death. A list of these references is available from *WoodenBoat* magazine's research library.

Burgess's later work, much of which consists of military devices in blueprint form, but which includes as well the Yankee One-Design and Small Point One-Design classes, is here at Mystic Seaport as part of the Burgess-Wolff collection. Besides the drawings, there are models, technical data, calculations, scrapbooks, extensive correspondence, and photographs in other of the museum's collections relating to WSB's work.

---

* Never holding to convention just for the sake of it, Burgess's drawings show a refreshing freedom of expression. Some boats are drawn with their bows facing west (that is, toward the left-hand side of the paper), while others point in the more usual easterly direction. There seems to be no set pattern. The Burgess drawings are larger than those of most designers, some of them being more than 5' in length, and the inked lines are more delicate—especially on lines plans—making them potentially more accurate.

THE BURGESS & DONALDSON PLANS

SMALL CRAFT

LOA	Beam	Description	Designer	Date	Plan Codes	Cat. No.
11'0"	4'8"	Round-bottomed sailing dinghy	W. Starling Burgess	n.d.	L	11.26
13'10"	6'2"	Brutal Beast-class V-bottomed sailing dinghy	W. Starling Burgess	1920	L S A	11.21
15'0"		Centerboard sailing dinghy; alt. lines	Burgess & Packard	1907	L	11.49
16'0"	2'6"	Sliding-seat sailing canoe; cat-ketch rig	Burgess, Rigg & Morgan	1927	LP	11.24
17'4"	6'0"	Double-cockpit launch; round bottom w/chine	Burgess, Rigg, & Morgan	1927	LOCP	11.34

SAILING YACHTS

LOA	Beam	Description	Designer	Date	Plan Codes	Cat. No.
22'0"	7'1"	Flush-decked cruising sloop (*Dormouse* type)	Burgess & Donaldson	1933	LOSA	11.60
23'0"	7'0"	Flush-decked cruising sloop *Dormouse*	Burgess & Donaldson	1932	LCSADr	11.60
24'0"	9'0"	Flush-decked cruising sloop	Burgess & Morgan	1928	LSDR	11.62
30'0"	6'0"	Atlantic-class one-design sloop	W. Starling Burgess	1928	LOCSADhDr	11.39
32'0"	5'0"	22-Square-Meter sloop (Skerry cruiser)	Burgess & Morgan	1929	LOCSDr	11.61
32'0"	7'0"	Keel/centerboard sloop with cabin	Burgess & Morgan	1929	LOSA	11.40
32'0"	7'0"	Keel/centerboard decked sloop, open cockpit	Burgess & Morgan	1929	SA	11.74
35'0"	8'7"	Cruising cutter (*Barnswallow* type)	Burgess & Donaldson	1932	LSA	11.103
35'0"	10'0"	Cruising sloop	Burgess & Donaldson	1931	LCSA	11.59
36'0"	6'0"	Six-Meter-class sloop	Burgess, Rigg, & Morgan	1927	LOCSADr	11.78
36'0"	7'0"	Sonder-class sloop	Burgess & Morgan	1927	LOS	11.66
36'7"	11'7"	Double-ended offshore cruising cutter	Burgess & Donaldson	1935	LOCSADh	11.93
39'0"	10'6"	Shallow-draft keel cruising sloop *Barnswallow*	Burgess & Donaldson	1932	LCSA	11.89
39'4"	9'9"	Cruising ketch	Burgess & Donaldson	1933	L	11.91
39'6"	10'0"	Cruising cutter	Donaldson & Co.	1935	A	11.42
40'0"		Proposed cruising cutter	Burgess & Donaldson	n.d.	S	11.92
40'0"		R-class sloop *Shrew*		1932	S	11.101
40'0"	6'0"	R-class sloop	Burgess & Morgan	1928	LOCSADhDr	11.96
40'0"	6'9"	R-class sloop *Gossoon*		1927	Dh	11.100
40'0"	11'0"	Cruising sloop	W. Starling Burgess	n.d.	A	11.57
40'1"	11'0"	Keel/centerboard cruising yawl *Marjelia*	Burgess, Rigg, & Morgan	1927	LCSA	11.43
40'2"	7'0"	R-class sloop *Robin*	Burgess, Rigg, & Morgan	1928	LOCSADhDr	11.97
41'0"	7'0"	R-class sloop	Burgess, Rigg, & Morgan	1926	LOCSDhDr	11.98
41'0"	9'0"	Cruising sloop or cutter *Tinavire*, alt. cutter rig	Burgess, Rigg, & Morgan	1926	LOCSADr	11.13
42'7"	9'7"	Flush-decked ketch with doghouse	Burgess & Morgan	1928	A	
44'8"	12'0"	Double-ended cruising cutter *Christmas*	Burgess & Morgan	1930	LOS	11.104
45'4"	11'6"	Schooner *Vryling*, with alternate ketch rig	Burgess & Morgan	1929	LS	11.63
46'0"	8'6"	Q-class sloop	Burgess, Rigg, & Morgan	1927	LOCADhDr	11.81
46'0"	11'6"	Cruising sloop *Cinz*	Burgess & Morgan	1929	LOCSADh	11.67
46'1"	11'1"	Cruising yawl	Burgess & Donaldson	1932	LS	11.32
47'0"		Schooner *Landfall*, gaff fore, marconi main	W. Starling Burgess	1930	LCSADhDr	11.28
47'0"	8'11"	Eight-Meter-class one-design (includes tender)	Burgess, Rigg, & Morgan	1927	LOCSADhDr	11.87
47'4"	8'0"	Eight-Meter-class sloop *Invader*	Burgess & Donaldson	1933	SADh	11.88
48'4"	7'2"	Proposed 30' LWL racing/cruising sloop	Burgess & Donaldson	1932	ADh	11.90
48'4"	8'9"	Proposed one-design Q-class sloop	Burgess, Rigg, & Morgan	1926	SA	11.1

PLAN CODES: L=lines; O=offsets; C=construction; S=sail; A=arrangement; P=profile; Dh=hull detail; Dr=rigging detail

50'0"	12'6"	Schooner, w/gaff or marconi mainsail	W. Starling Burgess	1931	LSA	11.7
51'9"	13'6"	Schooner *Cayuse*; alternate rigs, including ketch	Burgess & Morgan	1931	CSADhDr	11.71
52'0"	13'5"	Flush-decked schooner *Ninette*	Burgess & Morgan	1927	OCSADhDr	11.72
53'7"	12'7"	Cruising yawl *Right Royal*	Burgess, Rigg, & Morgan	1927	LOCSA	11.117
54'0"	13'2"	Schooner, alt. rigs w/gaff or marconi mainsail	Burgess & Morgan	1929	CSA	11.37
55'0"	11'0"	Flush-decked cruising cutter	Burgess & Morgan	1928	LOCSA	11.86
55'4"	13'4"	Schooner	Burgess & Donaldson	1931	A	11.55
56'0"	12'10"	Flush-decked cruising ketch	Burgess, Rigg, & Morgan	1927	SA	11.76
58'0"	10'0"	10-Meter-class one-design sloop	Burgess, Rigg, & Morgan	1926	LOCSADhDr	11.106
59'0"	14'10"	Staysail-rigged racing schooner *Niña*	Burgess, Rigg, & Morgan	1928	LOCSADhDr	11.118
60'4"	12'10"	Proposed flush-decked staysail schooner	Burgess & Morgan	1929	SA	11.75
60'6"	14'0"	Staysail schooner, alternate rigs including ketch	Burgess & Donaldson	1934	SADh	11.94
60'9"	13'1"	Flush-decked ketch with doghouse	Burgess, Rigg, & Morgan		SA	11.4
64'0"	13'0"	Flush-decked schooner	Burgess, Rigg, & Morgan	1927	A	11.51
66'1"	12'7"	Flush-decked schooner	Burgess, Rigg, & Morgan	1929	A	11.79
68'0"	12'3"	Flush-decked sloop	W. Starling Burgess	1930	SA	11.54
69'0"	12'0"	Class G flush-decked staysail schooner	Burgess & Morgan	1929	SA	11.38
69'0"	12'0"	12-Meter-class one-design sloop	Burgess, Rigg, & Morgan	1927	LOCSADhDr	11.116
71'0"	10'0"	Flush-decked ketch; alternate schooner rig	Burgess & Morgan	1930	LOCSADhDr	11.83
76'0"	15'3"	Flush-decked ketch with doghouse	Burgess, Rigg, & Morgan	1927	SA	11.6
76'0"	16'0"	Flush-decked schooner; composite construction	Burgess & Morgan	1928	LOCSA	11.85
77'0"	13'0"	Flush-decked schooner	Burgess, Rigg, & Morgan	1927	A	11.52
78'0"	15'10"	Flush-decked schooner; gaff fore, marconi main	Burgess & Morgan	1928	CSA	11.82
80'6"	14'0"	M-class sloop *Prestige*, composite construction	Burgess, Rigg, & Morgan	1927	LOCSADhDr	11.112
80'9"	14'0"	M-class sloop *Valiant*, composite construction	Burgess, Rigg, & Morgan	1927	LOCSADhDr	11.110
81'0"	15'0"	M-class sloop, composite construction	Burgess & Morgan		L	11.108
81'2"	14'7"	M-class sloop *Simba*, composite construction	Burgess & Morgan	1928	SA	11.109
81'2"	14'7"	M-class sloop *Avatar*, composite construction	Burgess & Morgan	1928	LCSADhDr	11.111
82'0"	14'0"	M-class sloop, composite construction	Burgess & Morgan	1929	LOCSDr	11.107
84'7"	20'9"	Gaff or staysail schooner (similar to *Niña*)	Burgess & Morgan	1929	LOCSADhDr	11.41
88'0"	16'9"	Staysail schooner *Advance*, composite constr.	Burgess, Rigg, & Morgan	1927	ADh	11.35
90'5"	17'6"	Proposed K-class sloop, flush deck, comp. constr.	Burgess, Rigg, & Morgan	1926	LCSA	11.33
91'5"	17'11"	Flush-decked cruising ketch	Burgess & Donaldson	1932	LA	11.5
104'9"	18'4"	Proposed one-design sloop, composite constr.	Burgess, Rigg, & Morgan	1926	A	11.47
112'0"	20'0"	23-Meter-class *Katoura*, including launches	Burgess, Rigg, & Morgan	1926	LOCSADhDr	11.105
120'9"	22'1"	J-class sloop *Enterprise*	W. Starling Burgess	1929	LCSADhDr	11.114
125'9"	26'6"	Shallow-draft steel brigantine *Cutty Sark*	Burgess, Rigg, & Morgan	1927	LOSA	11.44
126'7"	21'0"	J-class sloop *Rainbow*	W. Starling Burgess	1934	LCSDhDr	11.115
201'3"	33'1"	Flush-decked schooner	Burgess & Morgan	1928	LA	11.84
208'0"	35'8"	Three-masted schooner-yacht *Four Winds*	Burgess, Rigg, & Morgan	1927	SP	11.8

POWER YACHTS

LOA	Beam	Description	Designer	Date	Plan Codes	Cat. No.
26'0"		Power cruiser with forward cockpit	Burgess & Morgan	1929	AP	11.102
40'0"	10'0"	Power cruiser with long raised foredeck	Burgess, Rigg, & Morgan	1927	AP	11.3
40'11"	9'6"	Power cruiser; plumb stem, raised foredeck	Burgess, Rigg, & Morgan	1927	AP	11.2
48'0"	12'0"	Ketch-rigged motorsailer	Burgess & Morgan	1929	CSAP	11.73
50'1"	11'6"	V-bottomed express cruiser, forward cockpit	Burgess & Morgan	1928	LOCAP	11.30
56'0"	16'0"	Ketch-rigged motorsailer; alternate designs	Burgess, Rigg, & Morgan	1927	LOCSAP	11.77
56'6"	14'0"	Power cruiser; plumb stem, canopy to stern	Burgess, Rigg, & Morgan	1927	AP	11.36
111'0"	16'4"	Motoryacht with raised foredeck & stack	Burgess, Rigg, & Morgan	1927	LCAP	11.80
198'0"	32'0"	Clipper-bowed steam yacht *Laurentian*	Burgess, Rigg, & Morgan	1927	CSAP	11.53

COMMERCIAL & MILITARY

LOA	Beam	Description	Designer	Date	Plan Codes	Cat. No.
60'0"	11'4"	Patrol boat; twin screw, raised foredeck	W. Starling Burgess	1930	LOCAPDh	11.119
250'0"		Steam cargo vessel *St. John's Guild*	Burgess & Morgan	1928	LP	11.12

PLANS BY OTHER DESIGNERS

LOA	Beam	Description	Designer	Date	Plan Codes	Cat. No.
11'6"	4'5"	Lapstrake sailing dinghy; alternate pram hull	Megargle & Gruber	1932	LOCS	11.22
13'10"	5'3"	Bulldog-class sloop (keel daysailer)	Megargle & Gruber	1932	LOS	11.23
34'5"	10'5"	Double-ended cruising cutter	Megargle & Gruber	1933	S	11.65
40'3"	6'9"	R-class sloop *Alert IV*	Charles D. Mower	1931	SDr	11.99
42'0"	11'0"	Double-ended offshore cruising ketch	Megargle & Gruber	1932	LSA	11.64
45'6"	12'9"	Double-ended offshore cruising ketch	Megargle & Gruber	1932	LSA	11.31
58'6"	14'4"	NY 40-class sloop *Jessica*, alternate rigs	N.G. Herreshoff	1928	SDr	11.10
64'5"	15'6"	Schooner *Barlovento*	Cox & Stevens	1931	DhDr	11.68
67'2"	15'6"	Flush-decked cruising ketch with doghouse	Megargle & Gruber	1934	LCSA	11.69
69'3"	12'3"	12-Meter-class sloop	Megargle & Gruber	1932	LSA	11.70
72'0"	14'6"	NY 50-class sloop *Carolina*	N.G. Herreshoff	1927	DR	11.11
89'0"	21'6"	Brigantine; lovely shape, lovely drafting	Megargle & Gruber	1933	LSADr	11.45
89'9"	21'6"	Schooner-yacht *Albatross*, beautiful shape	Megargle & Gruber	1933	SA	11.46
106'6"	21'0"	Racing sloop *Resolute*, America's Cup defender	N.G. Herreshoff	1914	Sdr	11.95
118'0"	22'9"	Racing sloop *Vanitie*, America's Cup contender	William Gardner	1927	LCSDhDr	11.113
121'6"	28'0"	Steel-hulled brigantine; alternate rig	Megargle & Gruber	1932	LSCADhDr	11.29
129'11"	22'0"	J-class sloop *Endeavour*, America's Cup challenger	Charles E. Nicholson	1934	L	11.18
272'0"	36'0"	Diesel yacht *Viking*	Theodore D. Wells	1930	DH	11.9

MISCELLANEOUS DETAILS

Description	Designer	Date	Plan Codes	Cat. No.
Anti-rolling rudder for USS *Hamilton*	W. Starling Burgess	1931	Dh	11.27
Herreshoff-type anchor	Burgess & Morgan	1928	Dh	11.19
Bermuda One-Design-class sloop; keel design	Burgess & Morgan	1929	Dh	11.48
Cross track and triangular booms	W. Starling Burgess	1931	Dr	11.20
Class A sloop	Burgess & Donaldson	1931	Dr	11.56
Mast design data	Cox & Stevens	1930	Dh	11.14
Universal Rule design data	Cox & Stevens	1930	Dh	11.15
Spreader design data	Cox & Stevens	1930	Dr	11.17
Propeller design performance curves	Cox & Stevens		Dh	11.16

© Mystic Seaport, Rosenfeld Collection, Mystic, Connecticut. Negative 67633F

Rainbow, 1934

THE ATLANTIC-CLASS SLOOP OF 1929
30'0" x 6'6"

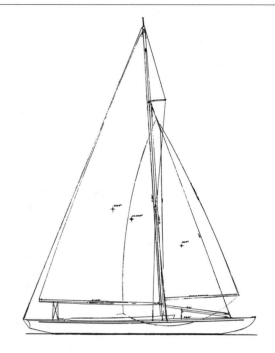

When the Atlantic class drawings appeared in the November 1928 issue of *Yachting*, 35 boats had already been ordered by Long Island Sound yachtsmen. Nearly three times that number—99 boats all told—were eventually built over a two-year period by Abeking & Rasmussen, and soon this round-the-buoys racer was on its way to becoming an all-time favorite. (The class still races, in fact, although the wooden hulls have been replaced with replicas built of fiberglass.) It's little wonder why they're popular: Atlantics are easy to sail, turn on a dime, and go like smoke—faster by far than predictions would indicate. According to the *Yachting* article, the planking was to have been cedar, and that is what these drawings call for as well. But as was A&R's custom for wooden hulls regardless of size, they substituted dense mahogany and fitted the planks wood-to-wood at their edges—a stunning bit of workmanship, but one that proved structurally flawed. When the mahogany got wet and swelled, there was neither soft caulking nor the resiliency of cedar to absorb the expansion, so broken frames plagued the

Atlantics from early on. No Atlantic escaped reframing—sometimes, in fact, a third set of frames was needed. A far more successful departure from these drawings was in substituting lead for iron in the ballast keel.   Catalog No. 11.39

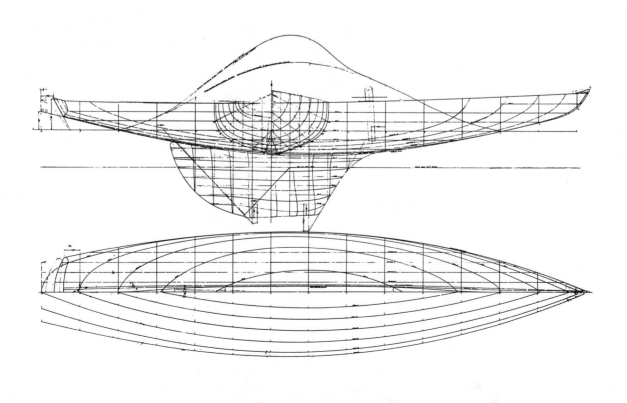

A KEEL/CENTERBOARD ATLANTIC-STYLE SLOOP OF 1929
32'0" x 7'0"

For reasons not yet apparent, Burgess designed what appears to be a shallow-draft Atlantic—one whose centerboard is housed entirely within its shallow fin keel. She carried an identical sailplan, but Burgess increased her beam to 7' to compensate for the shallower ballast keel. If any were built, I'll bet they were fine sailers and, with the advantage of drawing a foot less water, practical ones as well.

Catalog No. 11.40

AN R-CLASS SLOOP OF 1926
41'0" x 7'0"

The period 1924–27 was the heyday of the R class, and the R-boat shown here is typical, and an especially beautiful example of the type. Starling Burgess began designing to the R-class rule back in Boston during the final days of Burgess, Swasey, and Paine (BS&P), and turned out his last one from the newly established New York office of Burgess & Morgan. This featured design is similar to and followed close on the heels of L. Francis Herreshoff's famous R-class design *Yankee* (see page 42) which Herreshoff drew while both men were still at BS&P. This was a so-called "open" class, the goal of which was to create the fastest boat within a given rating formula. R-boats and other "letter" boats were generally custom-designed and custom-built to the Universal Rule. Competing for popularity in the 1920s with this strictly American measurement rule was the so-called International Rule under which most European racing yachts were being designed. Sadly for those who loved the svelte grace of the R-boats and the larger Qs, Ps, and Ms, the International Rule pre-empted the Universal Rule in 1928, whereupon Six-Meters, Eight-Meters, 10-Meters, and 12-Meters rapidly eclipsed the etter boats; the single exception was in the com—petition for the *America*'s Cup, for which J-boats became the class of choice in the 1930s.

Catalog No. 11.98

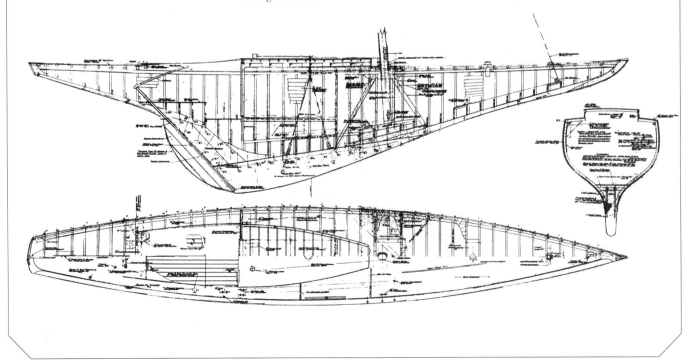

PRESTIGE, AN M-CLASS SLOOP OF 1927
80'6" x 14'0"

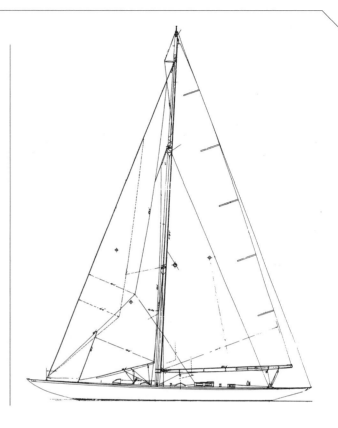

Harold Vanderbilt's patronage of WSB began with *Prestige*—an association that would last for a decade and culminate with the astonishingly swift J-class sloop *Ranger*, winner of the 1937 *America's* Cup by a wide margin. *Prestige*, partly due to having little in the way of accommodations and therefore lighter on her feet, made quite a name for herself among the eight boats of her class, half of which were designed by Burgess. In the final analysis, however, L. Francis Herreshoff's *Istalena* (see page 48) took honors as the fastest in this class. These M-boats were the ultimate "round-the-buoy" racers, larger by good measure than any class boat then in use and very much like scaled-down *America's* Cup J-class sloops. Drawings for this Herreshoff-built, steel-framed, mahogany-planked (and bright-finished) yacht are numerous and extremely detailed. Equally complete plans for three other M-boat designs are contained in this collection, and one of these, *Avatar*, now carrying the name *Pursuit*, is still afloat in Sausalito, California.   Catalog No. 11.112

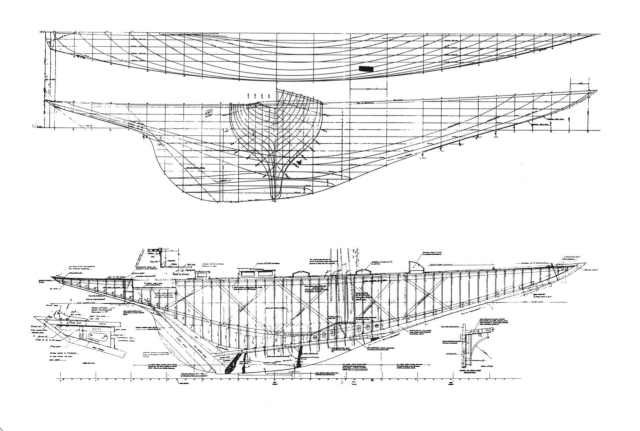

ENTERPRISE, A J-CLASS SLOOP OF 1930
120'9" x 22'1"

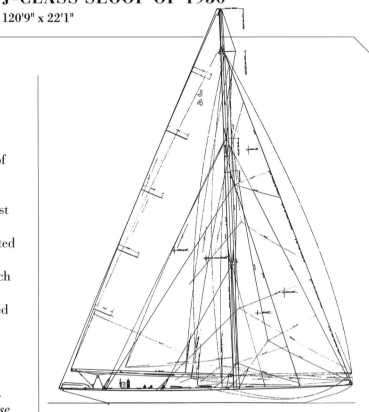

In spite of 1930 being the first full year of the Great Depression, the *America*'s Cup challenge stimulated the creation of four new contenders, and of these *Enterprise* got the nod, after trials against *Weetamoe*, *Whirlwind*, and *Yankee*, and became the successful defender against the last of Sir Thomas Lipton's *Shamrock*s. By his own admission, Burgess kept to a conservative hull shape and one that proved to be too small for best performance under the rule. What boosted her showing dramatically was the revolutionary riveted aluminum (called duralumin back then) mast, designed by Starling's brother Charles, with which she was fitted mid-season. Superb management by principal owner Harold Vanderbilt contributed to *Enterprise*'s success as well. He and Burgess had honed their respective skills in the M-class sloop *Prestige* and stood poised to design and campaign the larger but similar *Enterprise*. She sailed for only that one season of 1930, however. After being stored ashore for five years, *Enterprise* was broken up at the Herreshoff yard where she was built.

Catalog No. 11.114

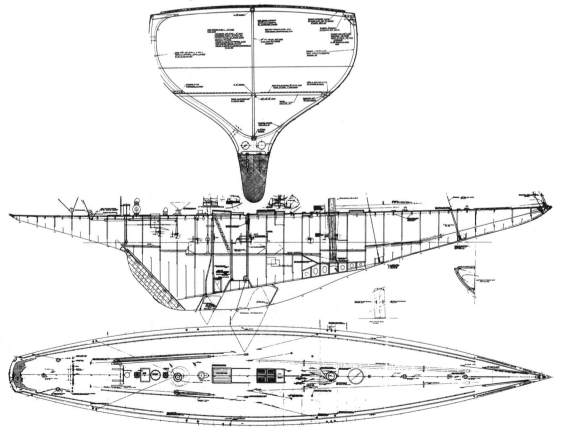

RAINBOW, A J-CLASS SLOOP OF 1934
126'7" x 21'0"

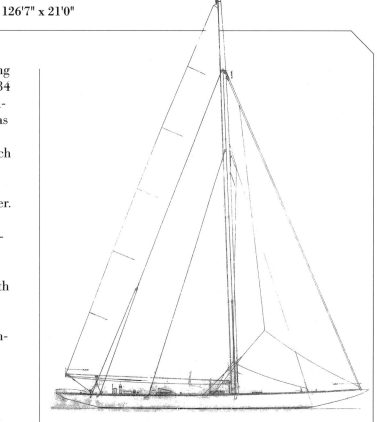

Burgess's next foray into *America*'s Cup designing was with *Rainbow*, the only new boat for the 1934 challenge—again with Harold Vanderbilt as managing owner. Once again, Herreshoff Mfg. Co. was selected as builder. *Rainbow*'s shape has great appeal—especially the modeling of her bow, which is not only longer and sleeker than *Enterprise*'s, but has some marvelously subtle flare as well. *Rainbow* didn't live up to her good looks, however. In spite of being well-sailed, she could never demonstrate a clear superiority over the reconfigured, four-year-old *Yankee*, and, although ultimately selected as the 1934 defender, came close to losing the Cup to England's *Endeavour*. As with the *Enterprise* drawings, those for *Rainbow* are numerous and very complete. Although neither boat's hull form was superior in terms of performance, the drawings, many of which were prepared in Burgess's temporary office at Herreshoff's, indicate Burgess's thorough understanding of metal hull construction and rigging. The proportioning of every piece results in maximum strength for the lightest weight, taking into account practical factors such as ease of construction. In this, Starling Burgess was a worthy successor to N.G. Herreshoff. And in producing winners, albeit winners by narrow margins, the Burgess family tradition in defending the *America*'s Cup

was upheld. Drawings for WSB's final and by far most successful J-class Cup defender, *Ranger*, are in the collection of the Maine Maritime Museum.

Catalog No. 11.115

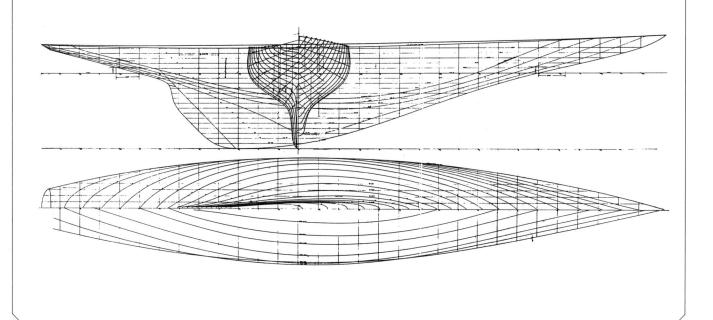

8-METER-CLASS ONE-DESIGN SLOOP OF 1927
47'0" x 8'11"

While many yachts designed to the International Rule suffer in appearance because of flat, level sheerlines and puffed-out sections, that malady doesn't at all show up in the lovely Burgess creations built in Germany by Abeking & Rasmussen during the winter of 1927–28. Perhaps it was because the boats were intended for use in this country as a one-design racing class that allowed aesthetics to prevail over the usual tendency to exploit the measurement rule. In any event, I've always loved the Burgess Eight-Meters, and came close to buying one that was gathering dust in a shed at Essex Boat Works, in Essex, Connecticut. But, before any deal was struck, this boat, then named *Seaman's Bride*, was reduced to ashes when the yard burned flat shortly after we'd "discovered" her. Later, a friend owned another Burgess "Eight" which was always a joy to look at, either ashore, at anchor, or under sail. She could be sailed by one or two, you had full headroom in the cabin, and she'd go like a witch!

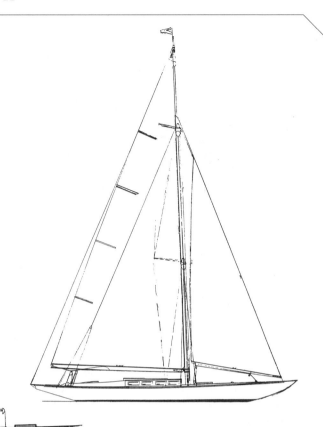

Catalog No. 11.87

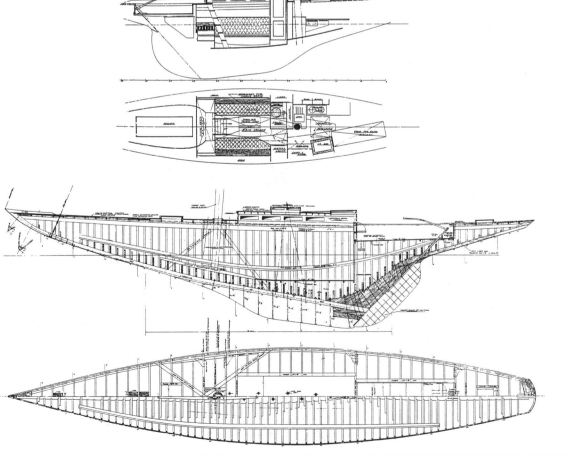

10-METER-CLASS ONE-DESIGN SLOOP OF 1926
58'0" x 10'0"

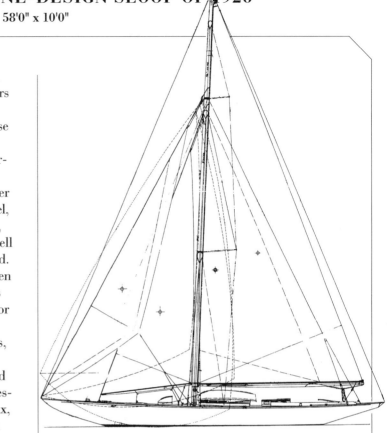

Much like the lovely Eight-Meter one-designs in hull shape, the proportionately narrower 10-Meters were enough larger than the "Eights" to require double-headsail rigs (a staysail and a jib). Because there was full headroom under the deck, the 10-meter didn't need a trunk cabin, and the deck forward of the cockpit could be pretty much flush, except for three companionways and a skylight over the main saloon. Every other hull frame was of steel, a feature not found in the all-wood Eight-Meters, but the planking, deck beams, and decking, as well as the backbone structure, were still made of wood. The Germans who worked at Abeking & Rasmussen during 1926 and the following two or three years surely appreciated the work Burgess sent them, for besides these 10-Meters and the Eight-Meters already mentioned, there was a fleet of 12-Meters, several M-boats, the Atlantic-class sloops, and a class of one-designs for Bermuda—all constructed in a very short span of time. Those A&R boats destined for the United States were shipped to Halifax, Nova Scotia, unloaded, and rigged, so they could clear customs on their own bottoms and thus avoid the import duty. As of this writing, I'm happy to report having sighted two well-cared-for 10-Meters within the year in San Diego, California, and there's one derelict awaiting restoration in Camden, Maine.

Catalog No. 11.106

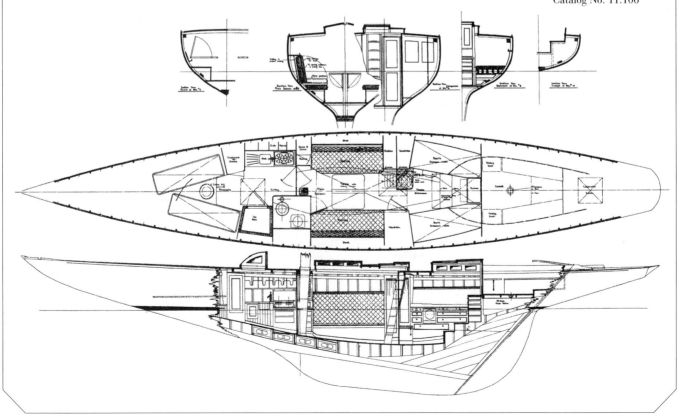

12-METER-CLASS ONE-DESIGN SLOOP OF 1928
69'0" x 12'0"

Their near-level sheerlines and more balanced
overhangs prevented these 12-Meters from having
as distinctive an appearance as the 10-Meters,
although they were generally considered, at least
by their original owners, to be better boats because
of their less cramped living spaces. They were the
first of what was to become a popular racing class
in this country. Not surprisingly, most of this batch
of 12-Meters went to New Yorkers (the very same
yachtsmen who voted in the International Rule) to
be raced in Long Island Sound. All were fitted,
almost sumptuously, for cruising as well as racing,
but the Burgess "12s" departed from purely one-
design status by adopting several interior arrangements depending upon owner preference. There
were also minor variations in mast location and
sailplan, but not enough to prevent the boats from
racing each other without handicapping. The hulls
are basically of wooden construction, but as with
the 10-Meters, are reinforced to a considerable
degree with steel. There are diagonal straps against
the planking and decking, several web frames of
steel, as well as a mast step of the same material.

Catalog No. 11.116

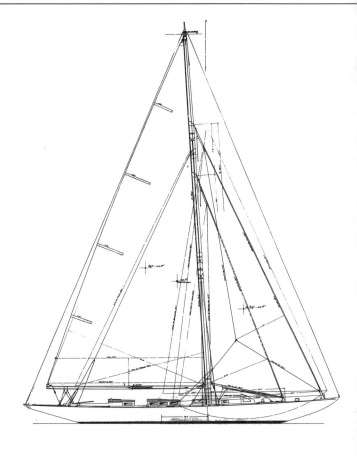

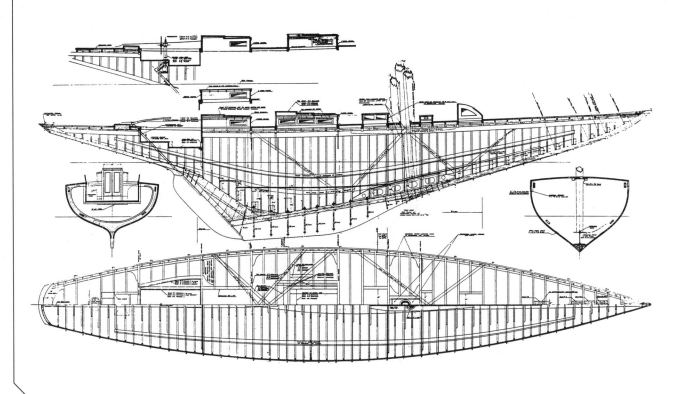

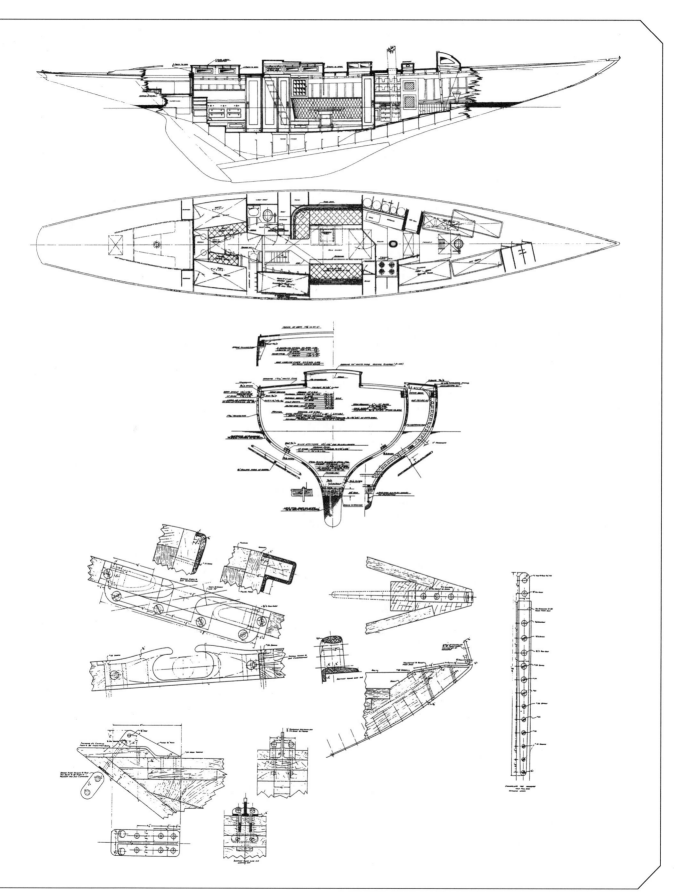

MARJELIA, A KEEL-CENTERBOARD YAWL OF 1928
40'1" x 11'0"

As owners of the N.G. Herreshoff-designed yawl *Aïda*, which was built a couple of years before *Marjelia* at a time when Starling Burgess would surely have seen her at the Herreshoff yard, we're convinced that *Aïda* (launched in 1926 as *Gee Whiz*) formed a good deal of the inspiration for this *Marjelia*: she has the same narrow deckline forward, a touch of hollow in the forward waterlines, a tightly radiused transom, 3' draft, and an underwater profile that, except for the straight keel and resulting knuckle at its forward end, is almost identical. Even the unconventional deck construction is similar, with a wide shelf taking the place of deckbeams in way of the cabin and cockpit. Although I've never had the pleasure of seeing *Marjelia*, there can be no doubt about her practical beauty. And she's enough larger than *Aïda* to give full standing headroom as well as pilot berths outboard of the settees. For the best in cruising and an occasional race, this design— perhaps fitted with a taller and more efficient rig and dispensing with the boomkin—would be very hard to equal. Dauntless Shipyard in Essex, Connecticut, built *Marjelia* for Mrs. J.S. Fassett of West Falmouth on Cape Cod.

Catalog No. 11.43

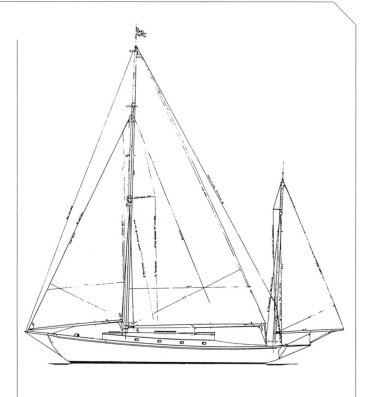

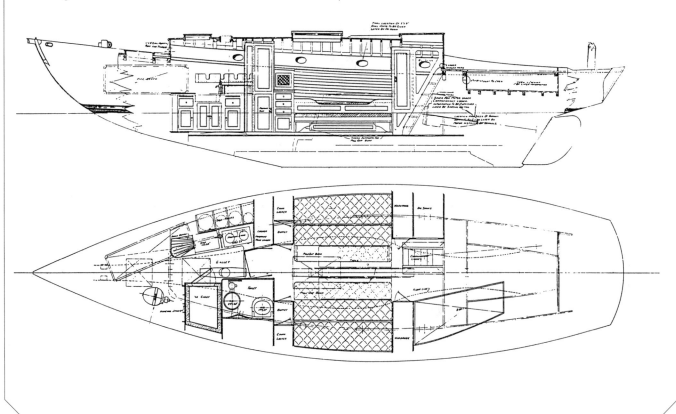

TINAVIRE, A NARROW AND DEEP CUTTER OF 1927
41'0" x 9'0"

Elihu Root, a New York lawyer, was Burgess's friend and patron all during the decade that Burgess had an office in that city. Together, they came up with some interesting and unusual designs, of which *Tinavire* (French for "Little Ship") is an example. This slack-bilged, steel-framed flush-decker was built at Herreshoff's in Bristol, Rhode Island. In *Tinavire*, one of Root's objectives was to get a good sea boat that would smash her way to windward at good speed in rough weather—thus the lean, deep hull and long waterline length. She was destined for a relatively short life, however, because her diagonal straps, deckbeams, knees, and half her frames and floors were of steel rather than wood or bronze. Nevertheless, these structural members, before deteriorating from rust, did give the boat superior strength. *Tinavire*, in fact, with her flush and pretty-much-uninterrupted expanse of deck and double-planked hull, was exceedingly strong all over. The plans show an alternate rig with the mast aft of amidships, giving her a curious sailplan, most of whose drive would come from the headsails. The drawings also indicate a tiller for steering under sail that was clutch-connected to a bulkhead-mounted wheel for steering under power. *Tinavire*'s galley is aft, which is recognized now as the proper location on a small cruiser/racer, but was somewhat unusual in 1927 when the paid hand would prepare and serve meals from "before the mast."

Catalog No. 11.13

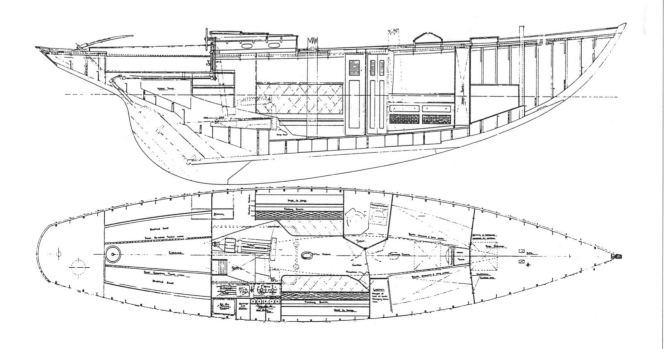

19

Ninette, the first of these nearly identical schooners, was designed about the time of *Niña*, shown on the facing page, and built for Burgess's soon-to-be partner Boyd Donaldson. Alternate sailplans allow a choice of either a gaff or marconi mainsail. Similar in shape to *Niña*, but enough smaller to require a long trunk cabin for headroom, both *Ninette* and *Cayuse* had the same underwater profile and the same distinctive outside chainplates. That my late friend Kim Norton decided to have *Cayuse* built was no coincidence, for he understood and appreciated *Niña*'s virtues, having been one of the young crew who helped drive her to a much-heralded victory in the 1928 race to Spain. *Ninette*, *Cayuse*, and at least one more schooner to this design—now named *Rose of Sharon*—were built in Shelburne, Nova Scotia, by Eastern Shipbuilding Corp., a then-favored yard with exceptionally high standards that also built the Burgess-designed sloop *Christmas* (page 24) and the Hoyt-designed schooner *Mistress*, all at about the same time.   Catalog Nos. 11.71 & 11.72

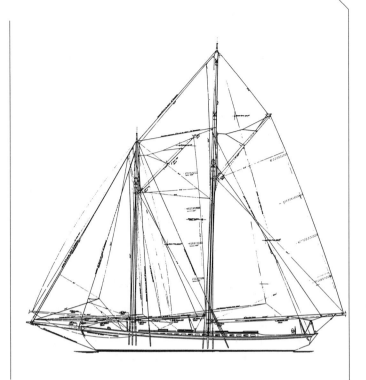

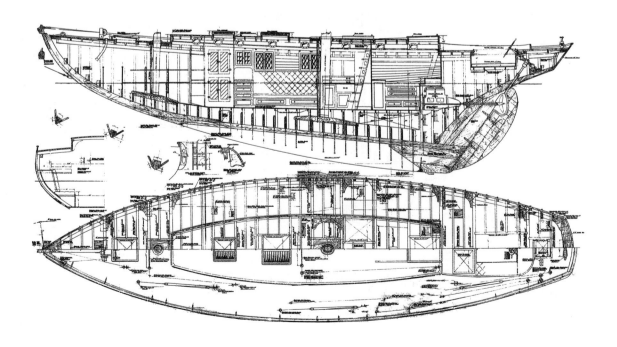

NIÑA, A STAYSAIL SCHOONER OF 1928
59'0" x 14'10"

Niña became legendary in her first year when she won a much-publicized transatlantic race to Santander, Spain. Winning soon came to be expected of her, however, under DeCoursey Fales's ownership which began in 1935. Fales owned *Niña* until he died more than 30 years later, consistently winning races and capping their victorious record together in the 1962 Bermuda Race with a first-in-class and first-in-fleet win. Even if *Niña* had been less swift, she'd still rate as one of Burgess's signal designs because of her stunning beauty. Her delicate wineglass-shaped transom has always been a favorite, but her svelte lines in general have much to recommend them. Part of her short-sterned shape resulted from a loophole in the prevailing measurement rule—a loophole subsequently exploited by Sherman Hoyt in his design of the similar *Mistress*. That same loophole, I suspect, accounts for the shape of Burgess's larger, somewhat less extreme (and as yet unidentified) schooner of 1930 (Cat. No. 11.41), as well as *Cayuse* and *Ninette* on the facing page.

Catalog No. 11.118

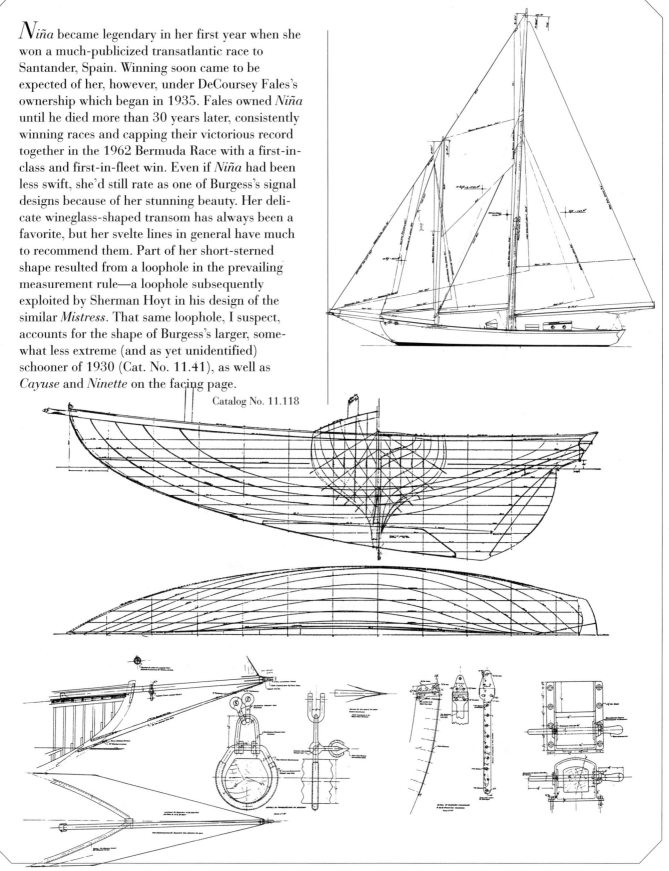

DORMOUSE, A FLUSH-DECKED SLOOP OF 1932

23'0" x 7'0"

Practical cruising always interested Starling Burgess, and never more so than in the early days of the Great Depression. Among others besides *Dormouse*, he created *Barnswallow*, *Binker*, and *Little Dipper*. By then, Burgess had moved to western Connecticut, drawn there by the Dymaxion automobile project in which he teamed up with Buckminster Fuller. Burgess also fell in with William Atkin, who lived nearby, and that association stimulated his interest in pocket cruisers, of which *Dormouse* is one. Several boats were built to this interesting design, some with the turtleback deck shown here, and others with a conventional trunk cabin. Starkly simple in layout, yet having a hull of considerable grace, the *Dormouse* design shows the diversity of Starling Burgess's vision and design skills.

Catalog No. 11.60

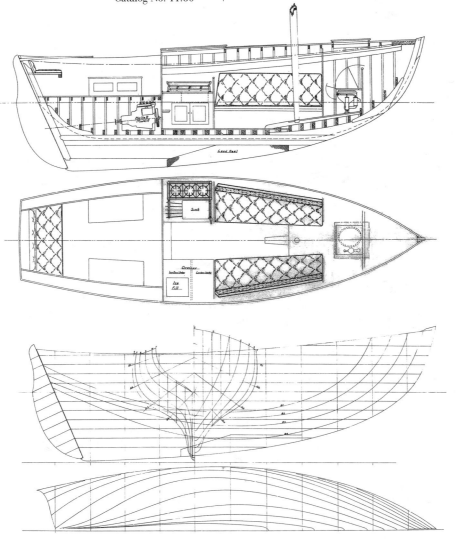

BARNSWALLOW, A SHALLOW-DRAFT KEEL SLOOP OF 1932
39'0" x 10'6"

Although we were one-time part owners of this well-known sloop and know a good deal about her history, more and more information keeps emerging. *Barnswallow*, it seems, grew out of a somewhat smaller but almost identically shaped boat (Cat. No. 11.103) that Burgess drew for his friend Elihu Root. Although the records show that *Barnswallow* was built and owned by Paul Hammond, Root definitely had a hand in her design (as he is said to have had in *Niña*'s some years before). Other designers were also involved as well, Bill Atkin, Frederic Fenger, and Phil Rhodes among them. In any event, *Barnswallow* turned out to be a most successful boat and one that has made many friends. To sail his Burgess-designed schooner *Niña*, Paul Hammond required 10' of water. *Barnswallow* floated in half that depth. But in spite of her shallow draft and having no centerboard, her speed and windward ability are well above average. Hammond owned her into the 1950s, always trying various gimmicks such as stainless-steel anchor rodes and twin whisker poles which spread the headsails for downwind running. Hammond's reputation for independent thought equaled that of his friends Elihu Root and Starling Burgess, all of whom shared a penchant for simple layout and ease of handling. Hammond donated *Barnswallow* to Webb Institute where she became a favorite of

Halsey Herreshoff and Jim Harvie, among others. Subsequently, Walter and Jane Page acquired her and sailed her for many years, finally donating her to Maine Maritime Museum. Her name comes from the fact that she was built in Paul Hammond's barn on Long Island. Building took three years, and besides the three professionals he hired, Hammond often put his boat-minded house guests to work helping out as well. Catalog No. 11.89

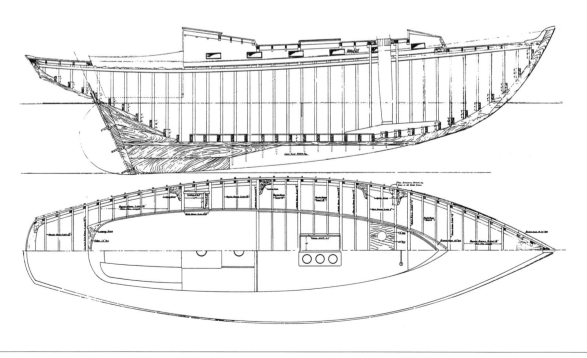

CHRISTMAS, A DOUBLE-ENDED CUTTER OF 1930
44'8" x 12'0"

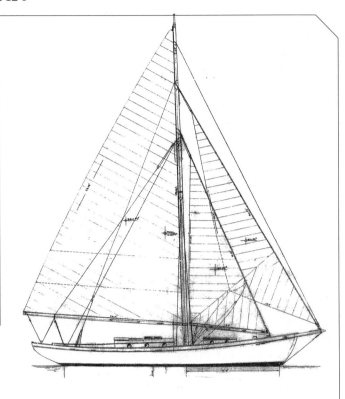

While double-enders were not Starling Burgess's forté, one can hardly fault his skill in shaping *Christmas*'s pointed stern—or, for that matter, in designing the rest of her. *Christmas* is still very much with us, and was featured on the cover of the 1988 *Calendar of Wooden Boats* as well as on the dust jacket of the book *Wood, Water, & Light* only a few years ago. More recently, a new owner had her fitted with a larger rig and heavier ballast keel, painted her white, and renamed her *Arawak*. But she remains lovely as ever and a fast sailer as well. The Eastern Shipbuilding Corp. of Shelburne, Nova Scotia, built her well to begin with, and there's been much refurbishing since. Although she's past the retirement age for humans, you can bet that, with any luck at all, she'll be sailing for many years to come.   Catalog No. 11.104

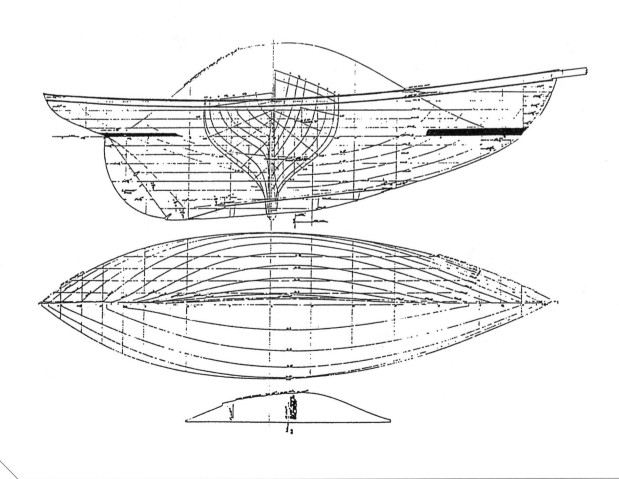

A DOUBLE-ENDED OFFSHORE CRUISING CUTTER OF 1935
36'7" x 11'7"

Starling Burgess and his partner of the early 1930s, Boyd Donaldson, had a serious falling out around the time of the 1934 *America*'s Cup campaign that resulted in the dissolution of the Burgess & Donaldson firm (and subsequently some legal action by Burgess as well). Burgess then teamed up with (Ralph) Megargle and (Henry) Gruber in what appears to have been a brief and rather loose association. It's hard to know just who was responsible for the designs from that 1935 period, but most of the drafting was Gruber's— and beautiful work it was! Here is a Norwegian-type double-ended cutter which most any deep-water sailorman would love to own and whose drawings any armchair sailor would love to hang on his wall. While most boats of the Colin Archer type are gaff ketches, this design is a single-sticker, carrying a big double-headsail rig of typical Burgess proportions, raked mast and all. And there's some hollow in the forward waterlines which, if nothing else, enhances her appearance. In all, she's a real dreamboat.   Catalog No. 11.93

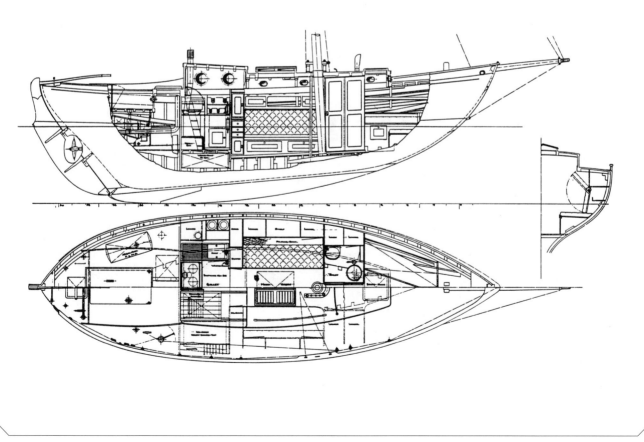

A SHAPELY BRIGANTINE OF 1933
89'0" x 21'6"

This vessel and her 121' big sister (Cat. No. 11.29) so far remain mysteries as to their genesis and whether or not they were ever built. It's safe to say that Starling Burgess's involvement was at most minimal; yet this design is, after all, part of Mystic Seaport's Burgess & Donaldson Collection. Its inherent beauty and the exquisite drafting by Henry Gruber were compelling reasons to include it. Although the interior is laid out for service as a yacht, an alternate arrangement could produce an unusually fine charter vessel—one handy in size and having an honest-to-God square rig. There are no construction drawings, but it's quite apparent that wood was the intended building material. How fine it would be to see a vessel take shape from this design.

Catalog No. 11.45

26

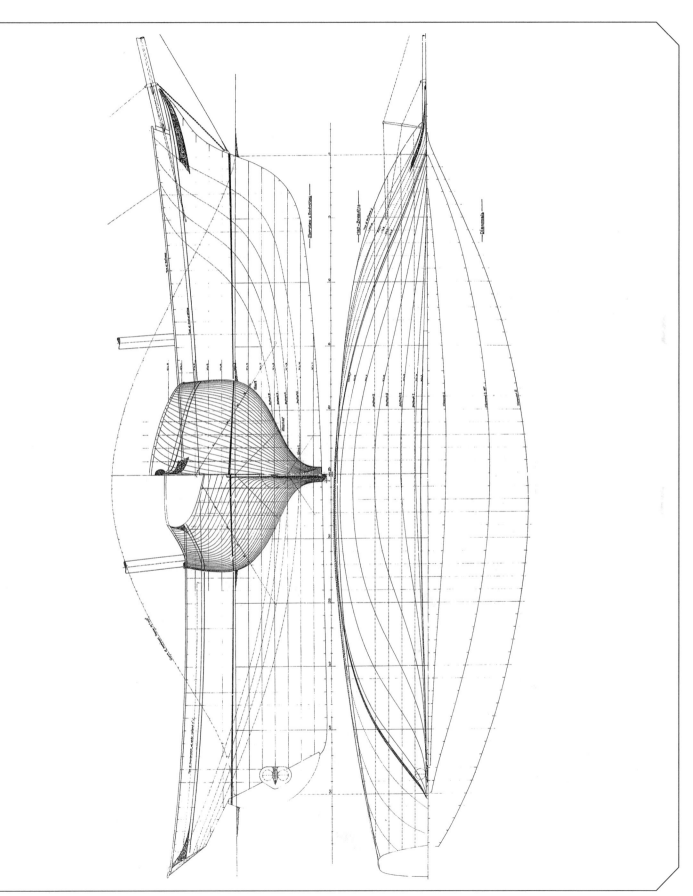

A DOUBLE-COCKPIT LAUNCH OF 1927
17'4" x 6'0"

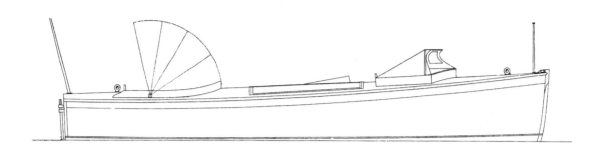

It would be interesting to know the background of this launch, under whose deck lies a giant inboard engine. Notations on the drawings imply that the customer may have been the United States Coast Guard. A rum-chaser, perhaps? No matter her service, the lifting rings fore and aft allow her to be hoisted on davits, maybe those of a larger vessel. And because she'd be spending most of the time out of the water, the cedar planking is ship-lapped and edge-fastened to restrain it from shrinking and leaking through the seams. Forward, the hull is round-bilged, while aft of amidships the bilge becomes decidedly sharp-cornered along the rabbeted chine log. If the size of the engine is any indication of its horsepower, and if the venturi-type windscreen is indicative of the boat's speed, this craft was more speedboat than launch.

Catalog No. 11.34

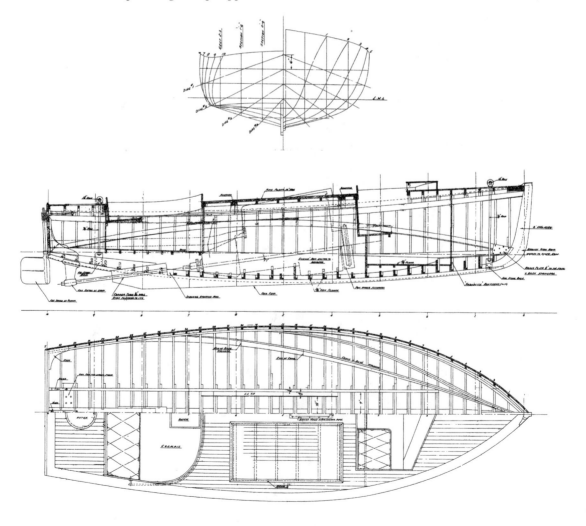

A TWIN-SCREW EXPRESS CRUISER OF 1928
50'1" x 11'6"

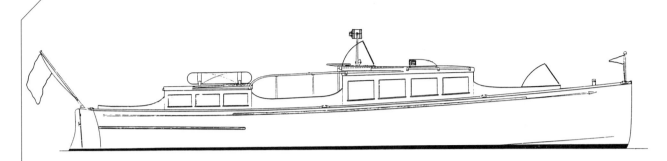

This design is typical of the swift, gasoline-powered commuters and so-called express cruisers of the late 1920s. She is unusual only in being one of Burgess's few surviving powerboat designs. Although she was considered practical in her era, nowadays one would expect more accommodations in a 50-footer. Wide open, she'd be a fast and noisy craft, quite appropriate for the "Roaring Twenties." The forward cockpit would have been relatively quiet, however, and in fair weather was really the best place to enjoy being aboard.

Catalog No. 11.30

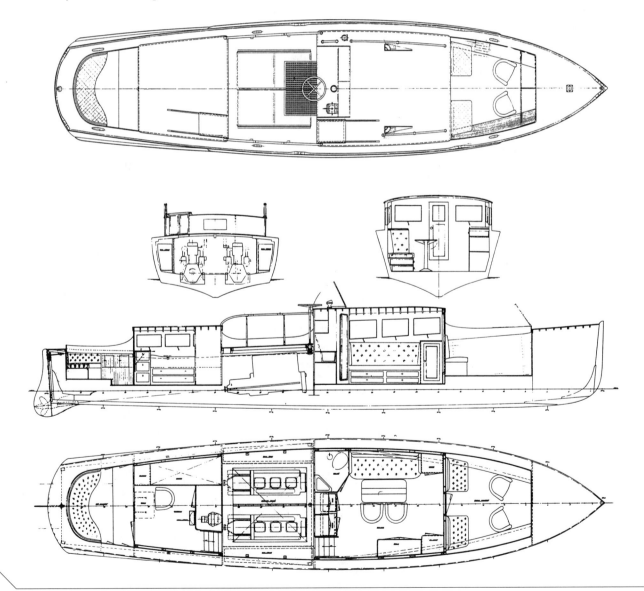

THE BRUTAL BEAST CLASS OF 1921
13'10" x 6'2"

In 1920, when Burgess was set up in Province-town at the tip of Cape Cod, he drew plans for this undecked catboat. One story is that he acted as delineator rather than designer, simply measuring an existing boat of the already extant class. In that scenario, the true designer's name remains a mystery. There are other stories as well. Here is L. Francis Herreshoff's version:

> The few original boats were built without any original design and then, after WWI, when several of these boats were to be built, they had Mr. Burgess make a set of designs. The work was done by Norman Skene and done very carefully and he made the original Brutal Beast (which Frank Paine at that time owned) but when these boats were built, they were barred out of the racing in the Brutal Beast class and the only designs that are available now are of boats that cannot race in the class, so the whole thing doesn't make any sense.
> —*from an LFH letter of 3/1/45 held by MSM Manuscripts*

Still another yarn is that Burgess prepared the design for his son about 1916 and that the class name came in jest from the Burgess family dog which, in fact, was a most benign animal. In any event, Brutal Beasts are safe and stable and, above all, cheap to build. Classes sprouted up in many New England harbors where these not-otherwise-especially-noteworthy boats trained youngsters in the basics of sailing. Brutal Beasts vary from builder to builder, and there were at least two rigs—the marconi shown here in the Skene drawings, and a sliding gunter for which there are no drawings. The earliest boats are said to have been gaff-rigged.

Catalog No. 11.21

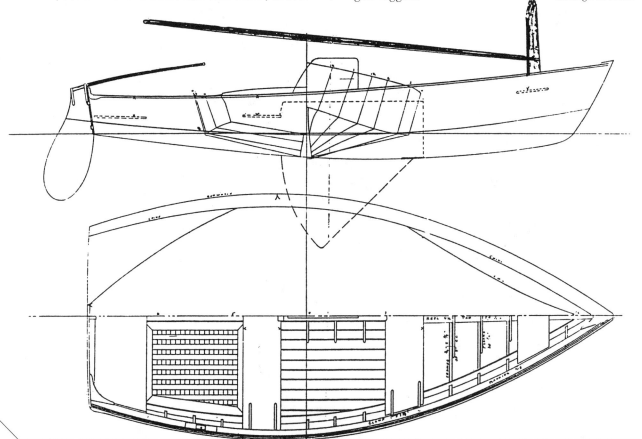

A BULLDOG-CLASS SLOOP OF 1932
13'10" x 5'3"

There's little doubt that the Herreshoff 12½-footers inspired Henry Gruber in this design. Although a bit smaller and, because of the abrupt knuckle where the keel joins the hull, a little less elegant in shape, the concept is the same: a huge cockpit, a pointed coaming, narrow side decks, a sunken after deck for the helmsperson, and an outboard rudder. Bulldogs are fine little craft with an appeal of their own, and could probably be built for less cost than the Herreshoff version.

Catalog No. 11.23

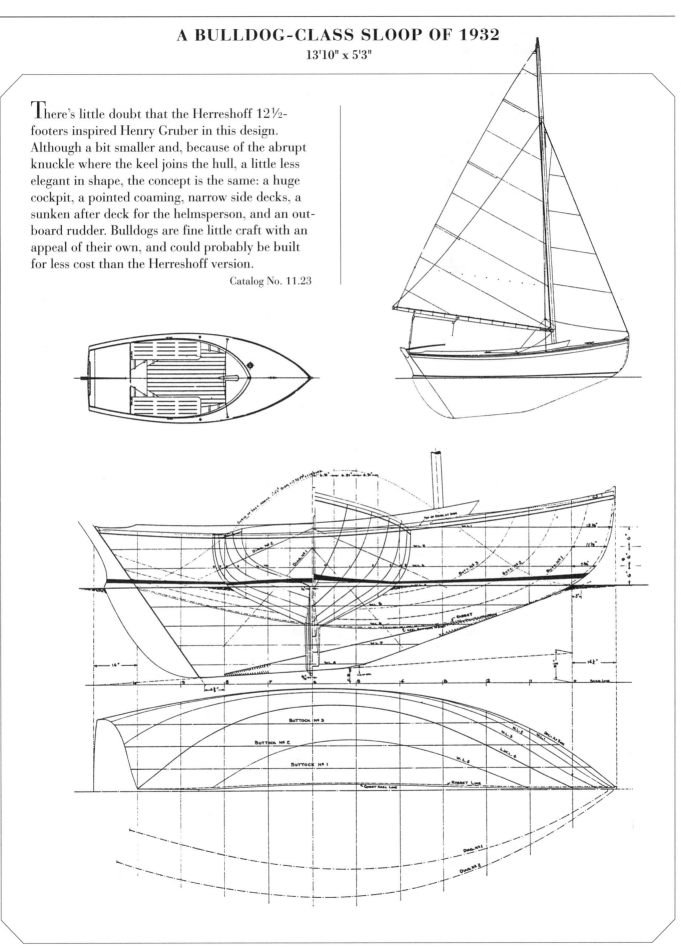

L. FRANCIS HERRESHOFF
1890 – 1972

Through his prolific writing, evocative drafting, and innovative designs, L. Francis Herreshoff has had an inestimable impact on recreational boating. His books, some still in print years after their first publication, have sold by the thousands and have profoundly influenced their readers, because in them he talks philosophically as well as technically about boats, boating, and life in general. His beautiful, detailed drawings, some of which appear on the following pages, clearly are works of art in and of themselves. The boats, fittings, rigging, and assemblies so carefully depicted on these plans show such a depth of detail, such innovative thinking, such a keen sense of form and proportion, and represent such a wide range of boat types, as to place L. Francis Herreshoff in a league of his own.

This is not to imply that all of his designs were successful—he had his share of bitter disappointments—but, just as with his writing, time has proven many of his yacht designs to be classics which remain revered to this day.

L. Francis, a lifelong bachelor, grew up with fine yachts and innovative thinking. His playgrounds were the shops and grounds of the Herreshoff Mfg.

Co. in Bristol, Rhode Island. Of the six children (five boys and a girl) of N.G. Herreshoff, L. Francis was always the least conventional—almost rebellious at times. He attended agricultural school and served in the U.S. Navy during the First World War, and he was nearly 30 years old before he began his yacht designing career—not in Bristol with his father, but in bohemian Provincetown, Massachusetts, with W. Starling Burgess.

L. Francis Herreshoff hit the ground running as he entered the field under his own name in Marblehead after a half-dozen years with the Burgess firm. The R-class sloop *Yankee* proved nearly unbeatable, and with her success came more orders for Universal racers in the R, Q, and M classes, and, finally in 1929—less than five years after he had set out on his own—the 130' J-class sloop *Whirlwind*. The late 1920s were heady days for the boating industry, and especially so for L. Francis. These were the years of his innovative creativity and of remarkable productivity: 30 major designs, all carefully detailed (they had to be very detailed due to all the custom features). To be sure, there were draftsmen who shouldered some of the more tedious work such as inking and the fairing of lines, but let it be known that the fledgling design office of L. Francis Herreshoff was very much a going concern until the Great Depression made itself felt in Marblehead and Massachusetts Bay.

Cruising boats became more his focus in the 1930s, and it was during this time that L. Francis refined his version of the clipper bow and the accompanying hull form embodied in *Bounty* and *Tioga*, *Mistral*, and, ultimately in the great 72' ketch known for most of her life as *Ticonderoga*.

In the 1940s, thousands of readers of *The Rudder* came to know L. Francis through articles nurtured by the magazine's editor, Boris Lauer-Leonardi. Notable how-to-build designs, such as the H-28, *Nereia*, *Meadow Lark*, and *Marco Polo* came from this era. He went on to write *The Common*

Sense of Yacht Design, followed by a wonderful biography of his father. From there he launched into the series called *The Compleat Cruiser* where his boating philosophy was given lively expression.

L. Francis Herreshoff was unconventional, as anyone who knew him will attest, and his designs reflect that individuality. Although there is aston-ishing variety among them, from Gloucester-fisherman-type cruising boats to state-of-the-art, out-and-out racers, you'll find that each drawing and each boat was carefully thought out and carefully drawn, and that each one is worth careful study as a kind of foundation to build on or to build from.

THE L. FRANCIS HERRESHOFF COLLECTION

Mystic Seaport had the good fortune to acquire nearly all of L. Francis Herreshoff's drawings, calculations, and correspondence, so that, with study, one can develop a fair understanding of the man as well as of the boats he designed. Other designers with draftsmen always at hand, or ones who never ventured far from the mainstream, may have eclipsed L. Francis in numbers of designs, but almost no one has surpassed his variety, his level of detail, or the sheer beauty of his drafting. The L. Francis Herreshoff collection of drawings is as much a study in maritime art as it is of naval architecture.

He prepared drawings for approximately 86 complete designs, developed an additional 85 or so preliminary designs, and accumulated a pile of reference drawings that were made by others. Drawings prepared by L. Francis Herreshoff, without design numbers, that couldn't be tied to one of his formal designs, constitute the remaining catalog numbers. They're all in the Museum's collection and are partly the reason why there are 537 different designs catalogued from the 1,562 individual sheets.

Most of those interested in Herreshoff boats are familiar with the designs that make up his book *Sensible Cruising Designs*, so we chose not to cover the same ground here. Instead, we recommend that you obtain a copy of that informative publication.

Mystic Seaport acquired this outstanding collection over several years, initially as a series of donations from Muriel Vaughn, to whom LFH left his entire estate. Upon the death of LFH's longtime secretary and loyal friend, Muriel's daughter Elizabeth became heir to all that remained. She continued with the same foresight and generosity, devoting energy and time to unearthing, sorting, protecting, and cleaning the approximately two vanloads of material she donated to the Museum.

All L. Francis Herreshoff plans may be ordered from Mystic Seaport's Ships Plans division—except for *Rozinante* plans, available from *WoodenBoat* Magazine, Brooklin, Maine, and *Ben-My-Chree* plans, which are also available from Ships Plans at Mystic Seaport, but with caveats. Contact the Ships Plans division for more information on *Ben-My-Chree* plans.

The L. Francis Herreshoff Plans

Small Craft (complete designs having all the key plans)

LOA	Beam	Description	Date	Des.No.	Cat.No.
8'0"	3'7"	Pram-type yacht tender for *Nereia*, flat bottom	1945	87	38.7A
8'4"	3'10"	Lapstrake pram-type yacht tender for *Istalena*	1928	34	38.17A
9'3"	3'2"	Pram-type tender for *Nor'easter*, flat bottom	1928	26	38.16A
10'0"	4'0"	Punt with arc bottom and straight sides	1930		38.8
11'5"	4'5"	Class B frostbite sailing dinghy *La Petite*	1932	54	38.172
11'6"	4'2"	Pram-type tender w/sailing rig for *Marco Polo*	1945	85	38.181A
12'0"	4'6"	Madoc duckboat with lug rig	1967		38.180
12'0"	4'3"	Lapstrake pram-type yacht tender for *Whirlwind*	1930	44	38.12A
14'0"	4'6"	Sailing dinghy H-14 with sliding gunter cat rig	1944	84	38.3
16'0"	2'5"	Decked double-paddle canoe of dory-type construction	1933	57	38.2
16'1"	4'6"	Development-class sloops *Butterfly* & *Flutterby*	1930	48	38.171
16'3"	4'5"	Launch/power tender for the diesel yacht *Siva*	1928	25	38.76A
16'6"	5'0"	Punt with arc bottom and straight sides	1928		38.9
17'0"	3'4"	A.C.A. 10-square-meter sailing canoe		60	38.96
17'0"	5'0"	Centerboard knockabout daysailer	1929	39	38.178
17'3"	5'10"	Buzzards Bay 14-class sloop (NGH's 12½-footer enlarged)		86	38.20
18'0"	2'4"	Lapstrake double-paddle canoe			38.205
18'0"	4'6"	Lifeboat-type sailing tender *Carpenter* for *Walrus*	1929	41	38.170
20'0"	6'9"	Sloop-rigged keel daysailer for Narragansett Bay			38.183
22'6"	4'8"	Sloop-rigged keel daysailer *Koala*	1936	70	38.196
28'0"	6'11"	Sloop-rigged keel or k/cb daysailer *Ben-My-Chree*	1934	53	38.194

Sailing Yachts (complete designs having all the key plans)

LOA	Beam	Description	Date	Des.No.	Cat.No.
20'11"	7'6"	Ketch-rigged cat-yawl *Dancing Feather*		102	38.157
22'0"	7'5"	Lapstrake centerboard cruising sloop *Prudence*	1929c	43	38.126
22'9"	8'0"	Shallow-draft keel sloop *Prudence*, H-23	1939	71	38.95
26'3"	13'6"	Iceboat *Slipper*	1925	285(BSP)	38.125
27'0"	16'0"	Catamaran *Sailski* w/cat rig on raked mast	1949	90	38.168
28'0"	5'11"	Northeast Harbor one-design sloop with cabin	1940	77	38.198
28'0"	6'4"	Double-ended ketch-rigged canoe yawl *Rozinante*	1956	98	38.167
28'0"	8'9"	Cruising ketch H-28, outboard rudder	1942	80	38.4
28'3"	9'3"	Cruising sloop *Solitaire*, outboard rudder	1940	76	38.141
28'9"	7'0"	Auxiliary canoe yawl like *Rozinante* for longitudinal construction	1955	96	38.163
29'6"	7'10"	Auxiliary ketch-rigged cabin daysailer *Quiet Tune*	1945	82	38.93
30'0"	8'9"	Double-ended cruising sloop w/cutaway deadwood	1951	93	38.179
30'3"	8'10"	Double-ended cruising ketch *Wagon Box*	1956	99	38.191
30'9"	7'8"	Double-ended cruising ketch *Dulcinea*	1931	55	38.92
33'0"	8'2"	Ketch-rigged leeboard cruising sharpie *Meadow Lark*	1948	88	38.192
33'0"	8'6"	Auxiliary ketch-rigged cabin daysailer *Araminta*	1954	89	38.143
33'5"	9'5"	Auxiliary cruising sloop *Santee*, outboard rudder	1924	269(BSP)	38.187
35'9"	6'7"	30-Square-Meter-class sloop *Rima* w/curved mast	1929	38	38.60
36'0"	11'0"	Auxiliary clipper-bowed cruising ketch *Nereia*	1945	87	38.7

LOA	Beam	Description	Date	Des.No.	Cat.No.
36'6"	8'6"	Auxiliary double-ended cruising ketch (like *Diddikai*)	1925	65	38.117
36'6"	8'9"	Auxiliary double-ended cruising ketch *Diddikai*	1938	74	38.94
37'0"	6'0"	30-Square-Meter-class sloop *Oriole*, double-ended	1929	37	38.62
37'6"	6'8"	R-class sloop *Yankee*, longitudinal construction	1925	272(BSP)	38.67
38'0"	6'4"	Six-Meter-class sloop *Wasp*, double-ended	1927	27	38.11
38'0"	9'6"	Shallow-draft cruising ketch w/leeboards	1963	107	38.166
39'0"	6'8"	R-class sloop *Bonnie Lassie*, double-ended	1928	28	38.66
39'0"	6'11"	30-Square-Meter-class sloop *Oriole*, double-ended	1930	46	38.63
39'1"	6'9"	30-Square-Meter one-design sloop for Beverly YC	1932	52	38.61
39'6"	6'6"	R-class sloop *Live Yankee*, longitudinal construction	1927	21	38.6
41'3"	12'3"	Auxiliary cruising ketch *Albacore* w/centerboard	1929	36	38.207
43'0"	10'6"	Auxiliary cruising ketch *Stormy Petrel*	1923	18	38.45
45'3"	12'6"	Auxiliary clipper-bowed cruising ketch *Mobjack*	1936	63	38.18
46'6"	11'0"	Shallow-draft cruising ketch *Golden Ball* w/leeboards	1962	104	38.165
49'0"	12'5"	Offshore cruising ketch w/outboard rudder & raffee	1942	81	38.184
49'11"	13'0"	Clipper-bowed cruising schooner *Joann*, gaff rig	1924	257(BSP)	38.145
50'6"	7'8"	Q-class sloop *Nor'easter V*, double-ended	1928	26	38.16
50'6"	8'6"	Q-class sloop *Questa* w/long pointed trunk cabin	1929	33	38.59
51'0"	14'6"	Two-masted Block Island-type cruiser w/jib	1936	68	38.19
55'0"	10'0"	Three-masted double-ended ocean cruiser *Marco Polo*	1945	85	38.181
55'0"	12'9"	Racing/cruising yawl *Persephone* for CCA Rule	1937	69	38.51
55'3"	13'3"	Cruising ketch w/flush deck & bowsprit	1929	42	38.162
57'6"	13'1"	Clipper-bowed cruising ketch *Tioga*	1932	50	38.44
57'6"	13'1"	Clipper-bowed cruising ketch *Bounty*	1932	58	38.1
61'0"	15'6"	Shallow-draft schooner *Mañana* w/centerboard	1924	262(BSP)	38.79
63'6"	15'0"	Clipper-bowed schooner *Mistral* w/gaff foresail	1938	73	38.182
64'0"	15'0"	Racing/cruising ketch	1930	47	38.124
67'9"	16'3"	Clipper-bowed cruising ketch *Unicorn*	1960	106	38.142
71'0"	18'0"	Offshore cruising ketch *Landfall*, outboard rudder	1931	49	38.5
72'0"	16'1"	Clipper-bowed ketch *Tioga/Ticonderoga*	1936	66	38.15
72'0"	11'2"	Twelve-Meter-class sloop *Mitena*, double-ended	1935	62	38.43
86'0"	13'6"	M-class sloop, double-ended w/longitudinal construction	1926	22	38.70
87'0"	14'6"	M-class sloop *Istalena*, double-ended	1928	34	38.17
130'0"	21'8"	J-class sloop *Whirlwind*, double-ended	1930	44	38.12

POWER YACHTS AND MOTORSAILERS (complete designs having all the key plans)

LOA	Beam	Description	Date	Des.No.	Cat.No.
26'0"	5'6"	Fishing launch *Gadget*	1934	59	38.86
28'0"	5'10"	Launch *Retriever*	1929	30	38.84
40'0"	9'6"	Power cruiser *Melantho* w/low aft cabin	1959	103	38.120
44'0"	9'6"	Double-ended lifeboat-type motorsailer w/ketch rig	1925	288(BSP)	38.78
46'9"	9'6"	Streamlined fast power cruiser *Dispatch*	1927	20	38.91
47'0"	6'6"	Double-ended cruising launch *Piquant*	1950	92	38.89
49'0"	9'0"	Power cruiser *Barracuda* w/aft cabin	1950	91	38.88
50'0"	14'6"	Ketch-rigged motorsailer *Walrus* w/outboard rudder	1929	19	38.81
55'0"	14'6"	Towboat/tender *Twister* for J-boat *Whirlwind*	1930	45	38.13
57'0"	12'6"	Power cruiser w/deck-mounted pilothouse	1954	94	38.42
83'0"	15'0"	Ketch-rigged motorsailer *Albatross*, double-ended	1931	51	38.144
90'11"	17'5"	Diesel yacht *Siva* w/steadying sails	1928	25	38.76

INCOMPLETE DESIGNS AND MISCELLANEOUS PLANS BY LFH

LOA	Beam	Description	Date	Plan Codes	Des.No.	Cat.No.
		Inscription for N.G. Herreshoff's gravestone				38.33
		Swordfish weathervane				38.34
		Comparison, Q-class & 75-Square-Meter				38.40
		Retaining clip	1965			38.58
		Davit winch				38.114
		Noiseless winch	1923			38.121
		Double paddle	1931			38.130
		Fairlead for running backstay	1930			38.146
		Headboard				38.148
		Displacement study				38.149
		Anchor				38.158
		Fitting				38.175
		Comparison, five double-paddle canoes				38.206
		Spade rudder				38.227
		Self-steering gear for sailing model				38.136
		Comparison, streamlined & box masts				38.234
		Launch *Osprey*				38.171
		Sailing canoe *Damosel* w/ketch rig	1941	S		38.97
		Double-ender		L		38.217
		Double-ender		L		38.218
		Model, Chesapeake sailing canoe				38.138
		Model sloop	1925	S		38.135
1'8"		Model sailing yacht *Dilemma*	1923	S		38.137
2'6"		Model sailing yacht-Marblehead 30		L		38.127
9'10"	4'0"	Cartop boat w/round bow	1957	LO		38.140
11'1"	4'4"	Pram-type tender for *Bounty*	1934	CA	58	38.1A
11'6"	4'8"	Frostbite sailing dinghy w/round bow	1933	CS	56	38.173
12'0"		Unidentified boat		L		38.139
13'0"	4'6"	Beach cruiser w/lug rig	1953	LSAP		38.164
14'0"		Sailing skiff for Bristol YC		S		38.235
14'0"	2'2"	Rob Roy double-paddle canoe		LAP		38.10
14'0"	4'7"	Frostbite sailing dinghy, class B		SA		38.115
15'0"	4'7"	Frostbite sailing dinghy *So & So*	1935	CSAPDhDr	64	38.174
15'6"	2'1"	White water racing canoe	1957	LO	101	38.186
15'6"	2'2"	Double-paddle canoe		LC		38.131
16'0"	2'2"	Double-paddle canoe	1950	LC		38.132
16'0"	2'4"	White water canoe		LO	95	38.201
17'0"	3'6"	Double-ended dory-type rowboat		L		38.152
17'7"	2'4"	Double-paddle canoe of glued lifts		L		38.133
18'0"		Racing kayak	1934	LDh	61	38.185
19'0"		Suicide-class sailboat		S	32	38.113
20'0"	6'11"	Rainbow-class daysailer sloop				38.233
25'0"	7'0"	250-sq-ft sloop for Corinthian YC	1931	S		38.56
25'0"	9'0"	Sloop		LS		38.109
25'0"	9'0"	Lapstrake sloop like *Prudence*		LSP		38.228
26'9"	8'0"	Cruising sloop w/outboard rudder	1939	SP	71	38.197
27'0"	6'6"	250-sq-ft sloop for Corinthian YC	1931	S		38.55
27'3"	6'0"	Sloop-rigged daysailer, gunter rig	1928	LSAP		38.169
28'0"	6'0"	Launch *Manatee*		LOAP	40	38.85
30'0"		Yankee One-Design spoof *Zumar*		SP		38.226

PLAN CODES: L=lines; **O**=offsets; **C**=construction; **S**=sail; **A**=arrangement; **P**=profile; **Dh**=hull detail; **Dr**=rigging detail

LOA	Beam	Description	Date	Plan Codes	Des.No.	Cat.No.
30'0"		New rig for Mass. Bay 18 *Hayseed*	1930	SDr		38.38
30'6"	4'10"	20-Square-Meter sloop	1927	CS	35	38.65
30'0"	6'6"	Knockabout sloop w/cabin		SP		38.225
30'0"	7'9"	Sloop	1931	SA		38.105
30'9"	7'9"	Auxiliary yawl	1931l	SA		38.104
31'3"	6'6"	250-sq-ft sloop for Corinthian YC	1931	LOA		38.54
32'9"	10'3"	Clipper-bowed cruising sloop		SP		38.204
33'0"	10'0"	Cruising sloop for Southern YC		S		38.53
33'3"	9'10"	Cruising ketch w/batwing sails	1924	SA		38.123
35'0"		Cabin launch w/outboard rudder	1927	P		38.215
35'9"		Cabin launch, longitudinal construction	1927	C	23	38.41
36'0"	7'0"	30-Square-Meter sloop		L		38.150
36'0"	7'6"	Launch	1950	LO		38.87
38'0"	9'6"	Sailing yacht		L		38.100
38'0"	9'6"	Ketch		S		38.166
38'0"	10'7"	Auxiliary ketch	1931	LSA		38.106
39'0"	13'0"	Flush-decked cutter	1934	SP		38.155
39'3"	7'4"	New sailplan for R-class *Mary*	1927	SDr		38.69
39'4"	5'10"	R-class sloop		L		38.57
39'6"	6'0"	R-class sloop w/patent rig	1925	S	303(BSP)	38.68
39'8"	6'11"	30-Square-Meter sloop	1930	S		38.64
40'0"	10'0"	Block Island-type fishing boat	1925	P		38.213
40'0"	10'6"	Ketch		SP		38.99
42'0"		Powerboat		L		38.153
43'0"		Shallow-draft ketch with centerboard	1932	S	75	38.46
43'0"	10'5"	Sloop		S		38.103
43'0"	11'4"	Cruising ketch, Norwegian pilot type	1931	SA		38.112
44'0"	12'3"	Auxiliary ketch	1934	SA		38.108
45'9"	10'6"	Cruising ketch w/bowsprit	1925	LSAP	310(BSP)	38.160
46'0"	8'0"	Three-masted schooner		LSA		38.98
47'0"	8'0"	New spars for Q-class *Hayseed VIII*	1926	CSDr		38.37
47'0"	9'9"	Launch		L		38.90
48'0"	10'0"	Q-class sloop	1960	S		38.102
48'0"	10'6"	Launch w/alternate cabins	1935	AP	67	38.195/109
48'0"		Cruising ketch	1929	SA		38.101
49'0"	8'11"	New sailplan for Q-class *Hawk*	1925	CSADr		38.39
49'2"	9'0"	New sailplan for Q-class *Leonore*	1925	SDh		38.35
50'0"	10'0"	Cruising ketch or schooner	1958	LO	105	38.203
50'0"	12'6"	Ketch	1934	S		38.107
50'1"	8'5"	New rig for Q-class *Nor'easter IV*	1926	SPDhDr		38.176
51'0"	8'0"	Cabin launch with high-crowned foredeck		LAP		38.221
51'0"	8'4"	Cabin launch w/pram on aft deck		LAP		38.221
51'9"	13'0"	Power cruiser		AP		38.77
55'0"	11'6"	Double-ended ketch, restricted sail area	1931	LSAP		38.154
55'3"	13'3"	Auxiliary ketch		S		38.162
57'0"	12'6"	Power cruiser w/pilothouse		P		38.159
58'0"	14'6"	Ketch-rigged motorsailer	L P		72	38.80
60'0"	2'6"	Eight-oared shell	1930	LOC		38.47
60'0"		Eight-oared shell		L		38.50
60'0"	2'0"	Eight-oared shell	1934	L		38.49
60'0"	2'6"	Eight-oared shell	1930	L		38.48
60'0"	12'0"	Vedette boat w/aft well	L A	1955 P	97	38.74
60'6"	12'0"	Double-ended cruising ketch		S	5	38.147

LOA	Beam	Description	Date	Plan Codes	Des. No.	Cat.No.
61'3"	15'6"	Cruising ketch w/raised foredeck	1922	LSAP		38.151
62'0"	15'6"	Shallow-draft schooner with centerboard	1922	SAP		38.161
66'0"	10'0"	Cabin launch		LOAP	100	38.82/83
68'0"	13'9"	Double-ended sloop for CYC rule		SAP		38.156
69'0"		Fishing boat		L	79	38.199
70'0"	15'0"	Brigantine *Varua* w/clipper bow	1942	SAPDh	1548	38.177
72'0"	14'6"	New rigs for the NY50 *Pleione*	1913	SDr	313(BSP)	38.72
80'0"	17'0"	New rig for schooner *Mistral*	1927	S		38.52
81'6"	13'0"	Inshore patrol boat w/dory & gun	1930	LAP		38.73
85'0"		Ketch-rigged dory fisherman	1922	S		38.212
85'0"	18'0"	Cruising ketch	1951	S		38.111
87'10"	15'0"	M-class sloop w/alternate sterns	1927	LS	31	38.71
100'0"		Three-masted cruising schooner	1922	S	16	38.122
110'0"		Three-masted schooner/ketch	1931	SP		38.190
130'0"		Three-masted schooner/ketch	1931	LSA		38.188
143'9"	25'8"	New rig for schooner *Mayflower*	1922	S		38.229
145'0"	20'0"	Submarine destroyer, steel hull	1940	P	78	38.75

PLANS BY OTHER DESIGNERS

LOA	Description	Date	Cat.No.
Various	Traditional Dutch yacht types by Kersken		38.23-32
28'3"	Traditional Dutch Boeier *Hawke* by Van der Zee	1876	38.22
	Paddling canoe by Thorelly		38.128
	Paddling canoe *Aland* by Thorelly		38.129
15'0"	Kayak by Pardee		38.134
33'0"	R-class sloop *Lightning* by Burgess, Swazey, & Paine	1933	38.116
38'5"	R-class sloop *Atalanta* by Burgess, Swazey, & Paine	1923	38.118
40'0"	Sloop *Decoon* by Stackpole	1915	38.36
41'0"	R-class sloop *Scappa II* by Anker	1925	38.119
40'0"	Proa *Cheers* by Newick	1967	39.21
62'0"	Aux. schooner by Burgess, Swazey, & Paine		38.161
135'3"	Fishing schooner by Roué	1920	38.193
138'0"	Fishing schooner *Puritan* by Burgess & Paine	1922	38.189
	Schooner yacht *Speejacks* by Hand	1928	38.200
	Schooner yacht *Hermes*	1884	38.81
152'6"	Tern schooner *Minas Princess*	1919	38.14

Sailski (27'0" x 16'0"), the now-obscure catamaran that LFH developed for *The Rudder* in great detail, was rakish and handsome, but complicated to build.
Catalog No. 38.168

Other L. Francis Herreshoff designs featured in the book *Sensible Cruising Designs*
published by International Marine, Camden, Maine, 1991

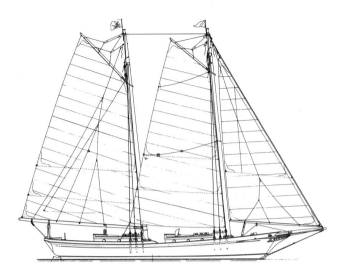

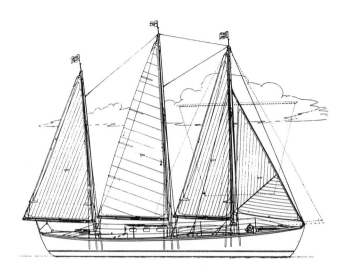

Joann (49'11" x 13'0"), the first LFH design to have a refined clipper bow, is the boat that really spawned one of Herreshoff's hallmark hull shapes—of which *Mistral* and *Mobjack* on this page and *Araminta* and *Nereia* on page 41 are examples.

Catalog No. 38.145

Marco Polo (55'0" x 10'0") is LFH's idea of a boat for ocean cruising. She's seaworthy, seakindly, and easy to handle. To be operated under power as much as under sail, this "how-to-build" design for *The Rudder* proved too ambitious for most of the magazine's readers.

Catalog No. 38.181

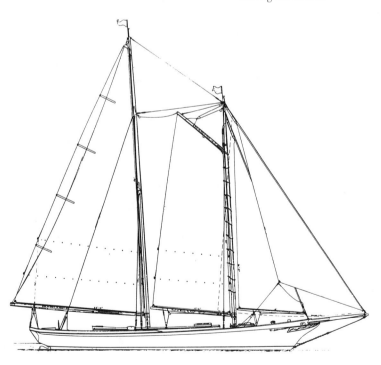

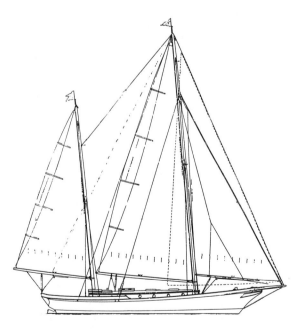

The lovely ***Mistral*** (63'6" x 15'0") followed a decade and a half after *Joann* and carries a more modern rig. Britt Bros. of West Lynn, Massachusetts, were the builders.

Catalog No. 38.182

Mobjack (45'3" x 12'6") made a single-issue appearance in *The Rudder* as an abbreviated "how-to-build." She was designed for a client who lived on Mobjack Bay in the lower Chesapeake.

Catalog No. 38.18

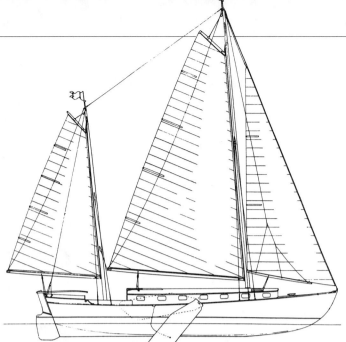

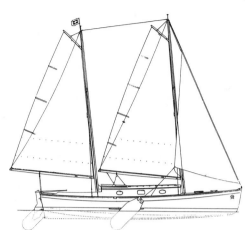

Golden Ball (46'6" x 11'0") is an easily-sailed, shallow-draft cruising ketch with full headroom and twin-screw power. LFH favored leeboards and with them achieved a hull that floats in only 2' of water.
Catalog No. 38.165

Meadow Lark (33'0" x 8'2") is a simply-built, ketch-rigged sharpie with leeboards and kick-up rudder for cruising sheltered, shallow waters. Like *Golden Ball*, *Meadow Lark* was designed for two engines and twin screws.
Catalog No. 38.192

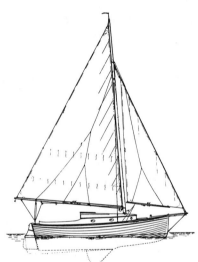

Prudence (22'0" x 7'5") is a center-boarder for spartan cruising. The lap-strake planking and round-fronted trunk cabin are uncharacteristic of her designer.
Catalog No. 38.126

Solitaire (28'3" x 9'3") is an early cruising sloop design whose hull inspired the slightly smaller and shallower, and ketch-rigged, H-28 some years later.
Catalog No. 38.141

H-23 (22'9" x 8'0") is a small, shallow-draft keel cruising sloop for two, drawn originally for *The Rudder* as a "how-to-build" article.
Catalog No. 38.95

Carpenter (18'0" x 4'6") was designed to serve as tender for the motorsailer *Walrus* (pages 66 & 67). With watertight compartments at each end, this is a serious lifeboat as well.
Catalog No. 38.170

The **H-14** sailing dinghy (14'0" x 4'6") is another design prepared in elaborate detail as a "how-to-build" for *The Rudder*. LFH gave her a gunter rig to avoid a long mast.
Catalog No. 38.3

This knockabout (17'0" x 5'0") was given no name, but is an uncommonly handsome daysailer with the shape and light weight that would allow her to plane in strong winds.
Catalog No. 38.178

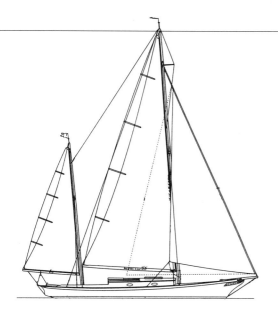

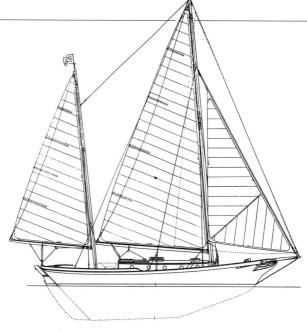

Araminta (33'0" x 8'6") is a handsome, clipper-bowed auxiliary ketch for daysailing and cruising, requires a skilled and experienced builder, but if completed according to the plans, she's a real beauty.
Catalog No. 38.143

Nereia (36'0" x 11'0") is a clipper-bowed auxiliary cruising ketch. More of a cruiser than *Araminta* and somewhat easier to build because of her flat transom and outboard rudder, this ketch shares the same lovely clipper bow.
Catalog No. 38.7

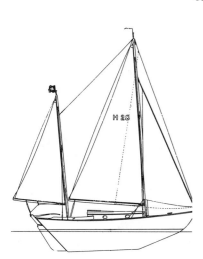

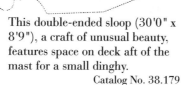

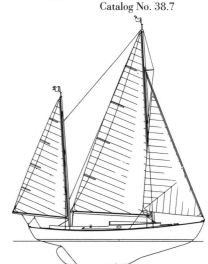

H-28 (28'0" x 8'9") was probably LFH's most popular design, due largely to its lavish presentation in *The Rudder* as one of Francis Herreshoff's first "how-to-build" articles.
Catalog No. 38.4

This double-ended sloop (30'0" x 8'9"), a craft of unusual beauty, features space on deck aft of the mast for a small dinghy.
Catalog No. 38.179

Rozinante (28'9" x 7'0") first appeared in *The Rudder* in one of LFH's *Compleat Cruiser* installments. In response to many inquiries, LFH completed the design and produced his final "how-to-build" article.
Catalog No. 38.167

La Petite (11'5" x 4'5") is a lapstrake frostbite dinghy whose spars can fit within her hull. Winter racing gave rise to similar dinghies from various designers.
Catalog No. 38.172

This pram-type sailing tender (11'6" x 4'2") came out originally as part of LFH's *Marco Polo* design for *The Rudder*. While response to *Marco Polo* (page 39) was disappointing, her tender attracted significantly more interest.
Catalog No. 38.181A

So and So (15'0" x 4'7") can be rowed as well as sailed, with the rower astride the seat that runs fore and aft atop the centerboard trunk.
Catalog No. 38.174

YANKEE, AN R-CLASS SLOOP OF 1925
37'6" x 6'8"

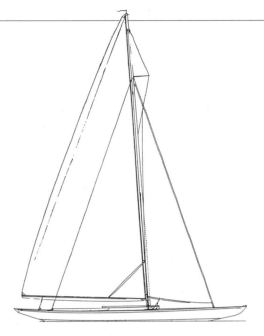

Under an arrangement whose details are yet to surface, LFH designed *Yankee*, or at least started on her design, while he was still working in the Burgess, Swasey, and Paine office in downtown Boston. Charles A. Welch, LFH's earliest patron, commissioned *Yankee* and with her raced and often won against other boats of the Universal Rule R class, boats of similar size and appearance that were also known as 20-Raters. Built (by Britt Bros.) more like a wood-bodied airplane than a traditional plank-on-frame yacht, her so-called longitudinal construction would lead LFH to apply for a patent—one that was granted in January 1929 as number 1,698,304. While this building method resulted in an exceptionally strong and lightweight hull, the deep web frames, even though more widely spaced than conventional steam-bent ones, made for more expense and so encroached on interior space that few other designers made use of it. Although less radical overall than his later racing yacht designs, and having a fairly conventional hull shape (the U-shaped forward sections are notable), *Yankee*'s sailplan indicates that LFH understood earlier than most designers how important a tall jib is in making a boat move fast, especially when sailing to windward. He also realized how much faster a boat goes if her jibstay is prevented from sagging or panting—so he eliminated the usual headstay (which runs from foredeck to masthead)

and substituted what he termed a "span stay" high up. With the doubling of the wires, this would soon become an essential element of any fractionally rigged yacht. (Today, we call them "jumpers," or "jumper stays" and "jumper struts.") No longer would the total load be shared with the headstay; the jibstay carried it all—to the distinct benefit of a tighter jib luff and, with it, greater boat speed. *Yankee*'s success boosted LFH's reputation as a designer of winners, and more commissions for racing sailboats soon came his way.   Catalog No. 38.67

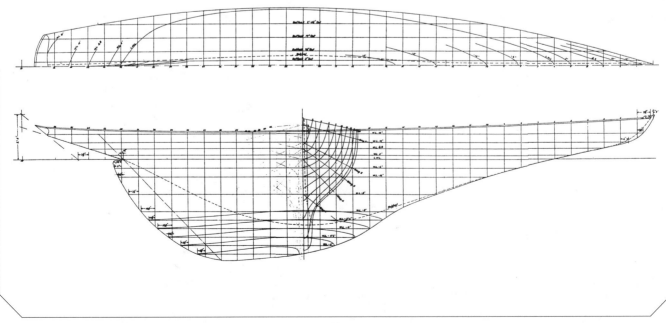

BONNIE LASSIE, AN R-CLASS SLOOP OF 1928
39'0" x 6'8"

This third and final of LFH's R-class sloops, while almost as innovative as *Live Yankee* (shown on the following page), with her huge rule-beating curved headboard and longitudinal construction, takes honors as having the handsomest hull of the three. Built by Graves of Marblehead in the waning days of the Universal Rule, *Bonnie Lassie* (for Dr. Morton Prince, replacing his earlier Burgess-designed R-boat *Bonnie Kate*) eventually shed her original rig and did quite well using a conventional sailplan, but one having a taller headsail than was then common. Her lead ballast keel serves as the mast step, there being no keel timber in the middle part of the boat. And it seems that LFH, as a precaution against her being over-ballasted, called for a couple of chunks of her lead keel to be easily removable for fine-tuning—to be carefully fussed with until the waterline length came to just within the R-class measurement rule.   Catalog No. 38.66

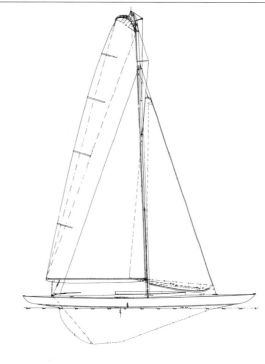

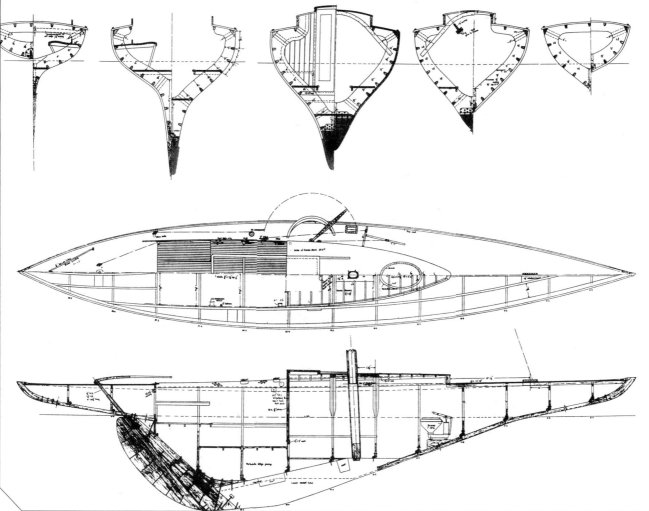

LIVE YANKEE, AN R-CLASS SLOOP OF 1927
39'6" x 6'6"

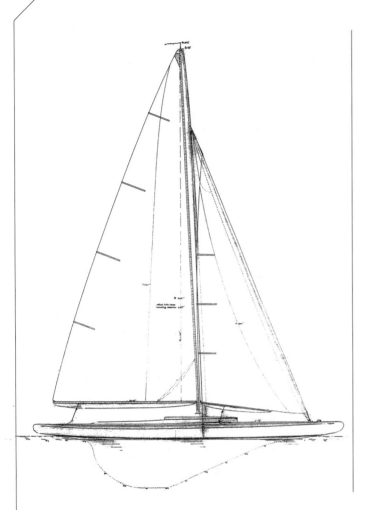

Here is the ultimate racing machine of her day, one with so much hard-to-build sophistication that both *Live Yankee* and her designer met with considerable derision in spite of an impressive racing record. As with her predecessor *Yankee,* LFH employed longitudinal construction and with it achieved a hull so light as to amount to only 20% of the total displacement—the 10,400-pound lead ballast keel was intended to make up the remaining 80%, although on launching it proved a bit too heavy, and had to undergo some surgery in order for *Live Yankee*'s waterline length to fall within the R-class limits. Britt Bros. were selected as builders, and photos show they made a fine job of it. A streamlined spar forestay, rigged to rotate, shows in both drawings and photos. A double-luff mainsail and a jib luff sleeve extended the teardrop shapes of the mast and the spar forestay well aft for an overall aerodynamic cross-sectional shape. The streamlined mainsail headboard, of bronze-reinforced maple, became virtually a part of the masthead when the sail was raised. *Live Yankee*'s rig, however, was new and untried (although patented: U.S. Patent #1,613,890 of January, 1927). As backup, an alternate and somewhat more conventional rig (although one still calling for a spar forestay, but for a single-thickness jib luff) was built and waiting in the wings for

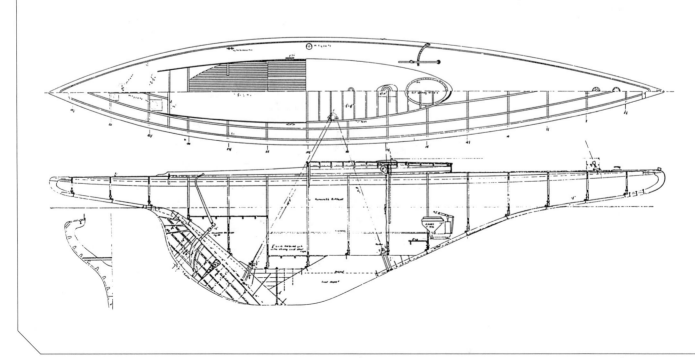

possible use. A seemingly endless number of custom fittings and the drawings depicting them, along with a double-planked hull whose inner layer crossed diagonally over the longitudinal stringers, made *Live Yankee* expensive to build, and her web frames, narrow beam, and slack bilges precluded any kind of cruising accommodations. Along with a general streamlining, some other speed-enhancing features included an articulated rudder whose blade bent increasingly from forward to aft and which was operated by a vertical tiller. Her thin-walled Spanish cedar mast also employed longitudinal construction (but with bronze frames called diaphragms) and rotated on a deck-mounted ball bearing so as to always present the least wind resistance.   Catalog No. 38.6

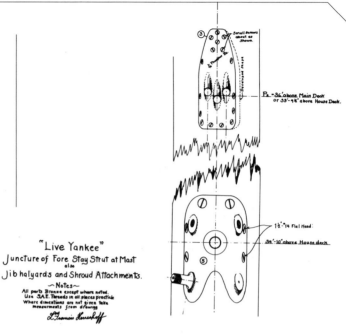

"Live Yankee"
Juncture of Fore Stay Strut at Mast
also
Jib halyards and Shroud Attachments.
~Notes~
All parts Bronze except where noted.
Use S.A.E. Threads in all places practicle
Where dimensions are not given take
measurements from drawings

L Francis Herreshoff

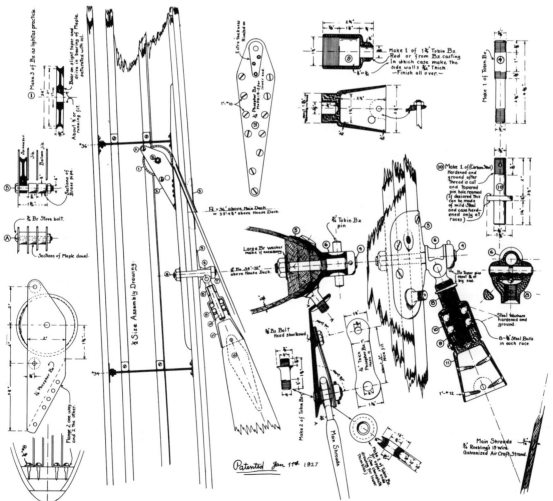

NOR'EASTER V, A Q-CLASS SLOOP OF 1928
50'6" x 7'8"

A lovely double-ender much like an enlargement of the R-boat *Bonnie Lassie*, and having the same longitudinal construction and no keel timber, *Nor'easter*, built by Lawley for Grafton Smith, did very well on the race course. In fact, one yachting writer called her "the smartest 25-Rater of the 1928 season in the usual Marblehead conditions." Her long, pointed trunk cabin allowed standing headroom, and in spite of her space-robbing web frames there were berths for four people, an enclosed head, and a small galley—not much for a 50-footer of the 1990s, but sufficiently commodious back then for Q-boats to capture LFH's loyalty as practical cruiser/racers. There are a great many detailed drawings that go with this design, all beautifully drafted, awaiting admiration and study.   Catalog No. 38.16

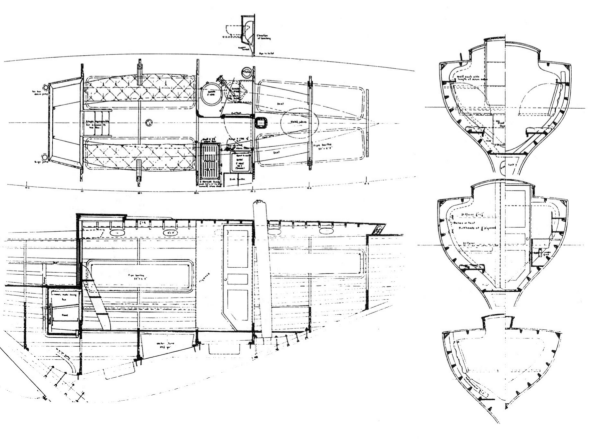

QUESTA, A Q-CLASS SLOOP OF 1929
50'6" x 8'6"

The James E. Graves yard in Marblehead built *Questa* for C.H.W. Foster, whose wonderful photograph albums of the boats that once raced in Massachusetts Bay waters (including *Questa*, of course) are held by the MIT Museums. A little wider with firmer bilges than *Nor'easter*, *Questa* is among the more beautiful of LFH's racing sailboats, transom stern notwithstanding. She was more than just beautiful; under the right conditions, she was fast as well, winning the Eastern Yacht Club's series her first season. But this was a big boat, not a light-weather performer; and although "when the breeze had plenty of strength, *Questa* was unbeatable by others in the class," she placed well down in the season's championship. A conventionally built hull reinforced with diagonal strapping and having double-planking where both layers run fore-and-aft, *Questa* is built more like the designs of N.G. Herreshoff and the yachts built by the Herreshoff Mfg. Co. than most of LFH's other contemporary racers. Although her below-deck layout is similar to *Nor'easter*'s, the living spaces, without the web frames, are far roomier. *Questa*'s double cockpit puts the helmsman sitting aft and at deck level, while the crew work from a deeper

forward cockpit. Not only are both *Questa* and *Nor'easter V* still sailing, but, most remarkably, these only Q-boats LFH ever designed sail together now on Montana's Flathead Lake!   Catalog No. 38.59

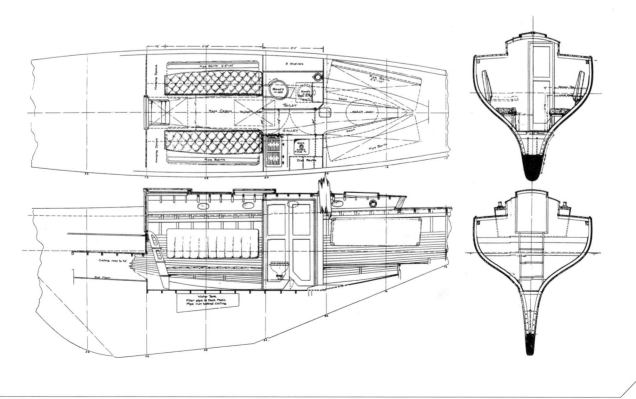

ISTALENA, AN M-CLASS SLOOP OF 1928
87'0" x 14'6"

Larger by far than any sailing yacht previously built to an LFH design, *Istalena* proved to be a champion and soon led to his commission to design the J-boat *Whirlwind*, as we shall soon see. This was, however, not LFH's first M-boat design; two that were never built (Nos. 22 and 31) had already been taken through the proposal stage a year or two earlier. Because *Istalena* was to be built at the Herreshoff yard in Bristol, Rhode Island, and LFH was very busy and at least three hours away in Marblehead, his father Nathanael agreed to oversee the construction on his behalf. A number of letters between the two show that Nat made a number of suggestions while LFH was developing the drawings that unquestionably improved the end product. *Istalena*, being about the upper limit for all-wood construction, was reinforced by steam-bent belt frames through-bolted over the ceiled-up hull in the manner N.G. Herreshoff prescribed in his recently published *Rules for Wooden Yacht Construction*. She was also diagonally strapped and double-planked, and featured a rabbeted lead keel sans keel timber. This was George M. Pynchon's third big sloop named *Istalena*, and although early on he had to suffer a broken mast (in the new boat's first race!) and finishing "last in class" during Larchmont Race Week, this *Istalena*

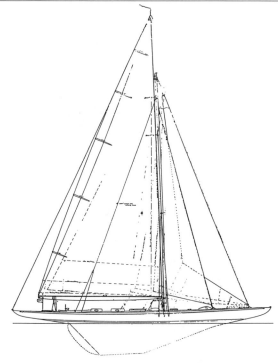

came into her own during the New York Yacht Club cruise. She went on to dominate the seven-boat class, which included four other brand-new M-boats, three of which had been designed by LFH's former mentor W. Starling Burgess. *Istalena* surely represented LFH's zenith in terms of successful racing yachts.

Catalog No. 38.17

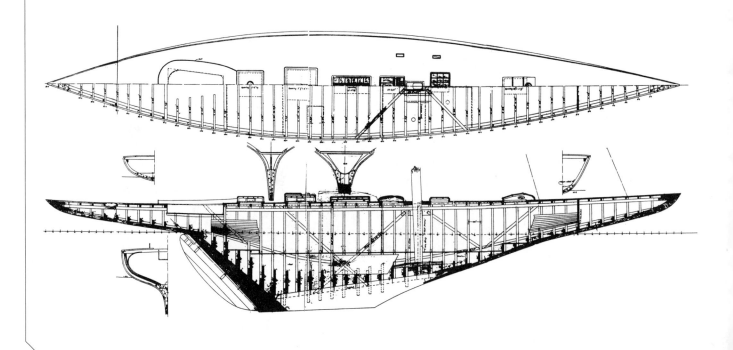

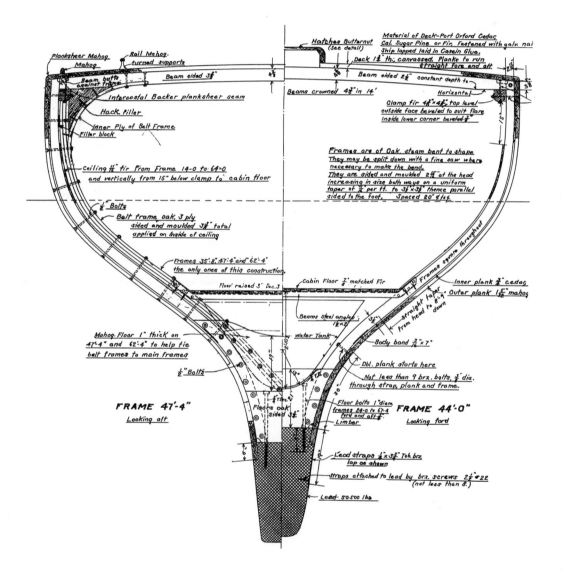

Hatches Butternut
(See detail)

Material of Deck-Port Orford Cedar,
Cal. Sugar Pine or Fir. Fastened with galv nail
Ship lapped laid in Casein Glue.
Deck 1¼" th; canvassed. Planks to run
straight fore and aft

Planksheer Mahog.
Mahog.

Rail Mahog.
turned supports

Beam sided 3½"

Beam butts
against frame

Beam sided 2½" constant depth to

Intercostal Backer planksheer seam

Beams crowned 4¾" in 14'

Horizontal

Hack filler

Clamp fir 4½"x4½" top level
outside face beveled to suit flare
inside lower corner beveled ¾"

Inner Ply of Belt Frame

Filler block

Ceiling ⅞" fir from Frame 14-0 to 64-0
and vertically from 15" below clamp to cabin floor

Frames are of Oak, steam bent to shape.
They may be split down with a fine saw where
necessary to make the bend.
They are sided and moulded 2½" at the head
increasing in size both ways on a uniform
taper of ¼" per ft. to 3½"x3½" thence parallel
sided to the foot.   Spaced 20" %oc.

½" Bolts

Belt frame oak, 3 ply
sided and moulded 3½" total
applied on inside of ceiling

Frames 35'-8", 47'-4" and 62'-4"
the only ones of this construction.

Floor raised 3" Dec.3

Cabin Floor ⅞" matched Fir

Frames square throughout

Inner plank ¾" cedar
Outer plank 1½" mahog

Beams steel angles;
1½"x2"

Straight taper
from head to 8-9
down

Mahog. Floor 1" thick on
47'-4" and 62'-4" to help tie
belt frames to main frames

Water Tank

Body band ⅞"x7"

Dbl. plank starts here

Not less than 9 brz. bolts, ¾" dia.
through strap, plank and frame.

½" Bolts

FRAME 47'-4"

Looking aft

Frames oak
sided 3½"

Floor bolts 1" diam
frames 24-0 to 67-4
fore and aft ¾"

FRAME 44'-0"

Looking ford

Limber

Lead straps ¼"x3½" Tob brz.
lap as shown

straps attached to lead by brz. screws 2½" #22
(not less than 8.)

Lead- 50,500 lbs

WHIRLWIND, AN *AMERICA*'S CUP CONTENDER OF 1930
130'0" x 21'8"

Through personality conflict, inept sailing, insufficient preparation, a lost fortune, and who knows how many other factors, a *Whirlwind* that could have put LFH in a league with his father ended in utter failure and became possibly the greatest disappointment of LFH's entire career. He got the commission because of *Istalena*'s success and because she, like *Istalena*, was ordered by George Pynchon. That order came too late, however, for the favored Herreshoff yard to take on her construction (the J-boats *Enterprise* and *Weetamoe* filled both shops), so the job went to Lawleys—as their second J-boat of the winter (*Yankee* had already been awarded). The stock market crash in the fall of 1929 soon left Pynchon without funds to continue, so his experience was denied designer and builder, and, more serious by far, the afterguard that was charged with tuning her up and racing. LFH collected $25,000—the standard designer's fee of 10% of the construction cost—and perhaps this money enabled him to become the retired designer that his subsequent magazine ads claimed, because with but few exceptions LFH ceased designing racing yachts after the *Whirlwind* experience. How ironic it seems that, as later J-boats demonstrated, LFH hit the mark with *Whirlwind*'s size (bigger hull than was then the J-boat fashion) and rig (two headsails instead of three). *Whirlwind*'s many lovely drawings are a

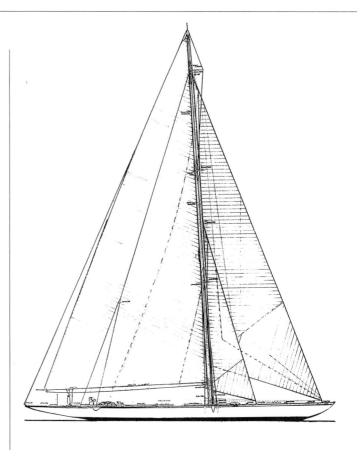

study in streamlining as well as in superb drafting. Even her binnacle and steering wheel have teardrop shapes.   Catalog No. 38.12

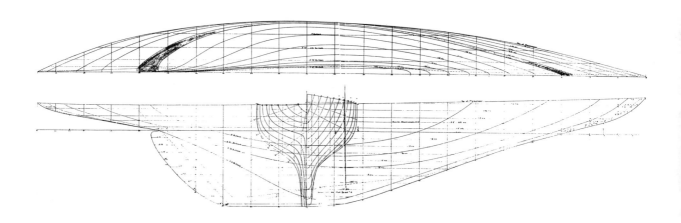

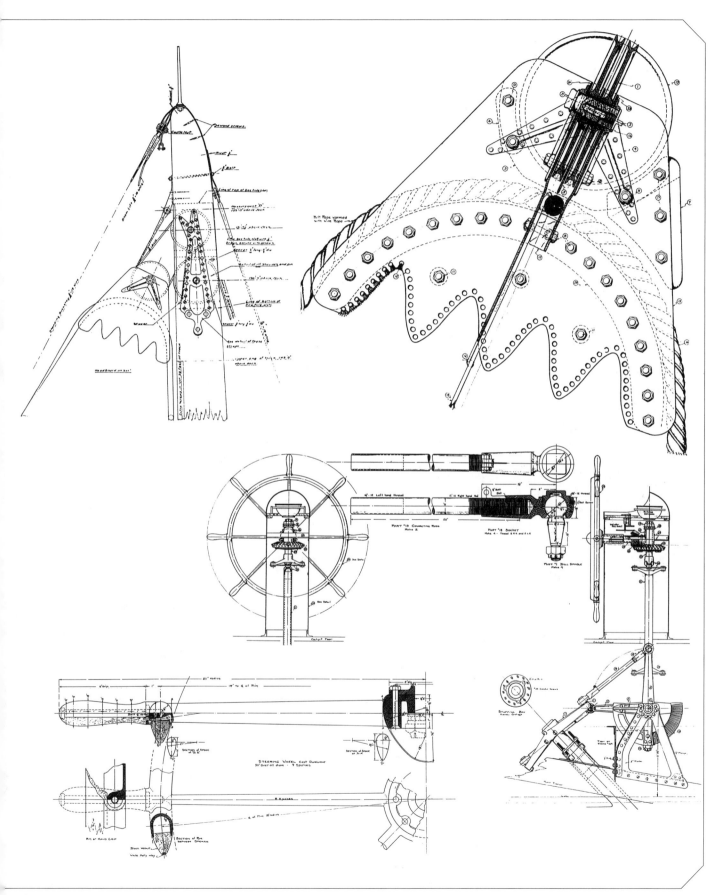

A 30-SQUARE-METER-CLASS SLOOP OF 1932
39'1" x 6'10"

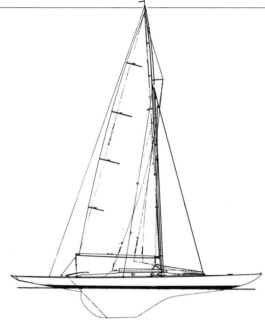

In 1928, as the Universal Rule began to give way to the International Rule and R-class sloops dropped from popularity (Marblehead being one of the last bastions for R-boat racing), LFH began to promote the long-ended, light-displacement 30-Square-Meters, feeling that they would be significantly less expensive and distinctly better craft than any of the rapidly increasing swarm of Six-Meter sloops that round-the-buoys yachtsmen were turning to. He began by purchasing a German-built 30-Square and comparing her speed against both R-boats and Six-Meters. Feeling thus encouraged, especially when the wind piped up and he left all others in his wake, he talked up these so-called Scharenkreuzers and landed his first design commission in the fall of 1928 from George McQuesten, a fellow Marbleheader who then owned the Alden-designed Q-boat *Tartar*. Immediately after he finished designing *Oriole*, as the double-ended, Lawley-built McQuesten craft was christened, LFH produced *Rima*, a transom-sterned, but otherwise nearly identical 30-Square for A.E. Chase, also of Marblehead. Only two more 30-Square designs by LFH followed. The first one—a Lawley-built double-ender now preserved at the Museum of Yachting in Newport, Rhode Island—also bore the name *Oriole*, much to the consternation of yachting historians. The second (the one shown here) came out as a stock offering by Lawley in which LFH was to receive compensation on a per-boat basis. LFH gave this boat and the second *Oriole* nearly identical hull shapes, except for *Oriole*'s pointed stern. This pair differed from the earlier pair in being slightly longer over-all, significantly longer on the waterline, and in having firmer bilges and more waterline beam aft. I suspect they were faster. Although Lawley's built four of these transom-sterned one-designs for sailing in Buzzards Bay, 30-Square-Meter popularity, while briefly intense in a few areas, never achieved the hoped-for, long-term popularity in this country. In Scandinavia, however, where the class originated, racing continued and new boats kept coming out until World War II. Besides the 30s, there are classes of 22-, 40-, 55-, and 75-Square-Meter sloops, each classification representing the boat's sail area. Even today, one can find these long and graceful craft racing and cruising among the Skerries of the Baltic, the islands from which Scharenkreuzers take their name.

Catalog No. 38.61

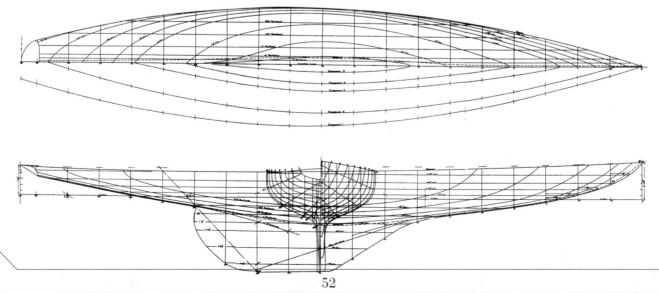

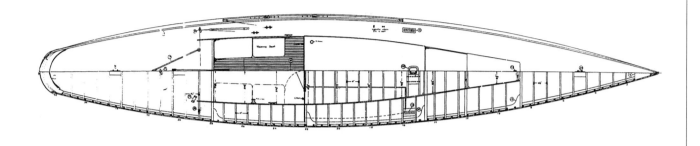

 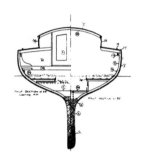 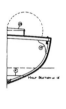

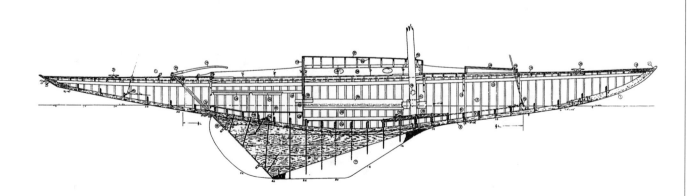

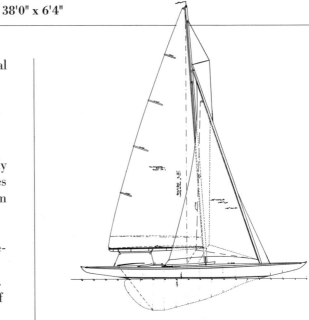

LFH much preferred designing to the Universal Rule, partly because the boats designed and built to this rule could be made good-looking (and beauty had a high priority with LFH), and partly because his father had written it. Boats created under the rival International Rule, especially the Six-Meters, generally came out with comparatively high, flat sheerlines, pinched-in ends, and topsides that tumbled home—that is, their maximum beam was apt not to be up at the sheer, but somewhat below it. In short, most Six-Meters tended to be less than beautiful. With *Wasp*, however, LFH created an especially handsome craft, but one that never made a name for herself on the race course. She's a double-ender, like so many of his racers of the late 1920s, and, except for her underwater profile, looks more like a Universal Rule boat than one designed to the International Rule. The benefit of tall jibs and jibs that lapped past the mast were beginning to be recognized, and although LFH believed the actual jib area should be measured instead of the foretriangle area, he gave *Wasp* what he thought of as a rule-cheating sail, soon to be known as a genoa. For effective close-hauled sheeting of this sail, the shrouds were led through the deck well inboard of the rail, to be tensioned by below-deck turnbuckles. The conventional plank-on-frame construction required by the International Rule must have irritated *Wasp*'s innovative designer, but he did manage to work a spar forestay into this design. Owned by a variety of Long Island Sound yachtsmen, this Lawley-built Six-Meter also featured headsail sheet fairleads that swung outboard for more effective reaching—an arrangement no longer allowed.

Catalog No. 38.11

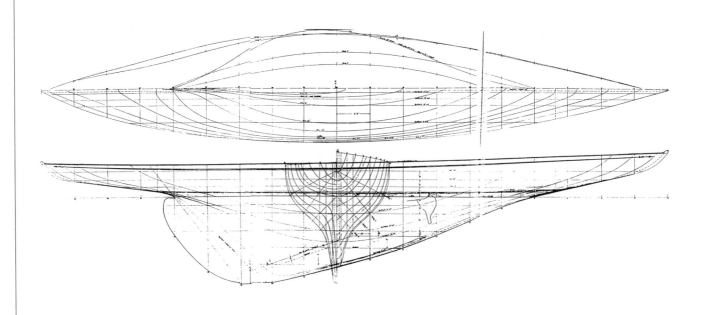

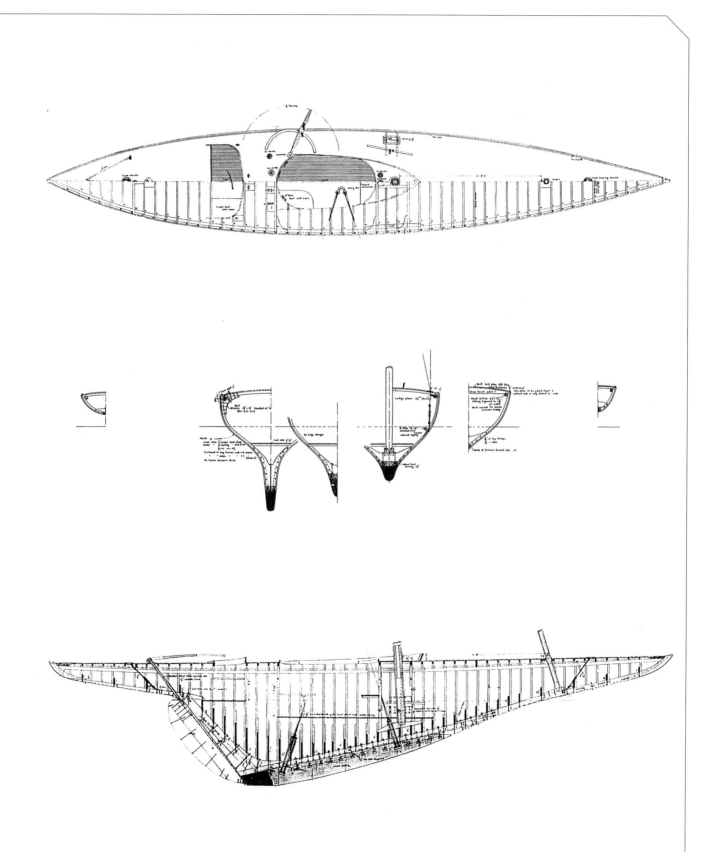

MITENA, A 12-METER-CLASS SLOOP OF 1935
72'0" x 11'2"

In commissioning *Mitena*'s design, William Strawbridge began a long relationship with LFH and became a patron second only to Charlie Welch. In all, LFH designed eight different boats for Strawbridge, whose yacht just prior to *Mitena* had been the M-class sloop *Istalena*. (The 55' yawl *Persephone* was his subsequent one.) *Mitena* is the last of LFH's racing double-enders and his last design done to the International Rule. In overall length, she's several feet longer than most 12-Meters because of the extent of her graceful pointed stern. Although *Mitena* never excelled on the race course, she's an exceptionally lovely craft—maybe the prettiest 12-Meter ever built. The drawings are beautiful as well, most from the fine hand of Fenwick Williams. Below, the U-shaped settee in her great cabin aft can seat a crowd, while the owner can enjoy privacy in *Mitena*'s small stateroom to starboard. Sleeping for all hands, however, is on pipe berths which, when not pulled down for sleeping, serve as backrests for the settees. Like *Istalena* and *Whirlwind* before her, *Mitena*'s deck structures show the streamlining that prevailed at the time. She's of composite construction (part metal and part wood) with bronze frames, deckbeams, diagonal strapping, and keel plate, with yellow pine planking, mahogany forward and aft keel timbers and sternpost, and oak stems at the bow and stern. Judging from the photographs, the craftsmen at the Herreshoff Mfg. Co., where she was built, did their usual fine job of it. Bill Strawbridge must have felt a good deal of pride as he picked up her 8'-long tiller for the first time, sheeted in her sails, and felt *Mitena* come to life.

Catalog No. 38.43

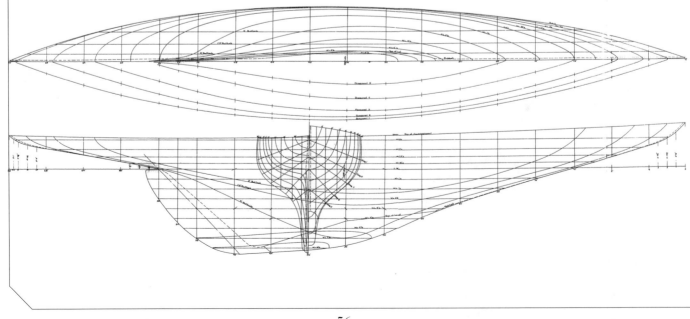

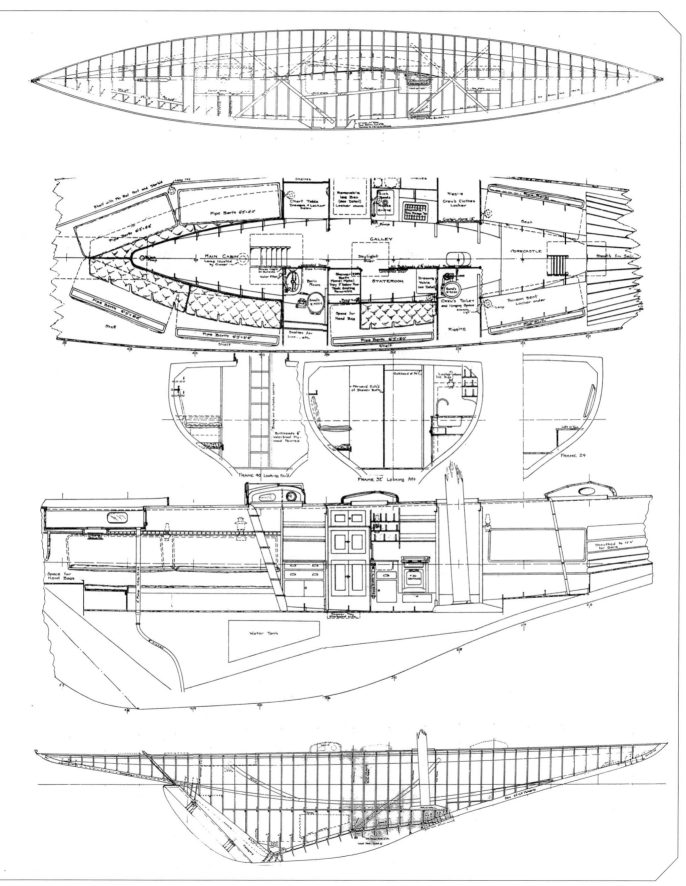

TIOGA (TICONDEROGA), A CLIPPER-BOWED CRUISING KETCH OF 1936
72'0" x 16'1"

LFH will be remembered for many contributions to yachting, but surely near the top is this striking ketch, launched as *Tioga*, but known to most as *Ticonderoga*—the name she's carried for most of her life. This yacht can be considered LFH's masterpiece for her breathtaking beauty, her record of performance over six decades, and the great attention to detail LFH lavished on her drawings. He drew full-sized plans for the trailboards and the carved eagle that graces her stern, for example, as well as drawings for the dolphins at the forward ends of the quarter rail, carved from teak and gilded. In 1935, while Fenwick Williams toiled over the drawings of the 12-Meter *Mitena*, LFH, assisted by Fred Goeller, turned out the many plans that were to be used by Quincy Adams Yacht Yard in building this enlarged version of yard owner Harry E. Noyes's 57-footer which he purchased used and which already carried the name *Tioga*. (The first *Tioga* was the shallow-draft and short-rigged one of a pair of otherwise nearly identical clipper-bowed ketches that LFH designed in 1932.) LFH, at different times, referred to *Ticonderoga* both as the last of the great clippers and as an improvement on the yacht *America*. He was proud of her record-breaking speed: eight con-

secutive days at 240 nautical miles each, while sailing to Honolulu from California; or a 48-hour run at 11 knots in a race to Tahiti. With the sheets eased and lots of wind, this boat's long waterline and sweet underbody allow her to really move! *Ticonderoga* has been raced, cruised, chartered, and more than once rebuilt, but she keeps on going, seducing everyone who has owned her, cared for her, sailed her, or looked at her. Other yachts have been built using the same drawings, and she inspired Bruce King to design *Ti*'s big sister *Whitehawk*. If ever the adage about a thing of beauty being a joy forever needed proving, you couldn't find a better example than *Ticonderoga*. The letters exchanged between designer Herreshoff and client Noyes, however, indicate considerable friction, mostly relating to LFH's compensation. The two men didn't part as friends, and I recall LFH saying that he'd never been aboard until years after her launching when she was under new ownership. In time, thanks to a succession of appreciative new owners singing her praises and driving her to new triumphs, LFH grew proud, shedding his earlier disenchantment, and I believe, in the end, did indeed feel that *Ticonderoga* was one of his greatest accomplishments.   Catalog No. 38.15

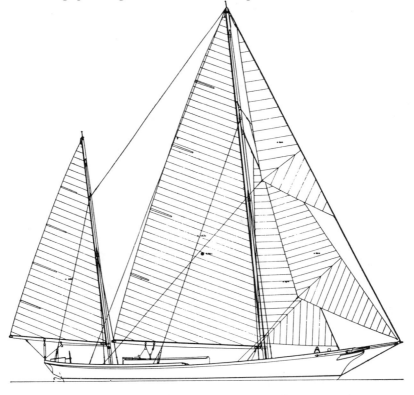

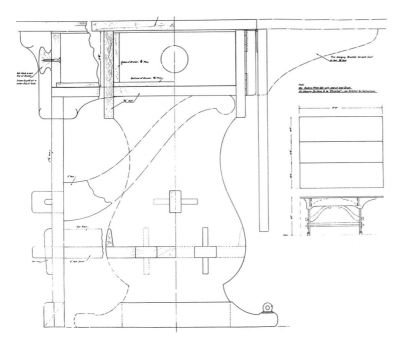

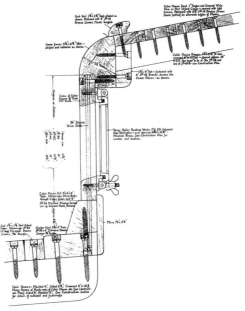

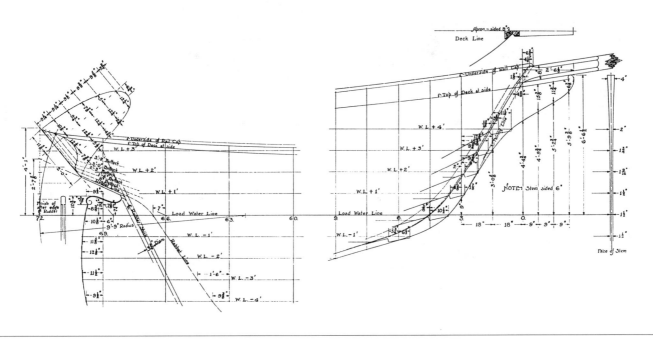

These launches, being of similar size and designed for the same client, invite comparison. Several years and almost 20 designs separate them, and it is apparent that, by the time *Gadget* came along, LFH had become more of a traditionalist, for she is really quite conventional in both appearance and construction. Aage Nielsen drew her lines plan, while LFH developed her construction drawing. It's hard to imagine a simpler little craft—she uses a tiller for steering, for example, thus eliminating a wheel and cables and sheaves. Herreshoff did hang onto his beloved contra-propeller, how-

ever, but that is about the only complication. (*Gadget* became the Concordia Company's yard boat in 1950.) On the other hand, as shown on the facing page, *Retriever*'s hull calls for the web frames, stringers, and double planking of LFH's patented longitudinal construction. She has two engines, with twin shafts and propellers, and is fitted with two rudders as well. There's a towing bitt amidships. Admittedly, she's more of a double-cockpit, decked runabout designed for faster speeds, so a certain increase in complexity is to be expected.   Catalog Nos. 38.84 & .86

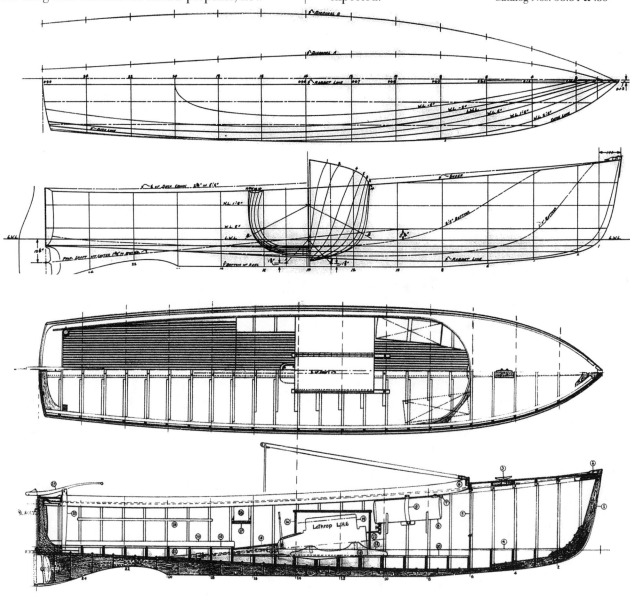

26'0" x 5'6" Gadget of 1934

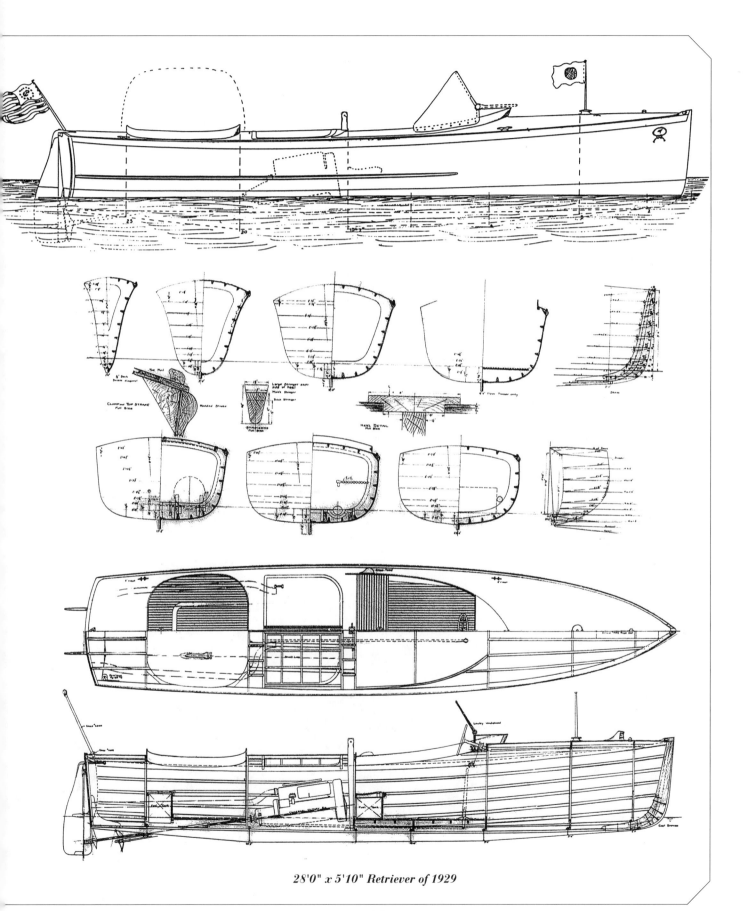

28'0" x 5'10" Retriever of 1929

DISPATCH, A FAST CRUISING LAUNCH OF 1927
46'9" x 9'6"

How the Britt Bros. must have chuckled when they started building this boat, perhaps thinking that she'd be better off upside down because of her rounded turtle deck and nearly flat bottom. Even Herreshoff, in retrospect, admits to designing this one before he knew any better. She left little in the way of records, having disappeared from *Lloyd's Register* only three years after being built. Supposedly, *Dispatch* was to be *Live Yankee*'s tender, sharing the same longitudinal construction and double-planked hull. Twin 200-horsepower, eight-cylinder Hispano-Suiza gas engines, bought used and installed with V-drives, powered *Dispatch*, and LFH gave her what he called a contra-propeller. This consisted of a twisted vertical fin just aft of each propeller which formed the leading edge of the twin rudders, and was supposed to straighten out the corkscrew water flow that the propeller discharged and thereby convert the wasted energy to more thrust. Although LFH is clearly labeled as the designer on all the drawings and *Dispatch* is listed as design No. 20 in his plan list, No. 314 turns up as the design number of a few plans, leading one to conclude that this design began in the Burgess, Swasey, and Paine office, to be finished a short time later in Marblehead. (That move to Marblehead made it very convenient for client Welch, who lived there, and designer Herreshoff to meet frequently while the Welch-commissioned designs literally poured out of LFH's new office.) Catalog No. 38.91

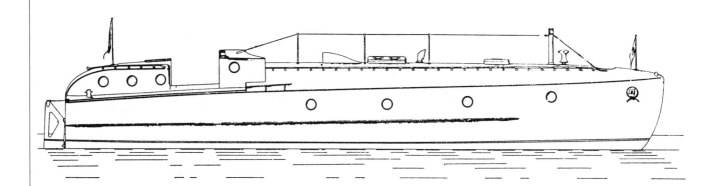

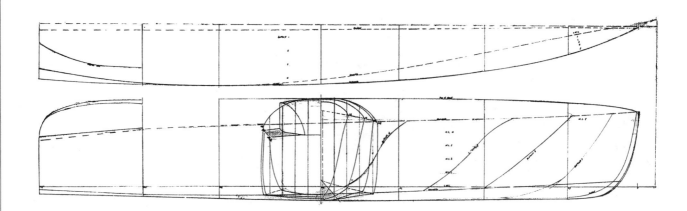

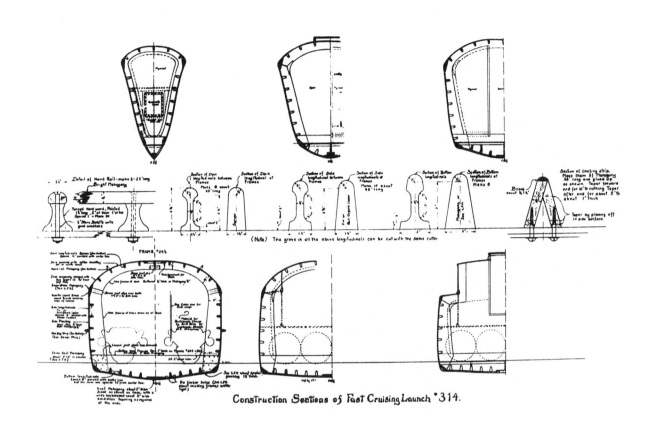

(Note) The grove in all the above longitudinals can be cut with the same cutter.

Construction Sections of Fast Cruising Launch No. 314.

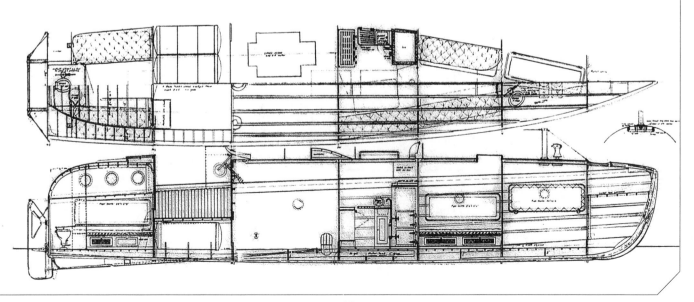

When launched from the Britt Bros. yard in West Lynn, Massachusetts, *Siva* was by far the largest power vessel in LFH's repertoire, and she remained so throughout his career. Her military appearance comes from the patrol boats of World War I, and LFH employed his patented longitudinal construction in *Siva*'s hull and deck. Although there's a good-sized smokestack, *Siva* wasn't driven by steam. A pair of six-cylinder Winton gasoline engines poured their exhaust into the stack, and drove her two propellers. With only a single rudder on the centerline and out of the direct wash of the propellers, and with such a long, straight underbody, I expect *Siva* might not have turned quickly at low speeds. LFH and client Donald Tripp went through a square-sterned iteration before they settled on *Siva*'s final design. Although LFH gave her a conventional curved sheerline, he kept the main deck, which runs aft only a little past halfway, perfectly level. This made for unusual comfort in the deckhouse where dining took place. The only steering station was outside, just aft of the deckhouse, but the paid crew—not the owner—steered the boat. Although not shown on the drawing, *Siva*

carried a small boat on each side of the stack, hoisted on custom wooden davits. The owner and his guests took fresh air atop the aft cabin, somewhat protected overhead by the awning, at the rails by canvas dodgers, and forward by a half-turret-shaped, open-ended deckhouse, where the owners' quarters access hatch was located. The galley and crew's quarters were forward of the engineroom. *Siva* carried a ketch rig and could fly some 700 square feet of sail as a steadying rig: two headsails on the mainmast, and a jib and trysail on the mizzen. Tripp sold *Siva* after only five or six years; then, until the Second World War, the yacht was homeported at Miami Beach. No record of *Siva* has surfaced after the war's end. With some 52 drawings, *Siva*'s design was exceptionally well detailed, and made for a busy little design office, coming as she did when LFH had commissions for a number of innovative and carefully detailed sailing yachts. She's worth studying more closely, as features such as her laminated oak anchor davit, and wormdrive, hand-cranked davit winch, could possibly find application today.

Catalog No. 38.76

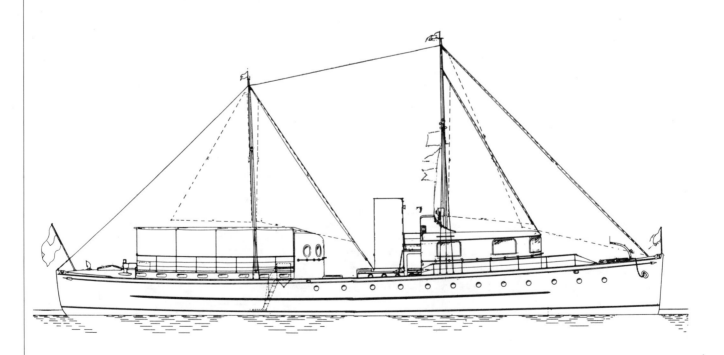

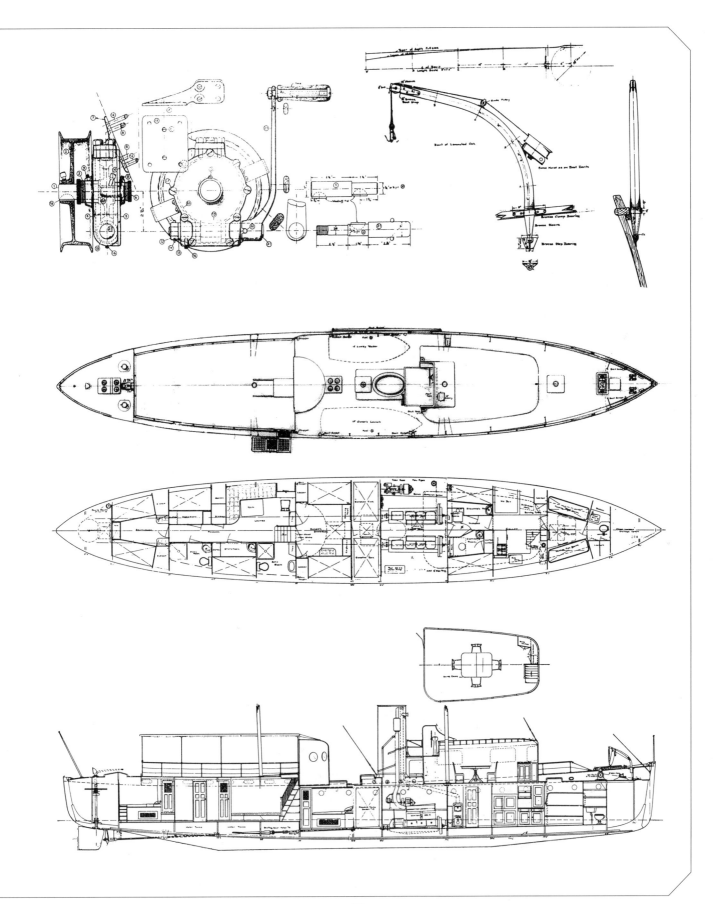

WALRUS, A KETCH-RIGGED MOTORSAILER OF 1929
50'0" x 14'6"

Although *Walrus* is featured in *Sensible Cruising Designs*, we've included her here simply to contrast her with *Dispatch* (preceding pages), which followed on her heels—a powerboat, for the same client, of almost the same overall length and weighing only one-quarter as much! *Walrus*'s concept originated while L. Francis was still with Burgess, Swasey, and Paine, her first iteration being a double-ender much like one of the Coast Guard's self-righting motor lifeboats and shown on page 339 of *SCD*. Later, in the very early days of his own design office, LFH carried the idea to completion in *Walrus*, a proportionally wider craft of about the same length. Lawley built her in 1929 for LFH's patron and Marblehead neighbor Charles A. Welch, who had also commissioned *Dispatch* (in all, Welch had LFH prepare 11 different designs). *Walrus* is seakindly, whereas *Dispatch* was anything but. For Welch, a true sailor, *Walrus* must have been a welcome replacement for *Dispatch*, which he disposed of in 1930.

To the best of our knowledge, *Walrus* ended her days in the Bahamas, or at least that's where she hailed from when last listed in 1979. Ford diesels had replaced her original twin Lathrop gas engines by 1962, and she was known as *Wind Quest* since 1964 when she headed south. Before that, for a short time in the mid-1950s, Mystic Seaport accepted her as a donation for resale. In shape and construction, *Walrus* holds to tradition, in spite of the rash of unconventional LFH designs that preceded and followed her. She's handsome as well, with hollow forward waterlines, a wineglass-shaped transom, and a salty sheerline. In terms of interior arrangement, she follows fishing-schooner layout forward, with a fo'c's'le lined with settees, a table at the mast, a potbellied stove, an opening skylight above, and lockers across the face of the bulkhead. The owners sleep aft of the engineroom, where there is a full-width stateroom with a pair of berths wide enough for two persons.

Catalog No. 38.81

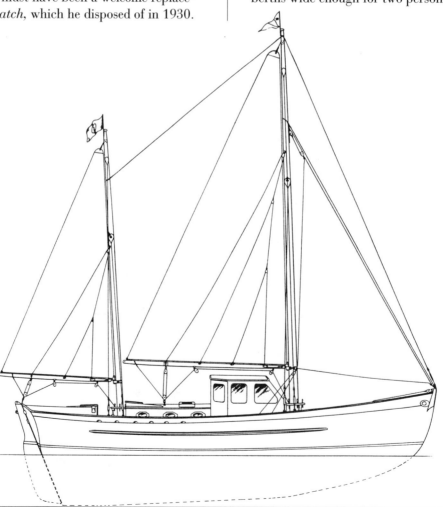

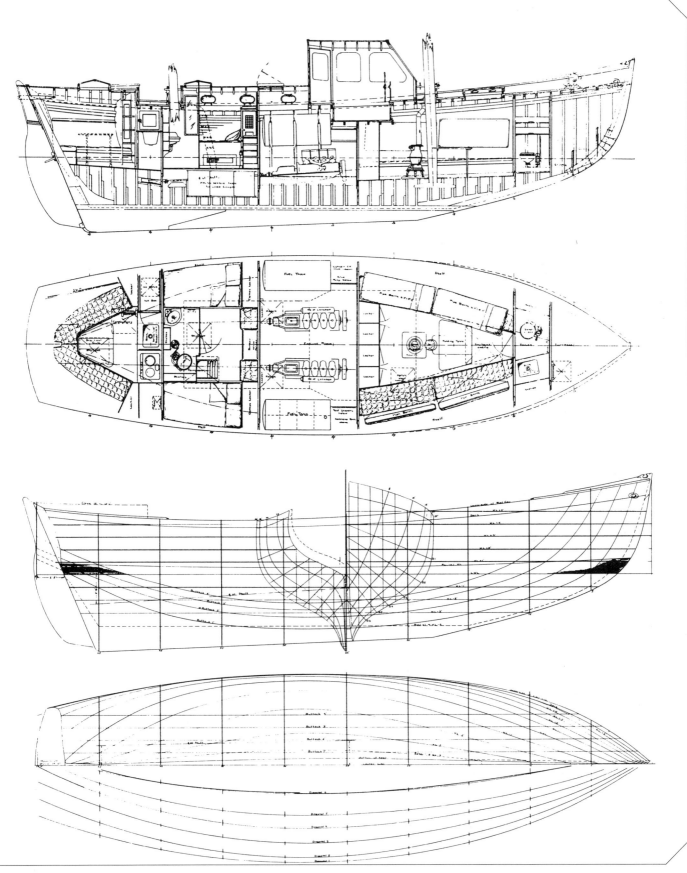

WINTHROP L. WARNER
1900 – 1987

With an artist mother and a father engaged in the manufacture of marine hardware, and himself growing up on the banks of the Connecticut River at Middletown, Winthrop Loring Warner was seemingly predestined to become a yacht designer. His drafting abilities surfaced during high school, and he worked at that trade for two summers around his senior year across Long Island Sound at the Greenport Basin and Construction Co. where both yachts and commercial craft were being built and repaired. Warner, or "Wink" as he was always known, entered MIT in 1920 and graduated four years later as a genuine Naval Architect and Marine Engineer.

Stints over the next five years at Electric Boat in Bayonne, New Jersey, the Portland Boat Works just across the river from Middletown, at the Massachusetts design offices of John Alden (in Boston) and William Hand (in Fairhaven), and at the New York design offices of Chester Nedwidek and, briefly, Philip Rhodes, provided the on-the-job-training so necessary for professional perspective. In 1929, full of confidence and with a 53' ketch to design, Warner set up his own office back in his hometown. The Depression that followed hurt, but by no means put him under. In fact, according to Ralph Jackson, who, hired in 1931 as draftsman, was associated with Warner for 15 years, some of the best times were on the eve

of the Second World War after the economy improved and the Warner office took up selling marine insurance and brokering used boats as well as designing new ones. Warner and Jackson could be on the drafting boards or in various boatshops supervising new construction during the winters, and come spring and summer could get out on the water with sailing trials. Except during the war years (1941-45), the Middletown office of Winthrop L. Warner stayed active with increasing recognition, especially to the readers of the yachting magazines where Warner designs appeared with predictable regularity. In time, Warner offered about a dozen stock designs; later, when he was in semi-retirement, that number was doubled and promoted by Seven Seas Press's booklet entitled *Cruising Designs from the Board of Winthrop L. Warner.*

Warner remained a bachelor until the age of 40, when in 1940 he married Louise Bunce. The Warners had two children, Loring and Mary Lou. Wink had always owned a cruising sailboat, and that pattern continued uninterrupted until the Warners moved to the year-round warmth of Vero Beach, Florida, about 1960. Warner personal yachts were the 35' sloop *Nancy R* (1931–34), the 28' cutter *Manisees* (1935–38), the 37' cutter *Manisees* (1940–47), the 40' cutter *Mary Loring* (1947–53), and the Warner 33 *Mary Loring* (1954–61).

THE WARNER COLLECTION

Since Warner generated a lot of paperwork and saved it all, including preliminary drawings, calculations, written specifications, and correspondence, and bequeathed every bit of it to Mystic Seaport, this collection is one of the Museum's largest, with the drawings alone numbering 3,479 sheets. Contained in it are over 100 complete Warner designs, mostly of cruising sailboats, but with a sprinkling of rowboats and engine-driven craft, including *Selden III*, the 64' ferryboat that runs between Hadlyme and Chester on the Connecticut River. There are about the same number of incomplete designs, some being proposals never finished nor used for building, and others prepared for alterations on existing boats. For reference, Warner amassed a big file of copies of plans by other designers, which form part of this collection; and, finally, there are a great many drawings of miscellaneous details and a few that, although drawn by Warner, have nothing to do with boats.

There is a sameness to Warner's designs that enable categorizing, especially with his sailboats and motorsailers. Short overhangs and springy sheerlines prevailed in pre-war designs, while after the War his boats are generally pulled out to have longer ends as in the Cambridge Cadet, *Rowdy II*, and *Snapper Blue*. For a given hull design, especially ones done before the War, there is usually a variety of rig and arrangement options, so a potential client could choose, say, between a sloop, cutter, or ketch (Warner's three favorite rigs), and select an interior arrangement he or she found most appealing.

Certainly there were more imaginative designers than Winthrop Warner—Burgess and Herreshoff, for example—but it is hard to find a more accurate or technically competent one, or one who could express himself more attractively on

paper. In terms of hull construction, Warner's drawings reflect standard practice for the time (he used the Nevins scantling rule), and their consistency indicates that it was the arrangement and rig variations that most interested this designer. Warner was a detailist, always providing builders with comprehensive written specifications and following up with revisions to accurately represent the boats as built. His correspondence with owners and builders leaves little doubt that this designer had no tolerance for unapproved alterations to the boats whose construction he was expected to supervise.

Getting work during the depressed 1930s, and to some degree into the early 1950s, meant that designers had to find ways to get their clients a usable boat as inexpensively as possible. This meant going to the small rural yards with low overheads and wage rates, and, unfortunately, it meant using short-lived galvanized steel rather than bronze for the screws and bolts that fastened things together. As Warner himself has written, "If prices were low enough, someone would dig back in the larder to buy the boat." As a result, the early Warner boats, while they were lovely to look at as long as they lasted, haven't held up well over time, and attrition has taken an early toll.

Although it was Warner who got Paul Luke his first dozen building jobs, Luke, with an eye always to associate himself with the wealthiest clients, suddenly switched to building designs by Nielsen, Sparkman & Stephens, and other designers who insisted on premium-quality materials and somehow had owners willing to pay a higher price. These were mostly people who were after racer/cruisers, with the emphasis on successful racing. For some reason, Warner never entered this design arena.

THE WINTHROP WARNER PLANS

SMALL CRAFT

LOA	Beam	Description	Date	Plan Codes	Des.No.	Cat.No.
4'1"	2'11"	V-bottomed pram (fiberglass)	1956	LCDh	181	46.190
6'0"	3'7"	V-bottomed dinghy, double-ended & fat (fiberglass)	1956	LOCA	182	46.179
7'10"	4'0"	Indian River-class sailing pram, marconi or gaff rig	1963	LCSDR	197	46.88 & .89
7'11"	3'9"	Flat-bottomed pram, ugly!	1949	LOCPDh	148	46.162
11'6"	4'6"	NADA Class A lapstrake frostbite sailing dinghy	1933	LOCSADh	44	46.14
12'2"	5'1"	V-bottomed lapstrake daysailer w/sloop rig	1948	LOCSADr	69	46.20
12'5"	4'4"	V-bottomed sailing skiff w/single lugsail	1937	LCS		46.232
13'0"	6'6"	Sloop-rigged daysailer w/outboard rudder	1935	LCSA	121	46.137
13'0"	6'7"	Sloop-rigged daysailer w/catboat-type hull	1932	LOCS	40	46.146
13'6"	5'10"	V-bottomed Indian River-class sloop	1959	LOCSADhDr	189	46.79
14'0"	4'10"	Undecked outboard runabout	1954	LOAP	165	46.70
15'4"	5'6"	Intracoastal-class sloop *Blue Peter* w/outboard rudder	1963	LCSDhDr	195	46.86
16'0"	7'9"	Inboard-powered launch w/fat hull	1938	LCP	92	46.147
16'6"	7'7"	Cape Cod catboat *Tid Bit* w/layout options	1962	LCSA	193	46.84
17'5"	7'8"	Cape Cod catboat *Bobcat* w/deck & sliding hatch	1976	LCSA	201	46.91
17'8"	7'0"	V-bottomed Baymaster 18 fiberglass cruising sloop *Bluebonnet II*	1967	LCSADh	205	46.95
17'9"		Outboard skiff w/flat bottom	1948	LC		46.283
17'9"	6'1"	Undecked flat-bottomed skiff for outboard motor	1949	LOCAP	135	46.57
17'10"	6'6"	Sloop-rigged daysailer *Peridot III* (like Alden O-boat)	1932	LOCSADr	32	46.7 & .157

SAILING YACHTS & MOTORSAILERS

LOA	Beam	Description	Date	Plan Codes	Des.No.	Cat.No.
20'0"	6'9"	Cruising sloop *Dirigo* w/outbd. rudder & alt. double-head rig	1936	LOCSADh	75	46.23
20'3"	6'10"	Cruising sloop *Wee Jan* w/outboard rudder & bowsprit	1940	LOCSADhDr	100	46.34
21'0"	9'6"	Catboat *Foam*		LCS		46.339
22'2"	8'0"	Cruising sloop w/outboard rudder & keel/centerboard option	1954	LOCAPDhDr	116	46.43
22'5"	7'9"	Trailer-sailer sloop w/centerboard, kick-up rudder, & doghouse		LOCSA	155	46.63
22'11"	8'0"	Cruising sloop w/V-bottom, outboard rudder, & centerboard		LCS	198	46.89
23'4"	7'6"	Trailer-sailer cruising sloop *Halcyon*	1956	LOCSADhDr	188	46.78
23'5"	8'1"	V-bottomed cruising sloop *Fellowship II* w/outboard rudder		LOCSDhDr	206	46.96
24'0"	11'6"	Cape Cod keel catboat *Mrs. O* w/gaff or marconi rig	1955	LOCSA	159	46.66
24'0"	11'6"	Cruising sloop w/Cape Cod catboat-type hull		LCSA	173	46.198
24'6"	9'0"	Short-ended cruising sloop *Typhoon* w/bowsprit & boomkin	1938	LOCSADhDr	85	46.2
24'10"	8'0"	Cruising sloop w/trunk cabin	1937	LCS	86	46.150
25'9"	9'1"	Cruising sloop *Pawnee* et al w/outboard rudder & rig options	1933	LOCSADhDr	58	46.17
26'6"	9'2"	Cruising sloop *Valiant* et al w/outboard rudder & rig options	1936	LOCSADhDr	81	46.26
27'9"	8'1"	Cruising sloop *Blimey II* w/moderate overhangs	1937	LOCSADhDr	87	46.29
27'11"	8'11"	Short-ended cruising sloop	1952	LCSA	6	46.3
28'0"	9'9"	Cruising cutter *Ningui* et al w/outboard rudder & bowsprit	1935	LOCSADhDr	68	46.19
28'0"	9'9"	Cruising cutter w/outboard rudder & rig options	1936	LOCSADhDr	80	46.25
28'4"	8'7"	Cruising sloop *Susan* w/doghouse & bowsprit	1946	LOCSA	123	46.48

PLAN CODES: L=lines; **O**=offsets; **C**=construction; **S**=sail; **A**=arrangement; **P**=profile; **Dh**=hull detail; **Dr**=rigging detail

LOA	Beam	Description	Date	Plan Codes	Des.No.	Cat.No.
28'7"	8'7"	Cambridge Cadet sloop, cutter, ketch, or yawl	1947	LOCSADhDr	126	46.50
28'7"	8'7"	Cruising sloop *Cadet* w/doghouse	1949	LCS	137	46.165
30'0"	10'3"	Sloop-rigged motorsailer *Kamibet* et al w/ various layouts & rigs	1936	LOCSADhDr	82	46.27
30'6"	10'0"	Knockabout sloop, cutter, or yawl w/trunk cabin	1935	LOCSADhDr	49	46.110
30'9"	10'3"	Cruising sloop w/doghouse	1949	CSAP	138	46.168-9
31'11"	9'9"	Cruising cutter *Yankee Girl III* et al w/ bowsprit & yawl option	1940	LOCSADhDr	102	46.36
32'0"	10'11"	Motorsailer *Yin Yang* et al w/sloop rig, trunk cabin, & other options	1935	LOCSADhDr	70	46.21
32'2"	10'3"	Motorsailer *Uno* w/sloop rig, raised deck, & pilothouse	1936	LCSA	76	46.138
32'6"	9'0"	Cruising sloop w/doghouse		LOCSADh	151	46.61
32'10"	10'4"	Warner 33 cruising cutter w/many options	1950	LOCSADh	152	46.62 & .167
33'1"	9'9"	Acadia 33 sloop *Vagrant* w/cutter & yawl options	1960	LOCSADr	191	46.81
33'1"	9'9"	Acadia 33 ketch *Nimbus IV* w/clipper-bow option	1967	LOCSADhDr	196	46.87
34'1"	8'11"	Knockabout-type cruising cutter	1953	LOCSADh	98	46.33
34'6"	10'8"	Sloop-rigged motorslr. *Lightning* w/raised deck & trunk cabin	1932	LOCSADr	43	46.13
34'8"	11'0"	Cruising ketch *Highlander* w/bowsprit & rig options	1934	LOCSADhDr	36	46.9
34'8"	11'0"	Cruising yawl *Meridian* w/bowsprit & rig options	1936	LOCSADhDr	71	46.124
34'8"	11'0"	Cruising cutter *Robinhood* et al w/bowsprit	1940	CSADhDr	101	46.35
35'0"	9'0"	Knockabout cruising yawl w/double-head rig option	1954	LOCSA	171	46.73
35'0"	10'9"	Cruising yawl *Vieserre* w/alternate cutter or ketch options	1954	LOCSADhDr	104	46.37
35'0"	11'0"	Gaff-rigged cruising ketch w/bowsprit	1954	LOCSA	15	46.4
36'4"	10'9"	Sloop-rigged motorsailer *Phalarope* with pilothouse option	1941	LOCSADhDr	108	46.39
36'6"	13'0"	Sea Witch-type schooner or ketch w/clipper bow	1941	LCSA	129	46.174
37'1"	10'1"	Cruising cutter *Blue Jay* et al w/various layouts & rigs	1938	LOCSA	90	46.30
37'4"	10'9"	Cruising cutter *Phoenix* w/ketch option	1964	LOCSADhDr	192	46.83
37'10"	10'10"	Cruising cutter w/doghouse & centerboard	1956	LCSADr	127	46.51
37'10"	10'10"	Cruising cutter w/doghouse	1954	LOCADh	156	46.64
38'0"	11'8"	Cruising ketch *Nimbus* w/alternate rig options	1935	LOCSADhDr	72	46.22
39'6"	12'8"	Ketch-rigged motorsailer *Edith M* w/trunk cabin	1932	LCSADr	38	46.12
39'8"	10'0"	Cruising sloop *Rowdy II* w/doghse. & cutter, ketch, or yawl options	1949	LOCSADhDr	130	46.53
39'10"	10'1"	Cruising cutter *Astral* et al; sloop, or yawl with bowsprit option	1941	LOCSADhDr	112	46.40
39'11"	11'8"	Cruising ketch w/aft cabin		CSA	194	46.85
40'0"		Plumb-stemmed motorsailer *Roaring Forty* w/rig options		CSADr	4	46.101
40'2"	10'6"	Cruising cutter *Snapper Blue*	1946	LOCSADhDr	124	46.49
40'2"	10'6"	Cruising sloop or ketch w/centerboard & low doghouse	1952	LOCSADhDr	145	46.59
40'5"		Sailing yacht w/outboard rudder		LCSPDh	184	46.180
40'9"	11'8"	Cruising ketch w/doghouse & clipper-bow option		LOCSADhDr	207	46.97
41'9"	12'1"	Sloop- or ketch-rigged motorsailer *Volana* et al w/pilothouse option	1939	LOCSADhDr	97	46.32
41'10"	11'3"	Sloop-rigged motorsailer w/pilothouse	1938	LOCSADr	91	46.31
42'8"	12'0"	Cruising cutter *Congar* w/outboard rudder & sloop/cutter options	1949	LOCSADhDr	132	46.55
43'0"	10'5"	Knockabout cruising sloop	1956	LOCSADh	107	46.38
45'0"	12'3"	Cruising ketch w/long trunk cabin & bowsprit	1936	LOCSADhDr	79	46.24
45'0"	13'0"	Motorsailer, cutter or ketch		LCSA	209	46.99
46'3"	13'1"	Cruising ketch *Blue Sea III* w/bowsprit	1932	LOCSADhDr	31	46.6 & .344
46'3"	13'1"	Gaff schooner w/main topsail-(looks like *Malabar II)*	1936	LOCSADh	84	46.28
48'8"	13'4"	Cruising ketch *Tere* w/'midship cockpit & aft cabin	1962	LOCSADh	190	46.80
49'7"	13'1"	Cruising ketch w/low doghouse	1953	LOCSADh	139	46.58
52'7"	13'4"	Cruising ketch *Felisi* w/flush deck & bowsprit	1930	LOCSADhDr	20	46.10 & .11
61'0"	15'9"	Dragger-type motorsailer w/ketch rig		LCSA	203	46.93
67'0"	18'0"	Ketch-rigged motorsailer w/'midship cockpit & aft cabin		LCSA	164	46.197

POWER YACHTS & COMMERCIAL VESSELS

LOA	Beam	Description	Date	Plan Codes	Des.No.	Cat.No.
20'0"	7'0"	Undecked yacht club launch w/towing bitt	1934	LOCAPDh	64	46.18
25'9"	8'3"	Launch *Charlotte* w/forward shelter cabin	1936	LOCAP	73	46.125 & .249
27'3"	8'9"	Power cruiser *Sting Ray* w/pilothouse or windshield option	1950	LOCAPDh	134	46.56
28'4"	9'4"	V-bottomed power cruiser w/raised deck & small pilothouse	1952	LAP	170	46.72
29'6"	9'9"	Power cruiser *Early Bird* for commuting, twin-screw	1951	LOCAPDh	169	46.69
30'0"	10'0"	Power cruiser *Broadbill* w/raised deck & small pilothouse	1933	LOCAPDh	46	46.15
30'0"	10'0"	Power cruiser *Gray Gull* w/long cabin & engine aft	1933	LOCAODh	47	46.16
32'1"	10'6"	Twin-screw power cruiser w/pilothouse or windshield option	1953	LOCAPDh	162	46.67
32'2"	10'6"	Power cruiser w/trunk cabin & pilothouse or windshield	1949	LCAP		46.158
32'2"	10'7"	Power cruiser w/flying bridge	1956	LOCDh		46.76
32'10"	10'4"	Power cruiser *Percheron* w/pilothouse & steadying sail	1955	LOCAP	177	46.75
35'2"	10'7"	Power cruiser *Walrus* w/open back pilothouse	1956	LOCAP	180	46.76
36'3"	11'0"	Power cruiser w/raised deck & steadying rig	1940	LCP	109	46.154
38'7"	10'5"	Power cruiser *Ailenroc II* w/raised deck & cockpit canopy	1932	LOCAPDh	25	46.5
50'10"	14'9"	Research vessel *Shang Wheeler* w/mast & various layouts	1951	LOCAPDh	150	46.60
50'10"	14'9"	Twin-screw power cruiser w/large deckhouse & rig	1956	LOCAP	185	46.77
54'8"	15'8"	Western-rigged dragger *Carl J* w/transom stern	1941	LOCAPDh	113	46.41
56'3"	14'9"	Power cruiser w/raised deck & aft cabin	1956	LOCAPDh	35	46.8
56'9"	15'8"	New England 57 (dragger-type power cruiser) *Blue Star*	1969	LOCSAPDh	202	46.92
60'0"	16'0"	Houseboat w/tunnel stern & open steering		LOCAP	1	46.1
64'1"	15'4"	Power cruiser w/plumb stem, deckhouse, & aft canopy		LOCAP	26	46.127
64'6"	30'0"	Car ferry *Selden III* w/square ends & off-center deckhouse	1949	LCAPDh	128	46.52
64'10"	12'10"	Power cruiser w/trunk cabin, flying bridge, & options		LCAPDh	200	46.90

Note: The Warner Collection includes such an enormous number of reference drawings
that listing them all was impractical. Among them are copies of various drawings by
John G. Alden, Colin Archer, S.S. Crocker, William H. Hand, George I. Hodgdon, Jr.,
Chester Nedwidek, Philip L. Rhodes, and Sparkman & Stephens. Inquire for specifics
from Ships Plans Division, Mystic Seaport Museum.

© Mystic Seaport, Rosenfeld Collection, Mystic, Connecticut. Negative 116766F

Mary Loring, 1947

73

ROARING FORTY, A SWORDFISHERMAN OF 1924
40'0"

Seeing any designer's early drawings, done before his eye or his drafting ability evolved to refinement, serves to emphasize that all prominent yacht designers began by turning out rather crude work. Aspiring designers can take hope that, with time and practice, they too might turn out polished plans for successful watercraft. Here is one of Warner's early designs, done when fresh out of MIT at age 24, showing a conversion from what looks like a decommissioned navy launch into a sloop or schooner-rigged motorsailer, complete with a swordfishing pulpit. The construction drawing calls for raising the sheer, and adding a cabin, catboat-style rudder, and rig.   Catalog No. 46.101

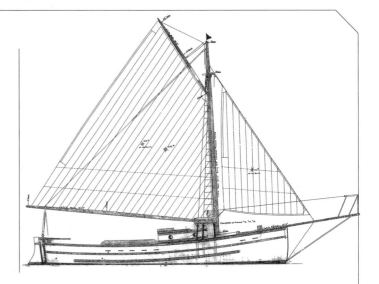

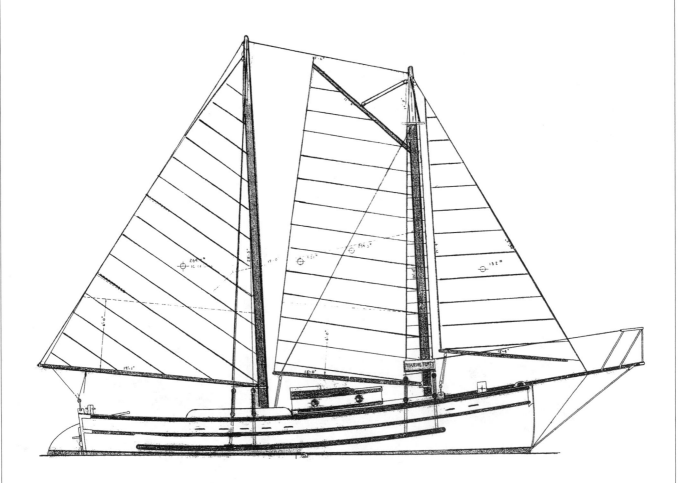

A KETCH-RIGGED MOTORSAILER OF 1929
24'0" x 7'0"

Warner's drafting improved dramatically, and by 1929 could be called refined. His eye, however, still had a way to go, as can be seen in this sailplan. His lifelong choice of flat, raked windshields perhaps began here, and while one can argue their aesthetic merits (personally, I never cared for them), there's little doubt that the tipped-back pilothouse could be improved. Warner labeled this as his design No. 6, but it is obvious that he'd had considerable drafting practice in the five years that passed since design No. 4. What didn't take place at MIT surely happened during his jobs in the design offices of John G. Alden, William H. Hand, and Chester Nedwidek, from which some of the very best drafting in the country emerged. Chances are that this is another conversion, since there are neither lines nor construction drawings. Although narrower than traditional Cape Cod catboats, this hull in profile resembles them. The boomed spritsails save in both running rigging and in mast length, and, for sails as small as these make very good sense.

Catalog No. 46.106

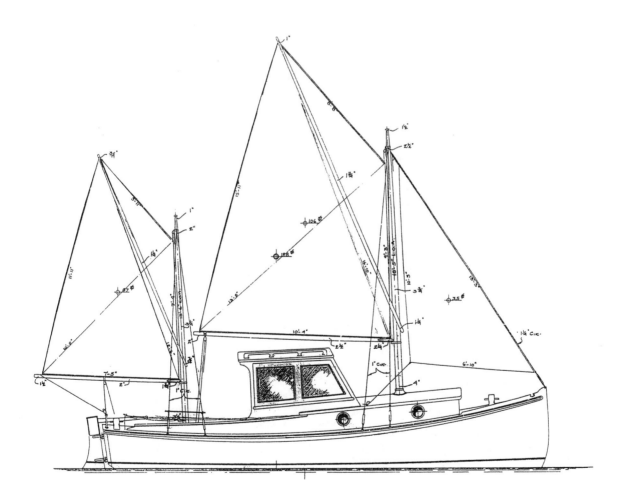

FELISI, A GAFF-RIGGED CRUISING KETCH OF 1930
52'7" x 13'4"

Warner's career as an independent designer really began with the design of *Felisi*, a commission awarded the recently educated and more recently experienced young designer by Middletown (Connecticut) Yacht Club Commodore T.M. Russell. With but two exceptions, *Felisi* would be the largest sailing yacht in Warner's repertoire. One can see in her hull shape the influence of both Alden and Hand, but the ketch rig probably came from the owner, who, it is written, cared for ease of handling and seakindliness more than speed. Following the practice of his former employers, Warner specified half her ballast to be in the cast lead keel and the other half to be inside the hull, partly as poured-in cement and partly as steel boiler punchings. *Felisi* is a flush-decker, having full standing headroom under the deckbeams and therefore not requiring the usual trunk cabin. Warner gave no rake to her masts as a gaff-rigger, but shows at least a little mast rake in a later conversion to tall-masted marconi. It is obvious that he put considerable effort into this design. There are 16 sheets in all, far more than would have come from the busy offices of Hand or Alden. Russell's choice of designers was a wise one, and having the designer nearby allowed him to work cooperatively on the details. The building job went to Dauntless Shipyard, only a short drive downriver in Essex, another convenience for owner and designer alike. After some 47 years in New England waters, *Felisi* was taken to the Great Lakes, her last known whereabouts.   Catalog Nos. 46.10 & .11

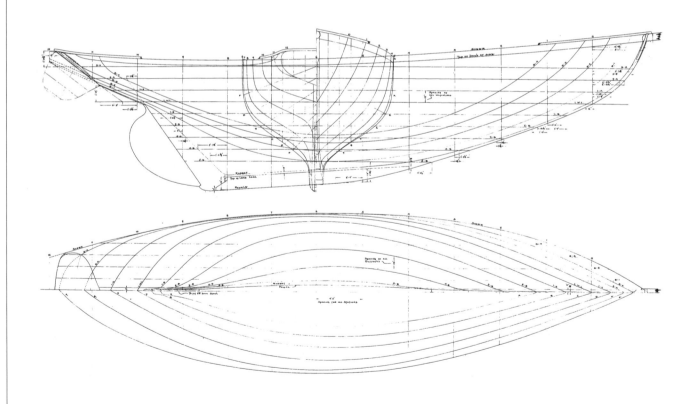

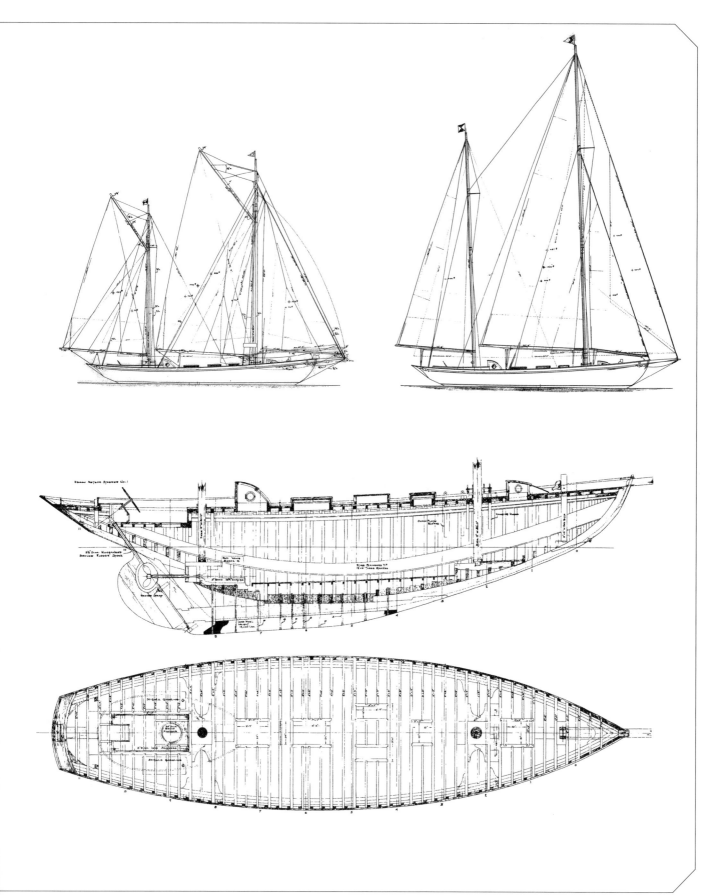

AILENROC II, A RAISED-DECK POWER CRUISER OF 1932
38'7" x 10'5"

The designing and building of new yachts plummeted with the Great Depression, and two years passed before a commission came in for *Ailenroc*, Warner's second complete design. Portland Boat Works, just across the Connecticut River from Warner's office, built *Ailenroc* for Charles Killam, and both *Yachting* and *The Rudder* gave the design good coverage after launching, with *Yachting* (September 1932) running a two-page spread with photographs. Having your design published in a magazine's design section was good for business—it amounted to free advertising—and Warner routinely sent photo prints of the key drawings, along with a general description, of each new design. As a result, most were accepted and published, and yachtsmen throughout the country soon came to know and appreciate Winthrop Warner's fine work. Some of those

readers became clients. As would also become Warner's practice, he used the *Ailenroc* design as a basis for several others. Not all were built, by any means, but by altering the length of the raised deck, repositioning the standing shelter, and rearranging things below deck, he saved the work of drawing new lines and construction plans and could offer a variety of what might appear to be new designs to potential clients having varying requirements and tastes. A favorite and enhancing Warner trademark appears on *Ailenroc*'s profile drawing, as it did earlier on *Felisi*'s—the carved scrollwork at the forward and aft ends of the covestripe which has been cut into the hull just below the sheer. Painted a contrasting color, and especially if done up in gold leaf, these coves and scrolls invariably add a touch of elegance.

Catalog No. 46.5

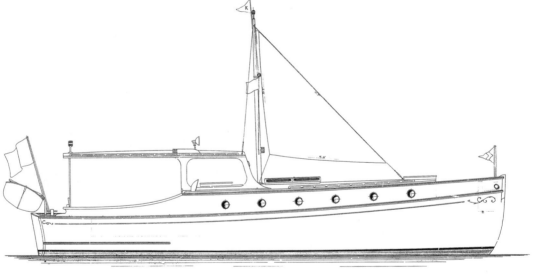

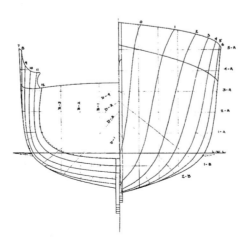

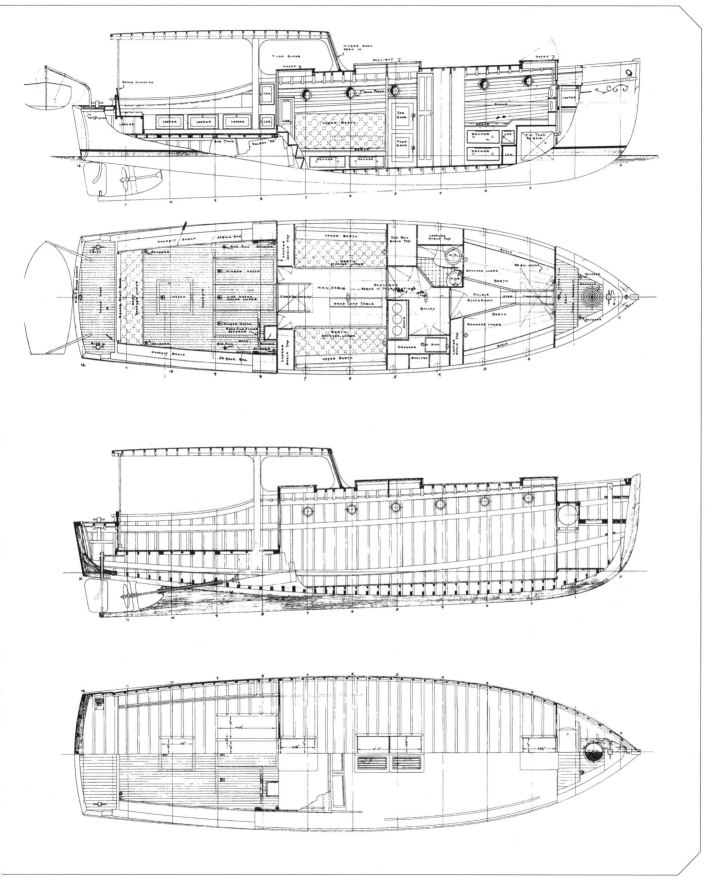

A FROSTBITE DINGHY OF 1933
11'6" x 4'6"

Racing open dinghies in winter became a popular sport in the early 1930s, and, in addition to this design by Warner which resulted in nearly 30 boats, there were many others built to the designs of leading naval architects of the day. Among them were John G. Alden, Sidney Herreshoff, Bill Dyer, Colin Ratsey, Fred Goeller, Norman Skene, Charles Mower, and Francis Sweisguth. This Class A dinghy, at times known as the Seaway Dinghy, conformed to the Rules of the North American Dinghy Assn. This meant, for Class A, that the boat had to be an all-around tender that could be taken on the deck of a larger yacht, be either towed or rowed, and carry up to five persons. A Class A dinghy had to weigh at least 150 pounds, have no more than 72 square feet of sail, and be protected from marring other boats' topsides and kept afloat after a capsize by means of a wraparound cork or kapok-filled canvas fender. Warner and the other designers participated in the racing, and records indicate that Warner, at various times, campaigned three different frostbiters. Most of these boats—28 of them, in fact—went to the American Yacht Club in Rye, New York. Like most dinghies of the era, the plans call for lapstrake cedar planking 9/32" thick, which was the minimum allowable. In 1934,

Warner adapted the Class A dinghy's lines plan to Class B for *The Rudder*'s Frostbite design contest, the winner of which would be adopted as a one-design racing class. Here, marconi rigs were permitted, and thwarts for five and fender rails were no longer necessary.

Catalog No. 46.14

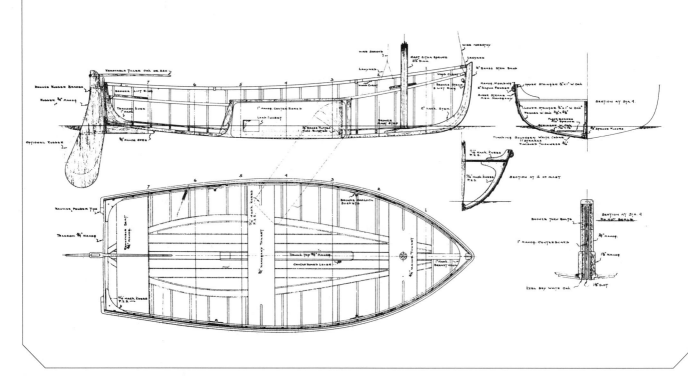

THE INDIAN RIVER CLASS SLOOP OF 1959
13'6" x 5'10"

In 1959, after he moved to Vero Beach, Florida, WLW drew the plans for this decked sloop to be built of ⅜" plywood over sawn frames of spruce. Most novel are the bilgeboards, in place of the usual centerboard, that have been incorporated into the cockpit seats and canted outboard so that when the boat is heeled, the leeward board will be more or less vertical. The bilgeboards are still pivoted, however, so they'll kick up when the water gets too shallow. Likewise, the rudder blade will kick up. Boats built to this design came out first from Indian River Maritime Associates right in Vero Beach, but later were produced in fiberglass as Cardinal Class Sloops by Regatta Plastics in Texas. By then, the bilgeboards had been abandoned in favor of a conventional centerboard. As decked sloops, these boats are somewhat akin to boats of the Blue Jay Class designed by Sparkman & Stephens. But they are wider and have more freeboard and, as a result, should be better in choppy water.   Catalog No. 46.79

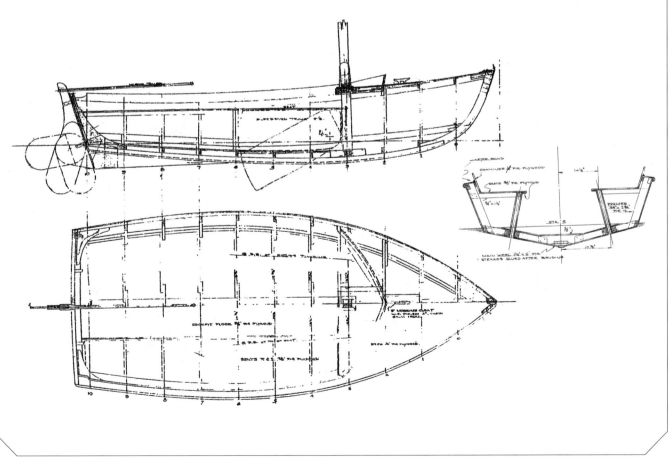

TID BIT, AN OPEN CATBOAT OF 1962
16'6" x 7'7"

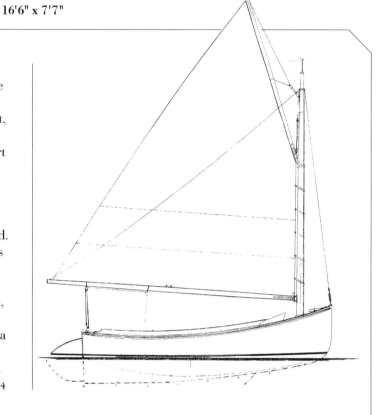

In 1962 on April 6, WLW drew a catboat in profile having a sheerline and oval coaming that were typical of the old-time catboats of Cape Cod. The next day, using exactly the same length, beam, draft, and sail area, he drew the profile you see here, which became the catboat *Tid Bit* built by Herbert Baum for Alfred Scofield. For reasons not clear, Warner boosted the height of the bow and sprung up the sheer to meet it, and abandoned the oval coaming for a less elegant but easier-to-build one that had V-shaped splashboards at its forward end. In spite of the more economical coaming, *Tid Bit*'s deck was of laid teak, sprung with the covering board and nibbed into a foredeck kingplank—a labor-intensive method. The floorboards, seattops, and varnished trim were also of teak. In her final iteration in 1964, Warner drew a profile showing a small cabin. Its flat forward face, however, indicates that the designer (or his client) was still in a cost-cutting frame of mind.   Catalog No. 46.84

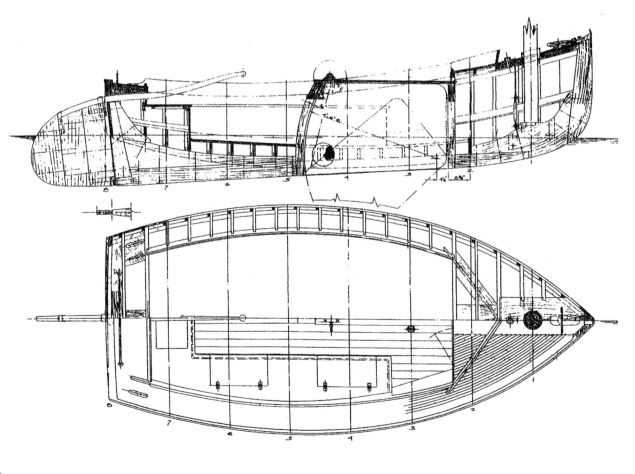

BOB CAT, A DECKED CATBOAT OF 1976

17'5" x 7'8"

Clearly, *Bob Cat* grew out of the earlier *Tid Bit*. In 1965, Warner stretched those lines out nearly a foot, enough forward for a prettier tumblehome bow profile, but most of the added length is aft. *Bob Cat*'s sheer looks better having been raised and flattened some while holding to about the same freeboard at the stem. The bilge is just a little softer as well, making the boat slightly easier to timber out and plank. This boat has better access under the foredeck since Warner gave her a sliding companionway hatch, but he still retained the square-cornered coaming. As is often found in Warner designs, there are alternate rigs and arrangements. In 1966, he drew a *Bob Cat* in profile, with a round-fronted cabin, and a year later came up with a marconi version having shrouds and a roller-reefing boom. No matter what version one favors, one couldn't go far wrong in building a *Bob Cat*. Someone, no doubt, has already done so, since the records indicate that Warner sold a number of sets of her plans. Catalog No. 46.91

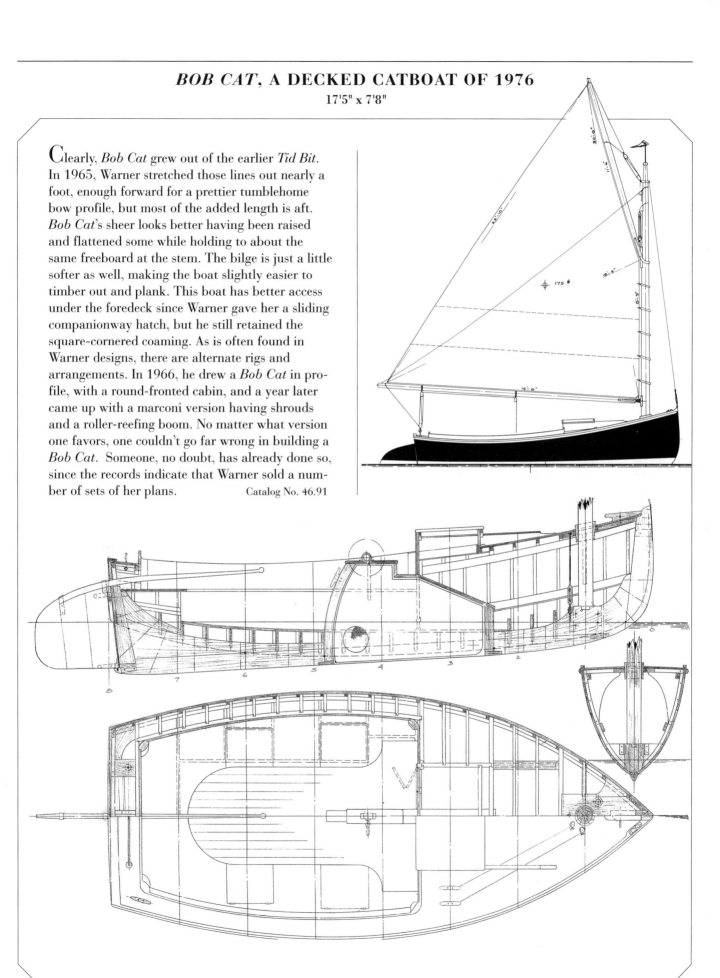

HALCYON, A TRAILER-SAILER OF 1956
23'4" x 7'6"

Because this was to be an owner-built boat, Warner drew some details not ordinarily provided, making this a logical design for someone to build today. As the name implies, she's designed with a long, straight keel that would make loading and unloading from a trailer exceptionally easy, and her mast pivots on a tabernacle mounted on the cabintop for easy raising and lowering. She weighs a little over 3,000 pounds, and her draft is only 2 feet with the centerboard raised. After Ramon Alan built the first boat in 1959, which like the ones that followed was strip-planked and sheathed in fiberglass, Warner offered the Trailer-Sailer as a stock design. At least two more were turned out by Smith & Rhuland of Lunenburg, Nova Scotia, a couple of years later. There's sleeping for two on the V-berth inside the cabin, and the cockpit is plenty long for two more to stretch out under a boom tent. Although rather minuscule, there is a galley below with a seat opposite, under which is a toilet. Best of all, Warner gave the boat an outboard well, complete with a carefully detailed plug for when the motor is out of the well and stored beneath one of the cockpit seats. There'll be no unsightly motor hanging off this boat's stern! The cockpit is self-bailing and is dish-shaped in cross-section so it will drain out through a couple of scuppers in the raised portion of the centerboard trunk. Forward of the cabin bulkhead, the trunk is contained beneath the cabin sole. Warner calls for a metal centerboard of either ¼" bronze or galvanized steel. In all, this is a dandy little boat, worthy of being built again. Although her designer is no longer around to answer questions, there is more than enough guidance in Warner's correspondence file.

Catalog No. 46.78

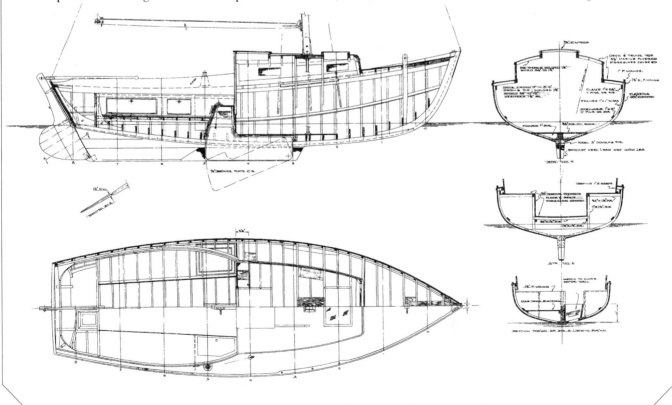

TYPHOON, TABLOID CRUISER OF 1938
24'6" x 9'0"

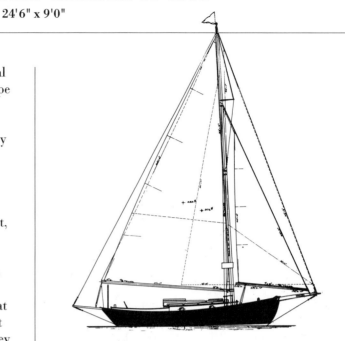

Embodying the family characteristics of elliptical transom, wheel steering, inset waist, and covestripe with scrollwork, *Typhoon* is the smallest of Warner's pre-war cruising craft. She came out in June 1938, built in East Hartford, Connecticut, by Whittaker Marine for Ed Jones. Jones must have liked the concept, for he ordered, new from Rice Bros. the very next year, one of the pair of 34' design no. 71 yawls the yard turned out in 1939. Back to *Typhoon*, now, and her cabin arrangement, for, besides sporting a whole raft of big-boat features above deck like a fife rail at the base of the mast, a pair of bowsprit heel bitts, and laid decks with a nibbed kingplank, she has lots to admire below. First off, she's been fitted with a dinette that converts to a berth—an unusual feature on a boat this small. Opposite, to port, is a full-fledged galley complete with a cast-iron Shipmate stove with an oven. You can't stand fully upright under the cabin in a boat like this, but you can function in the galley fully erect with your head and shoulders sticking through the open companionway. Rather than taking up space with a fully enclosed toilet room, the designer decided on a toilet located between the V-berths—not an ideal place by any means, this being the necessary compromise to having the dinette and comparatively spacious galley. For those requiring more privacy, Warner drew an alternate cabin arrangement later on which replaces one of the V-berths by an enclosed toilet room, and compensation is achieved by a quarter berth to port. It's not a very symmetrical layout, but some may prefer it. Besides drawing an alternate interior, Warner also designed a choice of marconi or gaff sloop rigs. Catalog No. 46.2

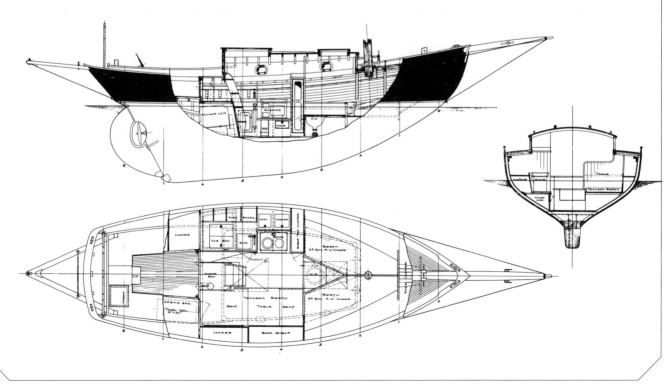

PAWNEE AND *MANDALAY*, A PAIR OF SLOOPS OF 1933
25'9" x 9'1"

This is an adorable hull shape—no doubt about it—and if I were to select a small cruising boat, this design would be high on my list. The lines plan shows a chunky hull, yet one that is unusually graceful. There's a bit of hollow at the bow, the sheerline is springy, the transom is radiused to avoid a "flat panel" appearance, and the sections are faired all the way to the bottom of the keel. Two boats were built to this design by J.G. Wyman of West Haven, Connecticut, and the lines plan reflects the first boat, *Pawnee*. These lines were used for *Mandalay*, but because Warner gave that second boat a heavier ballast keel (to compensate for her bigger sailplan), she floated some 4" deeper than the lines plan indicates. A number of sailplans and several arrangements exist, some preliminary, some reflecting what was built, and a few indicating subsequent modifications. I favor *Mandalay*'s layout and her final (1941) sailplan. This boat's cockpit is but a footwell, which is surely safer for offshore cruising than *Pawnee*'s full-width cockpit. Below decks, this boat's galley, although forward like *Pawnee*'s, is a little larger and more usable. Catalog No. 46.17

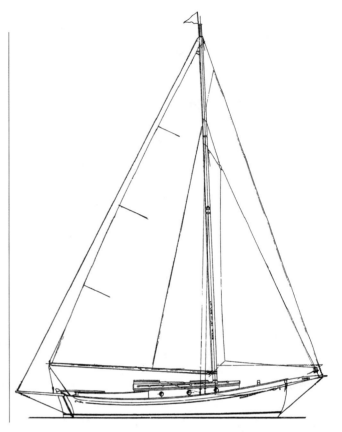

Mandalay

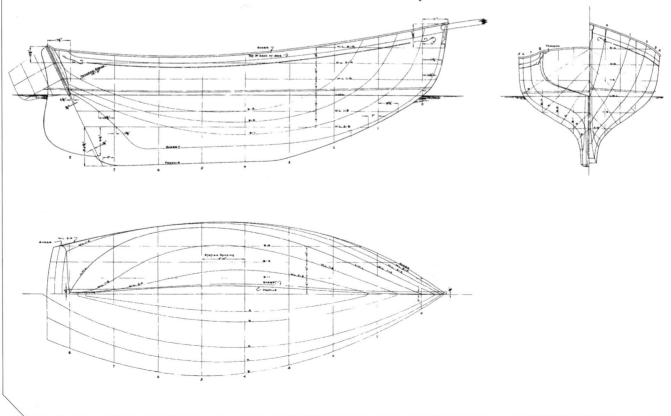

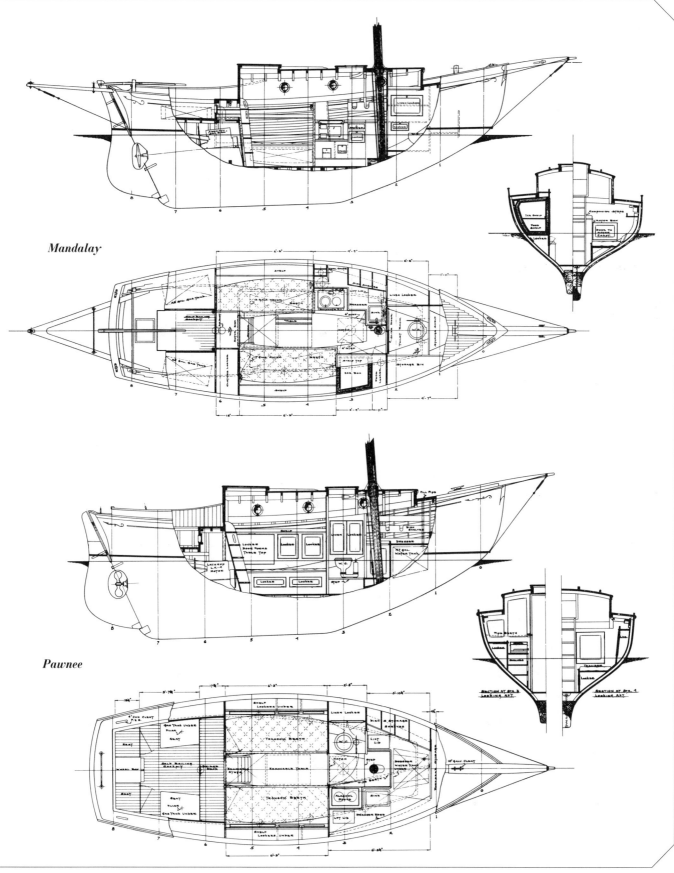

Mandalay

Pawnee

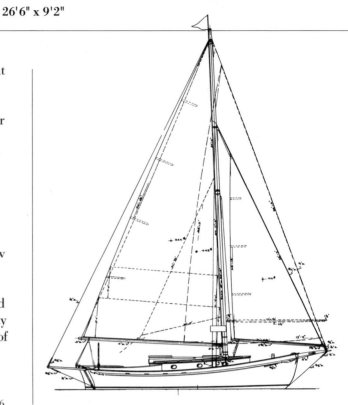

This trio's design grew, quite obviously, from that of *Pawnee* and *Mandalay*. Although, to my eye, the hull lines aren't quite as sweet, they are no doubt an improvement, having been developed for a 16,000-pounds-displacement boat instead of *Pawnee*'s 12,350 pounds, thus allowing a heavier ballast keel. If the specified keel weight of 5,760 pounds is used and construction is not beefed up over what the drawing shows, a boat built to this design can be expected to float where the lines plan indicates. Warner's arrangement drawings were individual for each of the three boats to show minor differences that were desired by their owners, but all three allow the *Mandalay* concept of having the galley forward of the settee/berths, and the toilet room in the forepeak. In spite of the salty appearance, there's six feet of headroom for most of the trunk cabin's length. All three boats were built at the East Greenwich, Rhode Island, yard of F.S. Nock, but launched with different color schemes.

Catalog No. 46.26

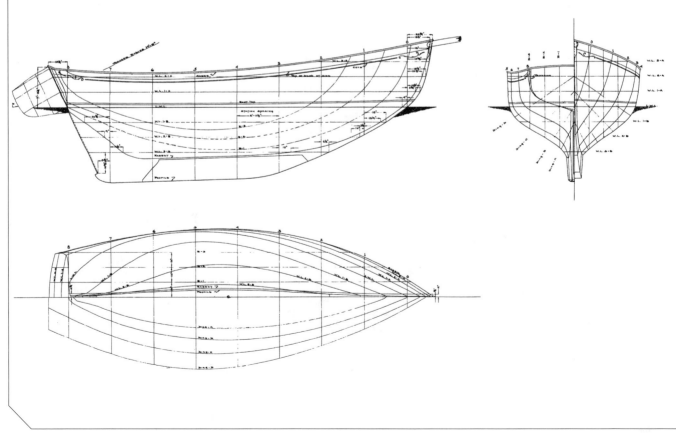

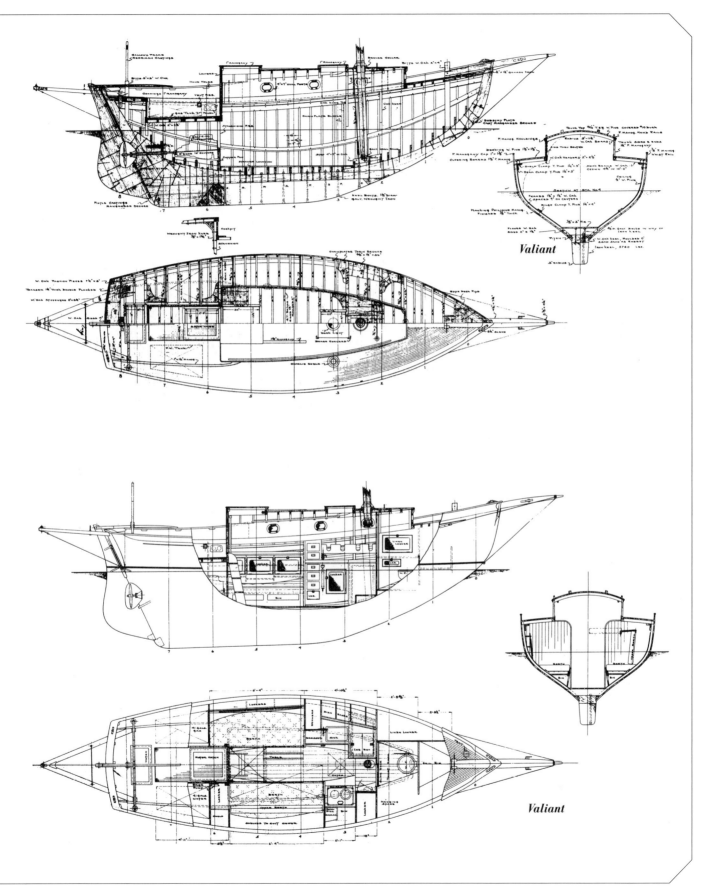

Valiant

Valiant

A SLOOP, YAWL, OR CUTTER OF 1935
30'6" x 10'0"

Warner's records indicate that no boat was ever built to this design, although it was twice published in *The Rudder* (April & December, 1935). Not only is she exceptionally pretty, but offers, in an overall length of slightly over 30', full headroom. Her galley is amidships with an enclosed toilet room opposite to port. She'd be a little cramped for comfortable sitting, however, if more besides the four that were cruising in her came aboard, since the after third of the main-cabin settees, which at night are used for sleeping, run in under the bridge-deck. Surely this is one of Warner's better designs. She deserves to be built. This design started out as a sloop with no bowsprit and 20% less sail area, but Warner wisely changed her to a yawl—a better rig for cruising. He also drew an alternate cutter rig with three headsails, running backstays, no boomkin, and a trunk cabin that runs farther aft—a change that eases the congestion a little at the base of the ladder, which should make for more comfortable seating. There are arrangement and construction drawings for both the four-berth yawl and the three-berth cutter.

Catalog No. 46.110

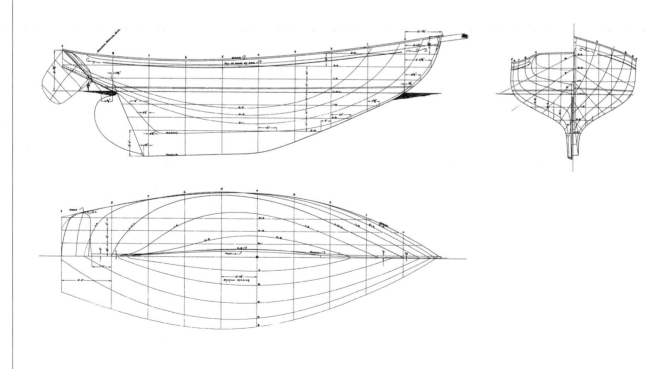

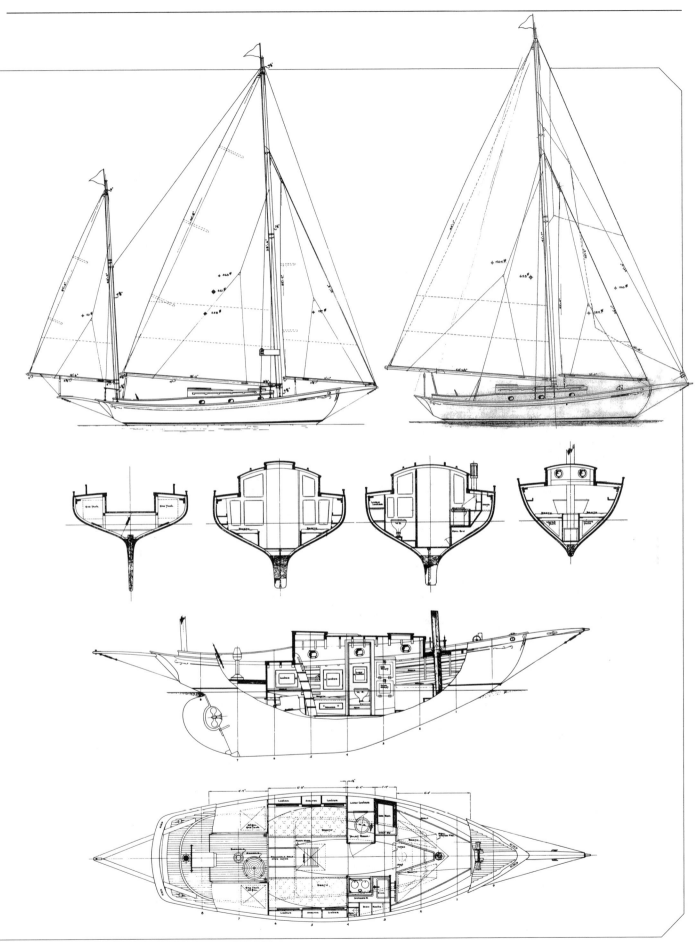

91

HIGHLANDER AND HER SISTER YAWLS, CUTTERS, AND KETCHES
34'8" x 11'0"

The February 1933 issue of *The Rudder* featured what was called "The Architect's Own Boat." It was the first appearance of the 34'8" short-ended cruiser—a design from which many variations have since been built. Half a year later, *Yachting* published the same design, saying that Warner intended to build her for his own use. He never did. (Instead, Warner had the smaller *Manisees* built for himself in 1935.) Through its publication, however, Warner apparently got the commission for *Highlander* the next year. The lines were identical and the arrangement was about the same, but *Highlander* was rigged as a ketch instead of a cutter. She was launched from Portland Boat Works in the fall of 1934, and her drawings were also published. *Meridian* resulted from the exposure *Highlander* received and was launched in 1936. She was yawl-rigged, and for her Warner refined *Highlander*'s lines by giving the transom a touch more deadrise. He also lightened up on her construction, *Highlander* being a heavily-built craft. The same chain of events took place after *Meridian*'s drawings, including her lines plan, were published in both *The Rudder* and *Yachting* in the fall of 1936, clearly demonstrating how effective

magazines were (and still are) as a promotional device. Using identical lines, but redrawing the sailplan for a higher-aspect mainsail, Warner produced the design for *Lenita II* and *Privateer*, both yawls, both built in 1939 by Rice Bros. of East Boothbay, Maine, and both to be homeported in Essex, Connecticut. *Robinhood* followed in 1940, but she carried a cutter rig—a taller and more modern one than Warner had drawn for his "Architect's Own Boat" nearly a decade earlier. Although, except for the change in rig and the usual minor changes in the below-deck arrangement, *Robinhood* was exactly the same as *Meridian*, *Lenita II*, and *Privateer*, Warner gave her a new design number: 101. It gets confusing to chase a design through Warner's work because of his sometimes arbitrary numbering system. For example, to understand this design's evolution, one has to start with No. 36 , move to No. 71, and conclude with No. 101. In the late 1970s, two more No. 36/71/101s were built by Gordon Swift of Kensington, New Hampshire— *Sandpiper* rigged as a ketch, and *Tenacity* as a cutter. And the records indicate that in 1940 one was built on the West Coast as *Señorita*, a yawl.

Catalog Nos. 46.9, 46.35, & 46.124

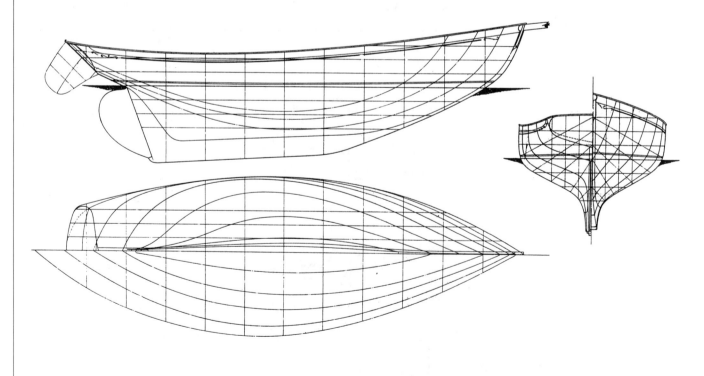

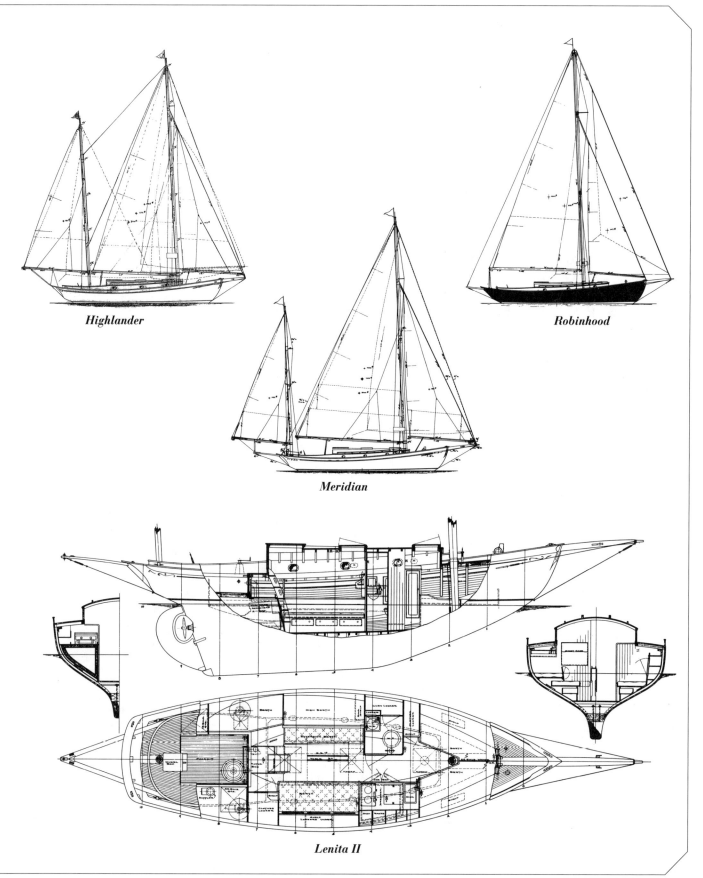

Highlander

Robinhood

Meridian

Lenita II

VIESERRE, A 35' YAWL OF 1960
35'0" x 10'9"

Compared to the preceding design, Warner's design No. 104 (a craft of about the same overall dimensions), this one's main difference is a narrower stern and a sharp-cornered transom. Both features detract some from her looks, although perhaps making for a faster and more seakindly boat. She represents a newer concept in design, and it is obvious that in her Warner was getting away from the Alden-inspired, Friendship sloop-type wide, elliptical transoms, and pursuing hull shapes with more equal buoyancy between bow and stern and less expensive construction back aft as well. And sterns with rolled-in quarters are notoriously difficult to make look right. The steam-bent, oval coaming has been replaced with one whose corners are square as another means of cost reduction. Although Warner's early drawings are dated in 1939, it was well after World War II (1960) before a boat was actually built. She was *Vieserre* and built in Japan for Coast Guard Lt. Thomas A. Seeman. Again, Warner came up with alternates. He has plans for a ketch as well as a cutter, and for the latter rig played around with both a doghouse and a concave, clipper-type bow. In 1962, when masthead rigs were in vogue, Warner updated the cutter's sailplan to show a single-headsail, masthead rig as well as a roller-reefing boom.   Catalog No. 46.37

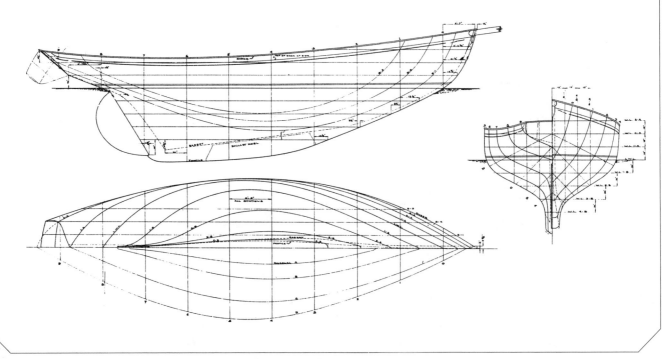

TRADITION AND *NIMBUS*, A SCHOONER AND A KETCH
38'0" x 11'8"

In hull shape this design comes from the same era and is very much the same as Warner's design No. 71, already described. The interesting feature here is, of course, the rig. Frederic Fenger, a contemporary yacht designer, developed and promoted the main-trysail rig, singing its praises in the yachting magazines whenever he could. As a result, he sold the concept to clients like Frank Palmer who, in turn, insisted Warner incorporate this rig in *Nimbus*. Palmer's plan was to use *Nimbus* in South America, but he never had the

boat built. More than a decade later, in 1947, Warner drew up a schooner rig for this hull and managed to work it into the earlier arrangement with very few changes below deck in spite of the masts having to be placed in vastly different locations from those of *Nimbus*. Although Warner refers to the schooner version as *Tradition* (a name that seemed to fit her to a T when *Nimbus*'s rig is considered), he indicates that there was never a boat built from the schooner plans.

Catalog No. 46.22

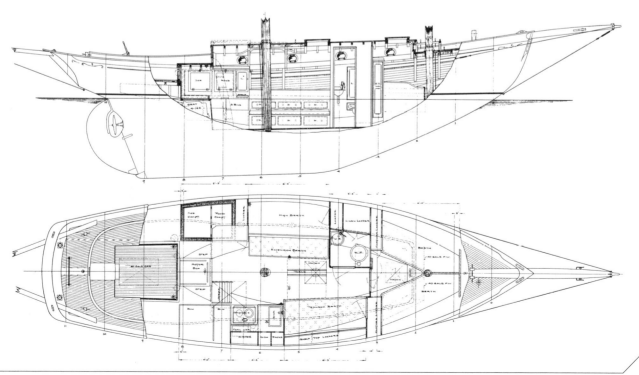

BLUE SEA III, A CRUISING KETCH OF 1932
46'3" x 13'1"

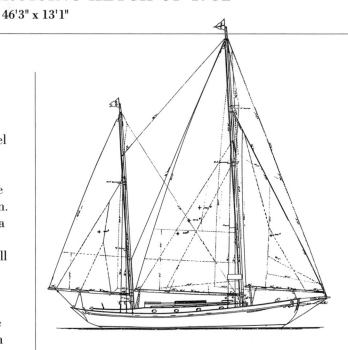

Built in Fairhaven, Massachusetts, by Casey in 1932, *Blue Sea III* was soon sold to California where, as far as we can determine, she ended her days. Warner gave her the hull shape that, in the years to follow, would be his standard for full-keel sailing yachts all during the 1930s. This meant a springy sheerline, a broad elliptical transom, a short, round bow profile, and a forward waterline that was slightly hollow as it approached the stem. His designs of this era also had inset waists with a covestripe just below it terminating in carved scrollwork at each end. Warner kept her draft well below 6', making her unusually shallow for a fixed-keel craft. This was no doubt one of the parameters the owner established at the outset. Her arrangement below decks shows what can be done in a larger-than-usual boat. Aft, in the main cabin, there's good seating on opposite sides of a folding table and, thanks to pull-out settees, sleeping for four at night; the galley, located in the space just forward, runs full width and is cut into only by the enclosed toilet room. There's a two-berth forward stateroom next, then a fo'c's'le which the paid hand, if there was one, would call home. The ketch rig's masts are out of the main living areas near the ends of the boat. Warner spent a good deal of time drawing the plans, several sheets

of which show what various sections through the hull would look like. Those kinds of plans are a real help to an owner not able to visualize such things, but most yacht designers never had the necessary time on their hands. Later in his career Warner gave up this practice as well, relying, as did the others, on a carefully drawn profile and plan view of the arrangement, with maybe only a single sectional view thrown in.   Catalog No. 46.6 & .344

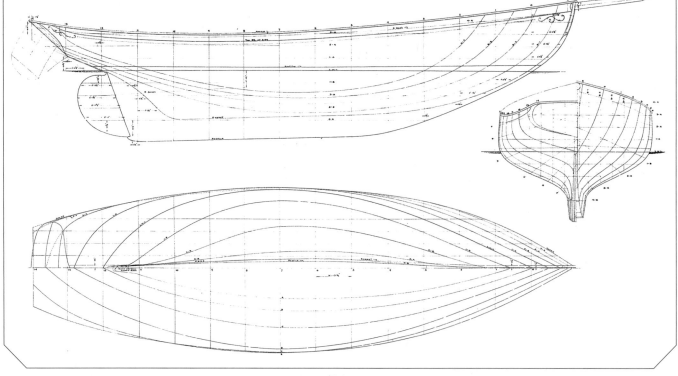

TERE, AN AFT CABIN CRUISING KETCH OF 1962

48'8" x 13'4"

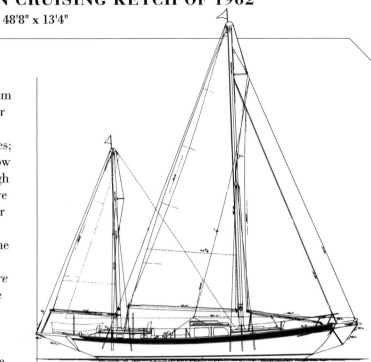

In the early 1960s, fully three decades after he drew the lines for *Blue Sea III*, Warner pulled them out, dusted them off, and used them as a basis for the ketch *Tere*. While most of *Tere*'s lines were traced off the old lines plan, there were differences; the most noticeable of these was the change in bow profiles, *Tere*'s bow having been pulled out enough to account for 2' more overall length. Warner gave the new boat somewhat less sheer, a slightly lower stern, and a touch more drag to the keel; otherwise, when you lay one drawing over the other, the two sets of lines fall right on top of each other. Similarities end with the hull shape, however. *Tere* steers from a 'midship cockpit, aft of which is the owner's double stateroom with its own enclosed toilet space and plenty of lockers and shelves for storage. There's a deckhouse just forward of the cockpit, and the cooking and eating are done here. Forward of that, under the trunk cabin, is another stateroom with its own toilet space. *Tere*'s owner, Louis Valier, had her built by American Marine in Singapore for use in Hawaii. Previously, he'd owned a smaller Warner-designed ketch, and the two men had often corresponded. The unconventional arrangement was more Valier's, by his own admission, than Warner's, but the reports are that it worked out very well. Valier was delighted with the new *Tere*'s performance, finding her very easy to handle and powerful enough to comfortably deal with Hawaii's blustery conditions.

Catalog No. 46.80

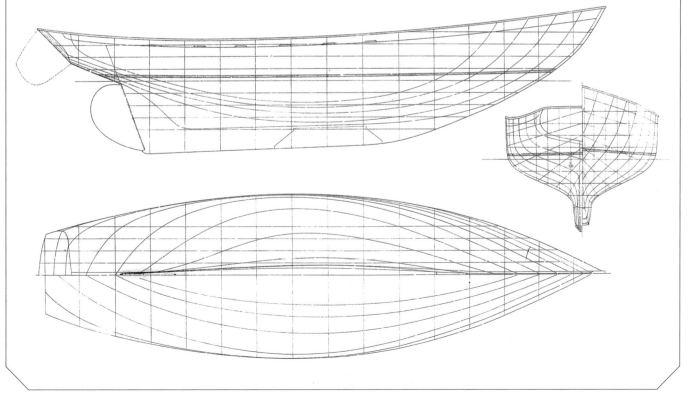

THE CAMBRIDGE CADET OF 1947
28'7" x 8'7"

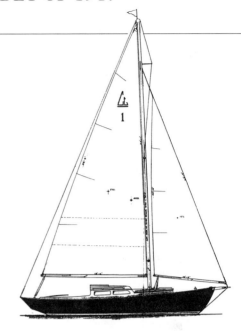

In designing the Cadet as a stock boat for Cambridge Shipbuilders in 1947, Warner surely created one of his best works. Everything about her looks right, even with the wisdom from almost half a century's hindsight. Her springy sheer, genuine bulwarks with railcaps, a short bowsprit for anchor-handling convenience, full headroom under the doghouse, and a sailplan that can be tacked without having to tend sheets or backstays, makes the Cambridge Cadet both handsome and functional. There are only three built-in berths, but a fourth can be set up for sleeping in the main cabin. Cambridge Shipbuilders of Cambridge, Maryland, managed to complete only a few Cadets before going under. Partly as a result of a Cadet write-up having been featured in a 1953 Universal Motors advertisement, more boats followed—this time from the Graves yard in Marblehead, Massachusetts, and the Dauntless yard in Essex, Connecticut. In Lunenburg, Nova Scotia, the Smith & Rhuland yard was also a Cadet builder. Warner, as architect, and Bill Slaymaker, as sales agent, teamed up to make these boats a stock offering at attractive prices—even soliciting bids from foreign builders. For anyone wishing a small and attractive cruiser with a distinctive appearance, the Cambridge Cadet would be hard to beat.   Catalog No. 46.50

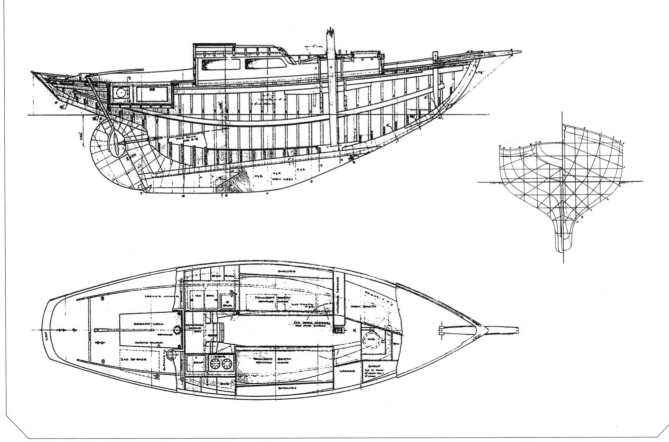

THE ACADIA 33, A STOCK CRUISER WITH OPTIONS
33'1" x 9'9"

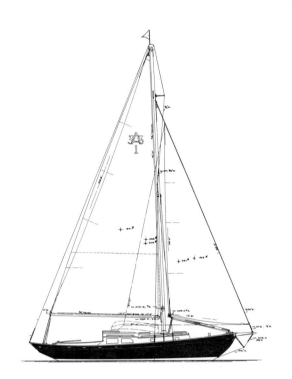

S mith & Rhuland had come to know Winthrop Warner and his work when that yard built his Cambridge Cadet design in the mid-1950s, so it was natural, a few years later, that they seek him out for a larger boat similar in appearance to be used as a stock offering. This became the Acadia 33, a boat you could have as a cutter (which looked very much like the Cambridge Cadet), or a ketch or yawl. There were a variety of cabin arrangements, and you could even order the boat with a clipper bow. Charles Marshall commissioned the first cutter-rigged Acadia 33, which he named *Vagrant*. Five years later, in 1966, he had Marriotts Cove Yacht Builders of Chester, Nova Scotia, build him *Nimbus IV*, a clipper-bowed ketch to this same basic design. To create the Acadia 33, Warner used a design of 20 years earlier, lengthening out the forward overhang about a foot, and working out a doghouse-type cabin configuration and all the options mentioned above. Three boats came from the earlier design, a pair of cutters built by Seth Persson named *Yankee Girl III* and *Snapper Blue*, and a yawl named *Moby IV*.

Catalog No. 46.81

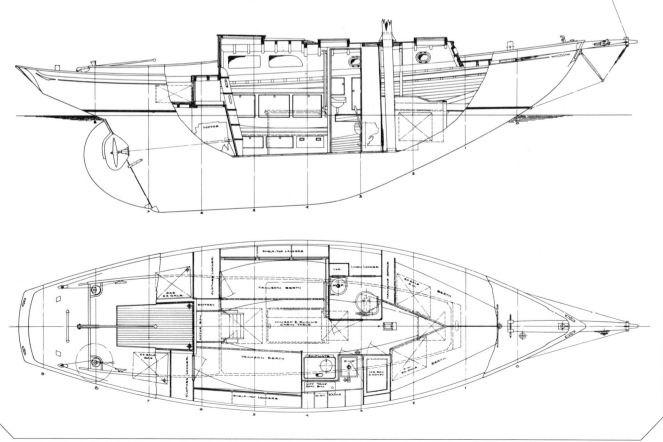

THE CUTTERS *MANISEES* AND *DIANA*, *BLUE JAY* AND *MARJORIE*
37'1" x 10'1"

July 15, 1939, surely was a great day for Winthrop Warner. He watched his own *Manisees* as well as her sister *Diana* slide into the water one after the other, as they were launched from Paul Luke's East Boothbay, Maine, yard. This attractive cutter was a replacement for a four-year-old smaller boat of the same name (Manisees is what the Indians called Block Island). Warner kept this second *Manisees* through the war years until 1947 when he returned to Luke for *Mary Loring*. In the meantime, in the spring of 1941, Luke turned out a third one of these 37-footers. *Marjorie* was actually the fourth (and final) boat to this design, and her cabin layout closely followed that of the first boat *Blue Jay*, built in 1938 by Anderson & Coombs in West Haven, Connecticut. These two boats slept six rather than five persons since there was a sea berth to starboard as well as to port. *Blue Jay*'s rig was a little different from the three boats that followed her, for, although a cutter like the others, she came out with a bowsprit and slightly more sail area. For those who prefer a divided rig, Warner prepared a yawl-rigged sailplan for this boat.

Catalog No. 46.30

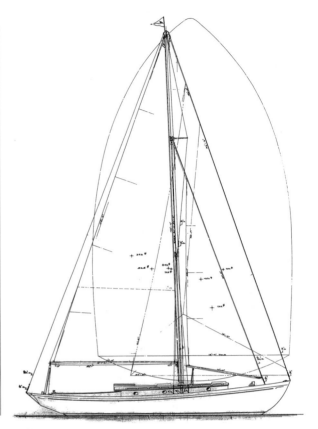

Manisees

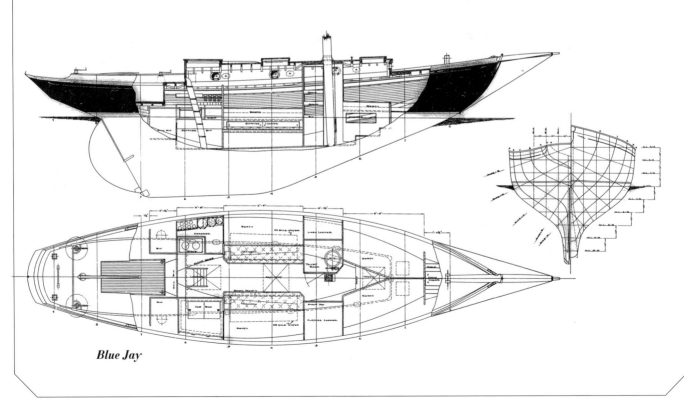

Blue Jay

A KEEL-CENTERBOARD CUTTER OF 1956
37'10" x 10'10"

Here's a change from Warner's usual full-keeled cruisers, in that this boat, prepared as a stock offering, was given a centerboard in order to reduce her draft. With the board raised, this cutter requires only 4'6" of water depth. As with many of Warner's interiors, the galley is near the mast, in this case running right across the boat. Likewise, the toilet area, just forward of the galley, is partly on one side and partly on the other. Having the cabin sole at two levels, high aft, and low forward, might be a nuisance; but it does justify the distinctive doghouse, provide space in the bilge for tanks, and keep the centerboard trunk entirely hidden.

Catalog No. 46.51

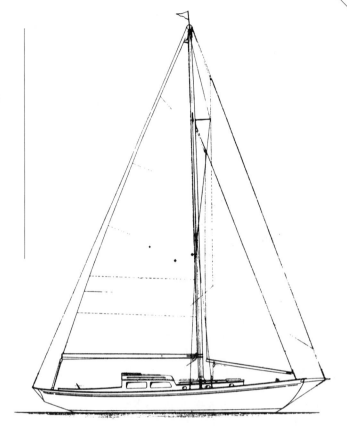

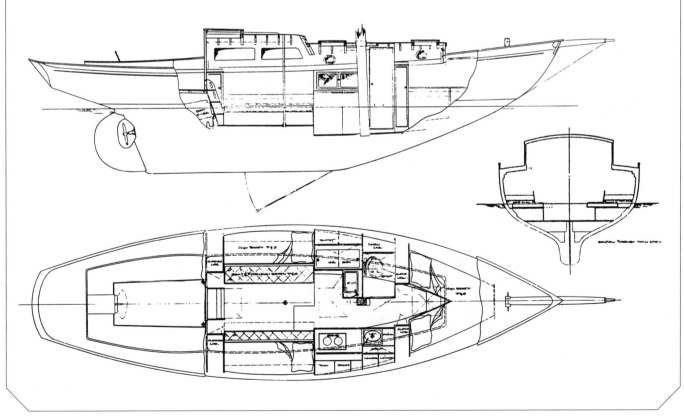

ROWDY II, A RACING-CRUISING SLOOP OF 1949
39'8" x 10'0"

Winthrop Warner left little to chance when he developed a new design, and along with an unusual number of individual drawings for each there are comprehensive written specifications. Only one boat was built to this design, and yet there are many sheets of plans and 43 pages of specifications. I found these specifications especially informative. *Rowdy II* was of the finest possible construction, with a lead ballast keel, double-planked hull, and non-ferrous fastenings throughout. Hodgdon Bros. of East Boothbay, Maine, built her, and made some suggestions before construction began that resulted in a better boat as well as a more buildable one. These show in Warner's addenda and include such things as tapered frames steam-bent over individual molds, and two layers of ⅜" Sitka spruce sprung to shape as the top for the doghouse. *Rowdy II* was launched in 1949, having been built for Herbert Mosley who was then Commodore of the Middletown Yacht Club. Warner's sloop *Mary Loring* of 1947, although rigged with two headsails and a mast that was farther aft, and was shaped with a finer aft overhang, might well have inspired Mosley to have commissioned *Rowdy II*, since Warner was a long-time member of the same yacht club.

Catalog No. 46.53

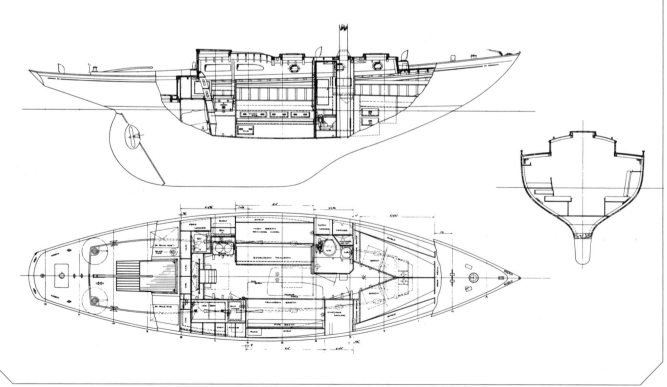

SNAPPER BLUE, A CUTTER OF 1946
40'2" x 10'6"

Snapper Blue is the largest of what might be called Warner's modern classic sailing yacht designs, ones with moderate overhangs, deep keels, and generous sailplans. These are boats meant to sail well and win an occasional race. For *Snapper Blue*, Warner arranged to have Paul Luke do the building. By now the two men had come to understand each other and had developed an efficient working relationship. Warner could get a yacht that suited both him and his client without spending an inordinate amount of time inspecting the work himself. *Snapper Blue* had a lead keel and bronze fastenings, a significant upgrade in materials from what Warner's customers were willing to pay for during the depressed 1930s.

Catalog No. 46.49

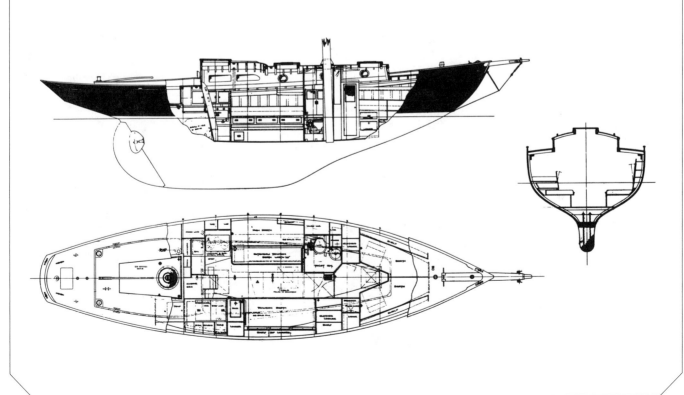

THE CUTTERS *ASTRAL*, *ALARM*, AND *MARY LORING*
39'10" x 10'1"

This design was prepared for John Newell, of Bath Iron Works in Bath, Maine, where the *America*'s Cup defender *Ranger* was launched only four years before *Astral* was built in 1941. The selection of Paul Luke as builder was only natural, as his East Boothbay shop was only about a half hour's drive from Newell's office. *Astral* was trimmed and decked with teak and was fitted with a lead keel. To me, her profile and deck plan look a good deal like a Concordia yawl in that the maximum beam is near amidships and the stern is drawn out to a very small transom. Warner even developed a yawl rig for her. But, unlike a Concordia, Warner's design has the softer bilges that were more commonplace at the time. Newell owned *Astral* for 10 years, selling her to Oliver Garceau in 1951. Although this design was based on Warner's own *Manisees*, she offered enough more to convince him to build one for the 1947 season as the Warner family's new boat, to be named *Mary Loring* after Warner's mother. There were minor changes in rig and layout from *Astral*, but the hull was the same, enabling savings in lofting and mold-building since Luke, once again, was to be the builder. Winthrop Warner brought another client to the Luke yard the following year when the third boat, the yawl-rigged *Alarm*, was built. Warner as well as Luke could offer savings to a client who was content with one of his existing designs. To be sure, there were the inevitable

owner-invoked modifications, which meant new sailplans and arrangement drawings, but the hull lines and offsets and many of the detail drawings didn't have to be created and paid for as new work.

Catalog No. 46.40

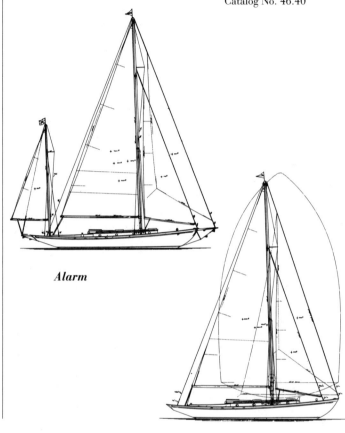

Alarm

Mary Loring

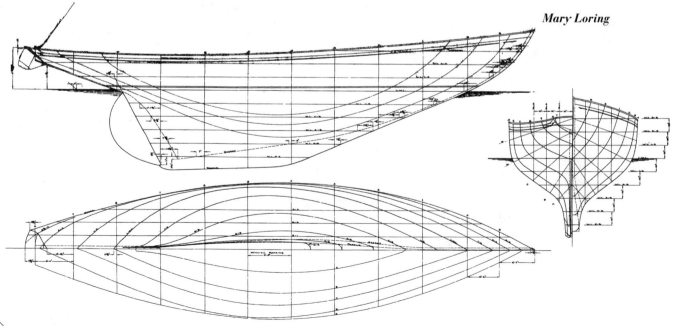

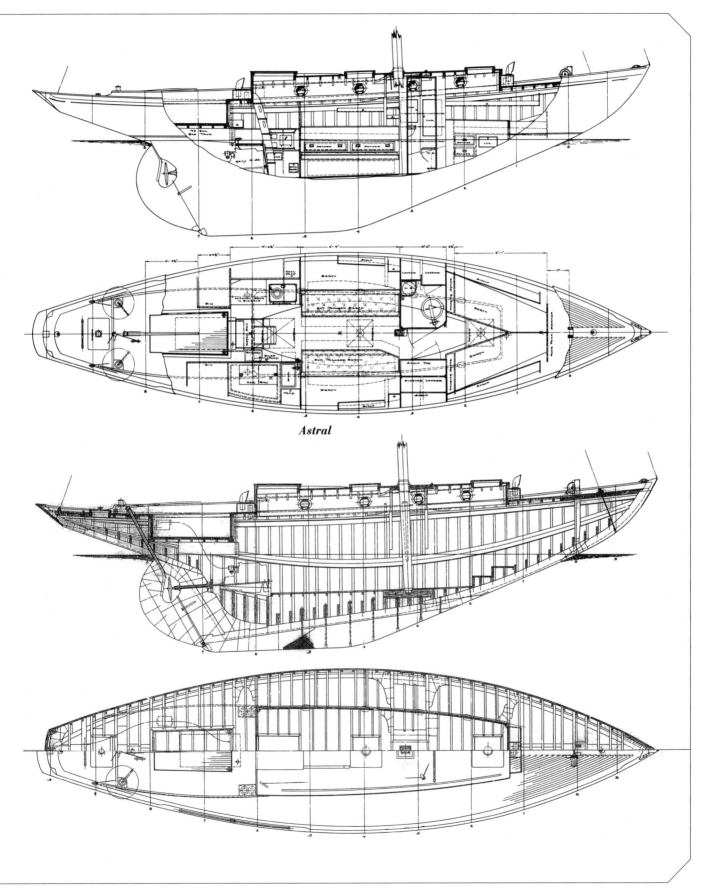

Astral

LIGHTNING, A SLOOP-RIGGED MOTORSAILER OF 1932
34'6" x 10'8"

Warner claims that the Maine Hampton boat served as a basis for *Lightning*'s hull shape, and one can see the Hampton's influence in her somewhat sharp deck line forward and her wide stern. In profile, however, that heritage is less apparent. This started out as a 30' preliminary design for Mr. Hasbrouck, but the the designer and client finally settled on these drawings, to which the boat was built. Raised decks are few among Warner's sail-carrying boats; I guess it made them look too much like motorboats. It seems to me, however, that this configuration has much to offer because of the additional interior space. Partly because of having unusual options below and partly a result of simpler cruising styles, *Lightning*'s arrangement merits a closer look. Forward of the mast, the V-berths are higher because of the raised deck, enabling a location nearer the bow. The toilet room's tiny size is made possible by the hinged washbasin, back then available from hardware suppliers as a stock item.

The galley is amidships, and the cooking is by means of a cast-iron Shipmate stove burning wood or coal and, of course, heating the cabin as well. The small hatch overhead lets the heat escape during warm weather. An old-fashioned two-tiered icebox with swing-down doors serves the galley, although it's located on the opposite side of the boat. The main-cabin berths are what would be called quarter berths, although they're arranged for comfortable seating (with pillows) for the four persons *Lightning* is equipped to sleep. A dining table, although not shown on the drawing, would fit between these settee/berths. *Lightning* has a genuine engineroom under the bridge deck with seats to use when caring for the engine and shelves behind them for tools and related gear. Flush hatches in the bridge deck give access and good light. The cockpit area is huge due to the boat's wide stern—and provides a place to sprawl and relax. All the way aft, a deck hatch gives access to a cavernous lazarette. Catalog No. 46.13

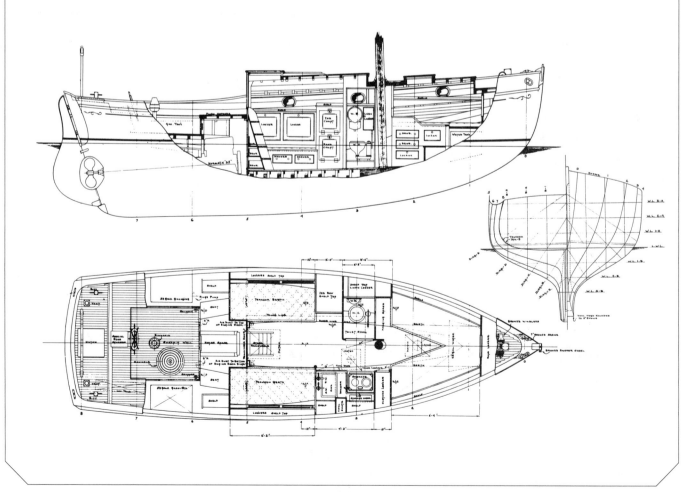

106

EDITH M., A KETCH-RIGGED MOTORSAILER OF 1932
39'6" x 12'8"

Here is a motorsailer of the same early time as *Lightning*, but one that is enough larger so that some of *Lightning*'s shortcomings are eliminated. The 12'8" beam allows pilot berths with pull-out settees inboard of them for more comfortable seating around the dining table. *Edith M.* has the same full-width engineroom, but access to it is through the bulkhead which has a door on each side of the companionway ladder—thus eliminating the potentially leaky flush hatches through the bridgedeck. Having a couple of full-height hanging lockers near the companionway can't be beat, and neither can the idea of having an onboard bathtub which, although small, is located in the enclosed toilet room. And, unlike *Lightning*, *Edith M.* has full headroom in most of the living space. *Edith M.* was designed for George B. Moffat, but there seems to be no record of her ever having been built. In 1932, when *Edith M.* was designed, Moffat owned a small, shallow cruising sloop that he sailed from Bayside, Long Island. He went for the same style, only larger, in this design. In spite of the fact that *Edith M.* came early in Warner's career, I think she's one of his most interesting designs.

Catalog No. 46.12

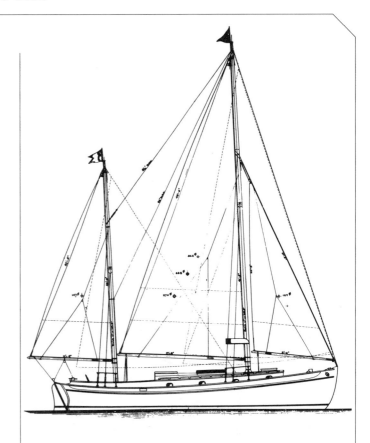

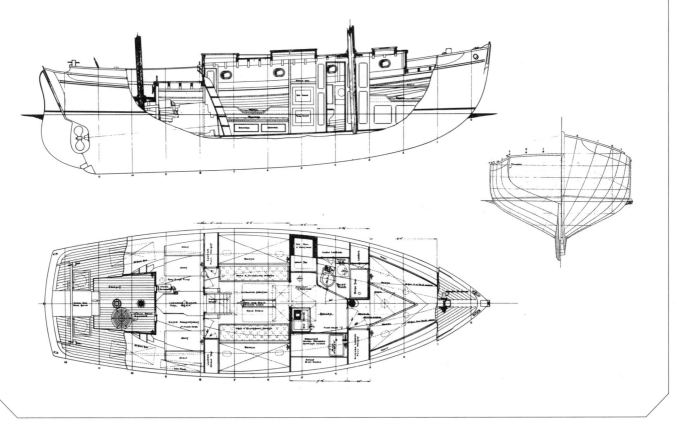

YIN YANG & *RUFINA*, TWO MOTORSAILERS OF 1935
32'0" x 10'11"

Warner's concept of the ideal motorsailer had been refined considerably by 1935 when he drew the plans for this pair of 32-footers. Although *Yin Yang* was built that year in New Haven, Connecticut, by J.C. Wyman, and *Rufina* came from the shop of the Fitz-Newman Corp. in Warren, Rhode Island, two years afterwards, they were identical except for their rigs—*Yin Yang* was marconi, while *Rufina* carried a gaff mainsail. Compared with Warner's earlier motorsailer *Edith M*, the galleys had moved aft to be near the cockpit; the bridge deck had been eliminated, making access between these two "nerve centers" much more convenient. The cockpit ran full width. In time, both boats were given more sail area, *Rufina* converted from gaff sloop to marconi cutter as her name changed to *North Star*, then *Blue Chip*, and making a Bermuda passage in 1958. As the first of

Burr Bartram's many *Exact*s, *Yin Yang* became a cutter with three headsails, a bowsprit, and boomkin. Later, under George Lauder's ownership, she became *Watermelon*. Later still she was given a modern masthead rig. In the end, both boats had graduated from motorsailer to pure sailer. Warner took this design in the opposite direction as well, demonstrating its versatility. *Sturdy Beggar*, with pilothouse and only a steadying sail, was pure powerboat, having been built by Kelsey of Clinton, Connecticut, in 1940. This boat was all business, with a small chunk of outside iron ballast, a three-cylinder, 30-hp, slow-turning Lathrop engine, and steering either by wheel or tiller. I remember seeing this boat years ago, and I thought she was wonderful. With the passage of time, that opinion has grown even stronger.   Catalog No. 46.21

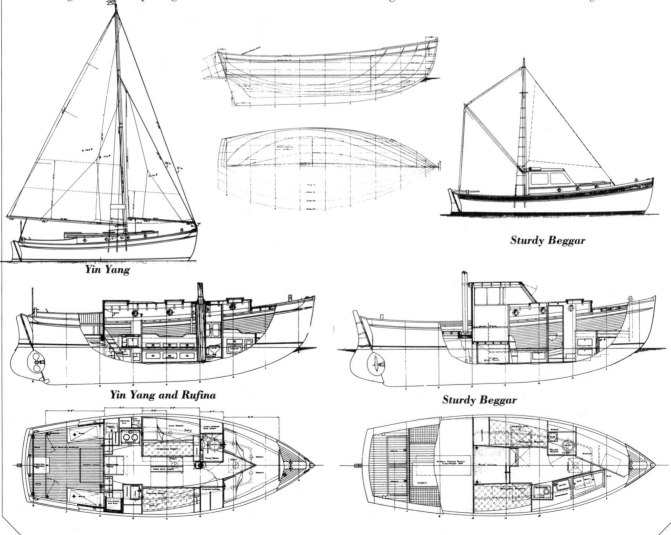

Yin Yang

Sturdy Beggar

Yin Yang and Rufina

Sturdy Beggar

KAMIBET, *DAMAJO*, AND *CONGAR*, THREE MOTORSAILERS OF 1936
30'0" x 10'3"

F.C. Luce commissioned *Kamibet*'s design late in 1936 and took delivery from Willis Reid's yard in Winthrop, Massachusetts, halfway through the 1937 season. Another of these so-called motorsailer-sloops, spreading some 25% more canvas by means of bowsprit and boomkin and carrying the name *Damajo*, followed next year, this one being built by Portland Yacht Service in South Portland, Maine, for Harold Cooley. The galleys were near the mast in both boats, but *Damajo*'s unconventional toilet room forward and full-width galley intrigue me most. Warner played around at some point with a pilothouse for this design as well as a raised-deck configuration for the hull itself. After the War, *Congar* was built in 1947 by Cambridge Shipbuilders of Cambridge, Maryland, as the most elegant of the trio—teak decks, binnacle, cockpit ice chest, etc. *Congar* was rigged with two head-

sails and carried even more sail area—564 square feet—than either of her predecessors. Strangely, her outside ballast keel was reduced in weight by nearly a half ton, doubtless due to feedback from the pre-war boats. *Congar*'s below-deck arrangement combines the ideas of both *Kamibet* and *Damajo*, sleeping four in the main cabin on a pair of settees and a pair of convertible uppers (as in *Damajo*), with a galley to starboard and a toilet room opposite to port near the mast (like *Kamibet*). Working with Warner, owner S.J. Silberman had laid out *Congar* for a paid hand whose quarters (pipe berth and toilet) were forward, shut off when desired so the galley was on his side of the door. A 30-footer is small for four persons in the owner's party and a fifth as crew, so it's not surprising that Samuel Silberman soon ordered his second and larger *Congar*.

Catalog No. 46.27

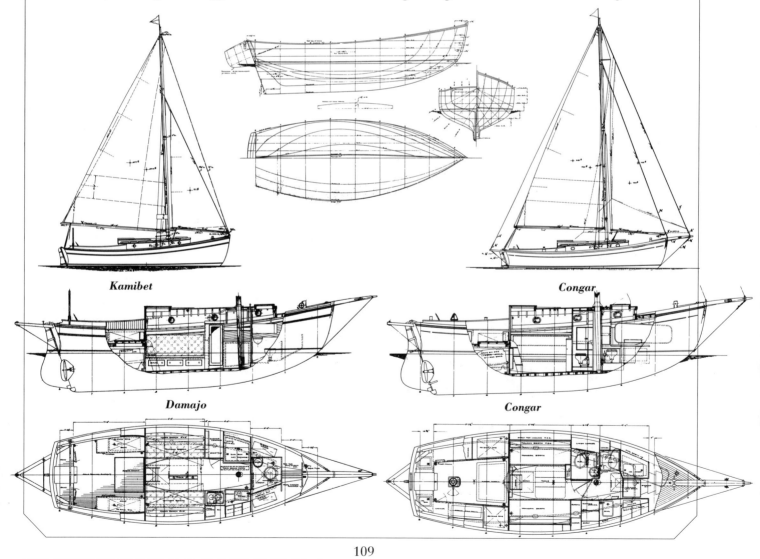

Kamibet

Congar

Damajo

Congar

THE WARNER 33 MOTORSAILERS OF THE 1950s
32'10" x 10'4"

Ten boats of this well-known and much-loved design were built in the mid-1950s by a variety of New England builders. Eight were wooden, but The Anchorage, in Warren, Rhode Island, built two in fiberglass that were known as "Sojourners." As was Warner's patient custom, he tailored the plans and specifications to some degree for each owner, with the result that there are well over a hundred sheets of drawings for this one basic design—although the 25-sheet package once offered by Seven Seas Press for *Starlight* would be sufficient for this one boat. The Warner 33 started out in 1951 as a "stretched" *Kamibet* (Warner design No. 82) for James Swan. In 1953 this design was the basis for the Sojourner class, one of the very early cruising sailboats to be manufactured in fiberglass. Morse Boatbuilding in Thomaston, Maine, launched the first two

genuine, wooden-hulled Warner 33s in 1954, one of which was for Warner himself—his final *Mary Loring*. For this pair and the six subsequent Warner 33s, the Swan/Sojourner design was tweaked to carry more sail, given an additional 6" of draft (to 4'6" with a "knuckled" keel profile), and lengthened to an even 33' overall. This design, although a compromise (as are all motorsailers), has a lot going for it and comes well recommended by the several enthusiastic owners who took the time to write long and glowing letters. Within Warner's many drawings for this design, a person stands a better-than-average chance of finding just what he's looking for. There's a wide variety of cabin layouts and rig configurations, a range of specifications, and sketches showing, among other things, a clipper bow, a stand-up steering shelter, or a raised sheer/aft cabin.   Catalog Nos. 46.62 & .167

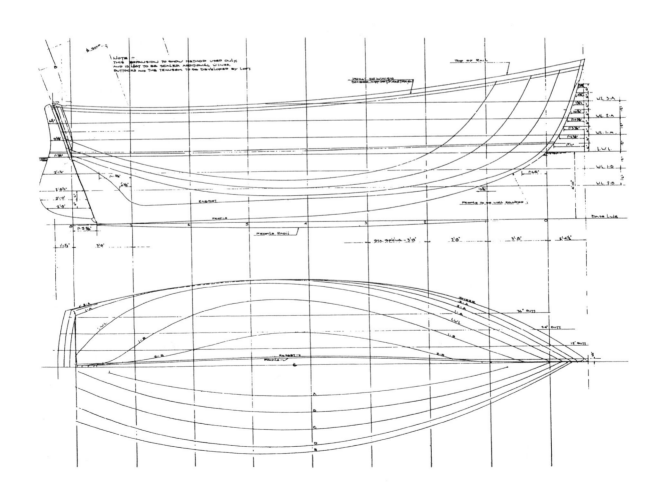

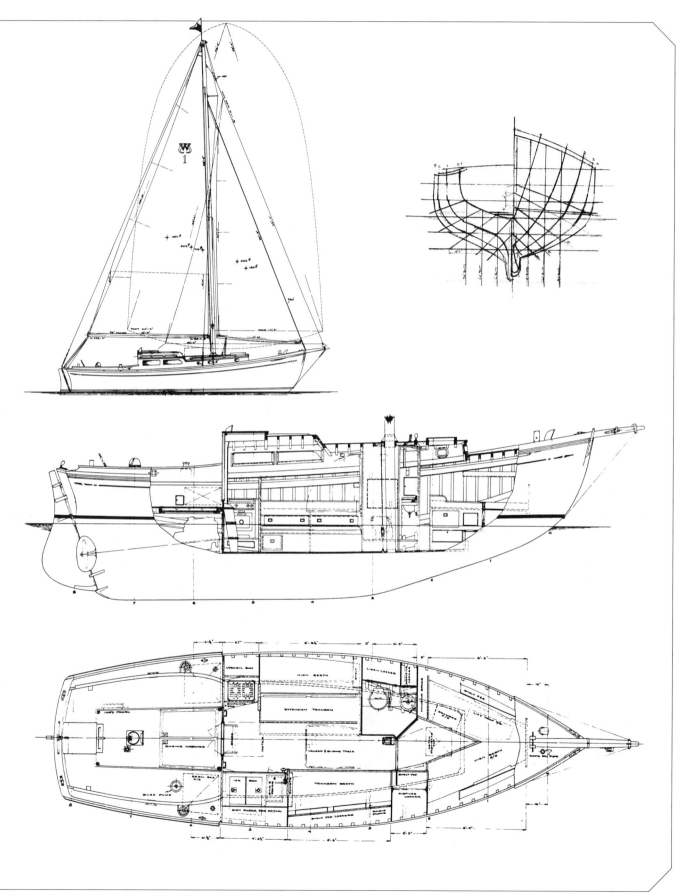

PHALAROPE, A MOTORSAILER OF 1941
36'4" x 10'9"

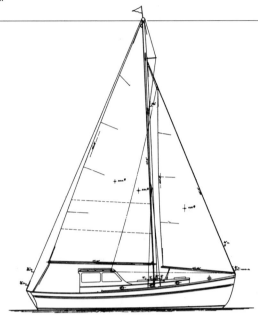

Somewhat larger and with finer lines than the Warner 33, *Phalarope* would show improved sailing ability. Thomas Bennett, who had her built in 1941 by West Haven Shipyard, loved to fish, which explains why the cockpit, although self-bailing, is deep and runs all the way out to the rails. It may also be why the rudder is under the boat instead of hung on the transom. You step down to enter the steering shelter, then down again for the below-deck living quarters which begin with the galley located at the base of the ladder. Going forward, the main saloon is arranged to sleep four on two settee/berths and a couple of seagoing pilot berths outboard of them; then come hanging lockers and a toilet room near the mast, and, finally, an owner's stateroom—complete with a double berth—in the forward cabin. In all, it's a very appealing layout. *Phalarope*, now named *Plantina* and homeported in Barrington, Rhode Island, is a no-nonsense, easy-to-care-for boat. She was plainly finished in paint without brightwork, her decks were of plywood, and there's neither

bowsprit nor boomkin. There are, however, various alternative configurations that Warner drew, including a raised foredeck, a Warner 33-type low doghouse, and a straightforward trunk cabin without the standing shelter.   Catalog No. 46.39

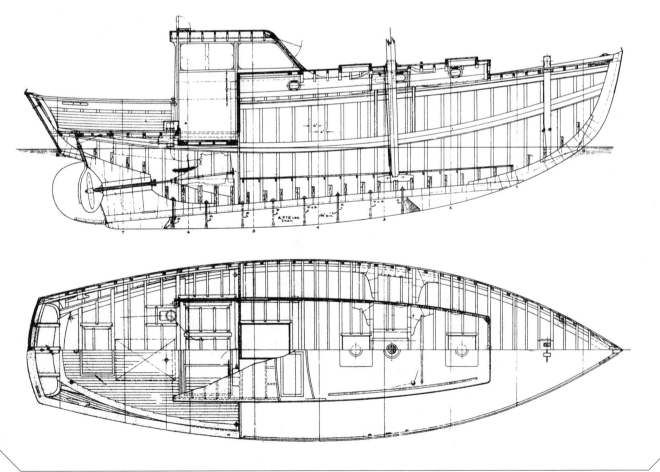

PHOENIX, A MOTORSAILER OF 1964
37'4" x 10'9"

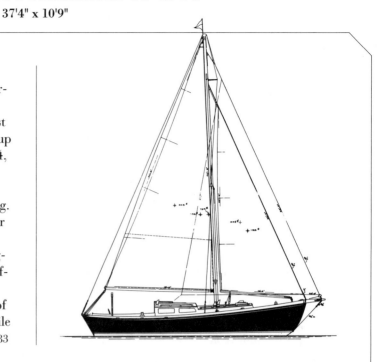

Whether to call this boat a cruising sloop or a motorsailer is a toss-up. Warner called her the former, but since she's so much like *Phalarope* I've chosen to place her in the latter category. The first boat built to this design, named *Hexerie*, burned up only days before her scheduled launching in 1964, but the name of the second boat, *Phoenix*—also built by Seth Persson, after his Saybrook, Connecticut, shop was rebuilt—seems more fitting. Bill Slaymaker ordered *Phoenix* the morning after the fire, and in her made some changes from the Warner drawings shown here. Other than the doghouse having replaced the pilothouse, *Phoenix* differed from *Phalarope* mostly in her cockpit. Instead of being laid out for fishing, it consisted of a conventional footwell, enabling one to steer while seated.   Catalog No. 46.83

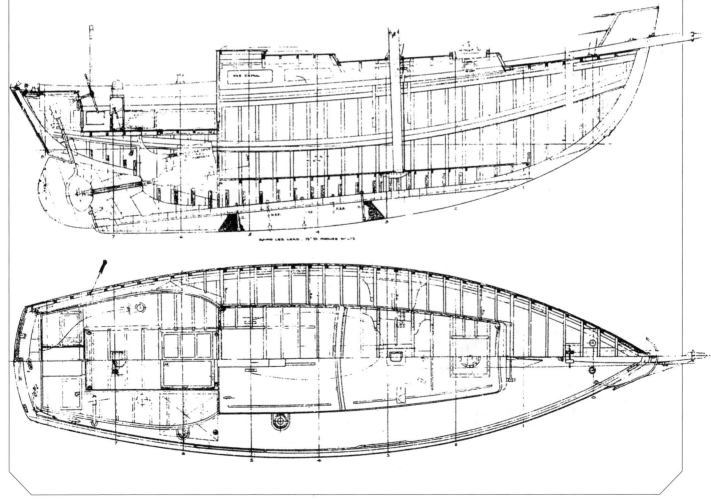

THREE MOTORSAILERS, *VOLANA*, *ALARM*, AND *JOLLY ROGER*
41'9" x 12'1"

Falling into the same family as *Phalarope* and *Phoenix*, this design started out as a ketch having only a low trunk cabin (*Volana*) and was subsequently modified for pilothouse and cutter rig (*Alarm* and *Jolly Roger*). All three boats were from East Boothbay, Maine, shops—*Volana* being launched from Rice Bros. in 1939, *Alarm* coming out of Paul Luke's shop a year later, followed in 1952 by *Jolly Roger*, also Luke-built. Unfortunately, galvanized steel fastenings were used for all three, as was the case with many of Warner's boats. With a black hull and some neglect, *Jolly Roger* was suffering from rust last time I saw her; *Volana*, however, still looks almost brand new and is well cared for in North Carolina. *Alarm*'s whereabouts is unknown to me. As one might expect with three owners, two builders, and a decade separating the first boat from the last, the differences in layout and rig from boat to boat are fairly significant. But throughout all the permutations, the forward well-deck was retained on all three.   Catalog No. 46.32

Jolly Roger and Alarm

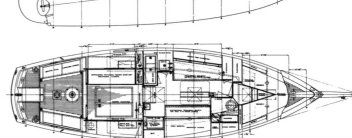

Jolly Roger

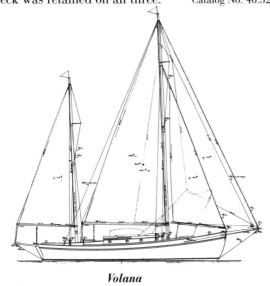

Volana

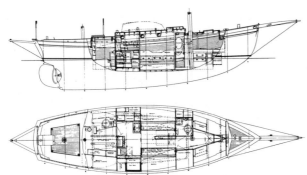

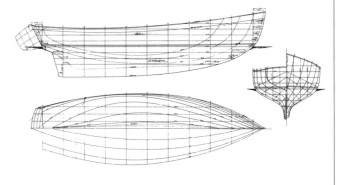

CONGAR, A MOTORSAILER OF 1949
42'8" x 12'0"

The largest of Warner's motorsailers to see fruition, *Congar* was elegantly built of the finest materials by Paul Luke of East Boothbay, Maine, in 1949. This was Sam Silberman's second Warner-designed motorsailer—the first *Congar* proving too small—and, working closely with the designer, he took great pains to see that this boat fitted his needs. Her layout is a bit unconventional in that the owner's stateroom, complete with its own toilet room, is aft under the doghouse. Entrance is possible by companionway from the cockpit, or by door from the main saloon. A companionway placed well forward on the trunk cabin leads directly to the saloon, and can be used when the owner's aft cabin is off-limits. The saloon, or main cabin, as it's called on the drawings, converts to sleep four and has its own toilet room and shower. The galley is forward of the mast, conveniently adjacent to the fo'c's'le where the crew is quartered. The spacious cockpit running all the way to the transom, the outboard rudder, and the steering wheel/binnacle setup were all concepts brought forward from Silberman's first *Congar*— a sure sign of experience and an indication of Warner's skill in developing that earlier design. But in reviewing the plethora of sketches and prelimi-nary drawings, including one showing a ketch rig, it's obvious that designer and owner considered many alternatives before firming up this design. That Mr. Silberman loved *Congar* is clearly evident from his letters to Warner written after extensive use. He donated her to the Coast Guard Academy in 1962. After serving there for a decade, *Congar* went civilian and remains today, much loved, in private hands.

Catalog No. 46.55

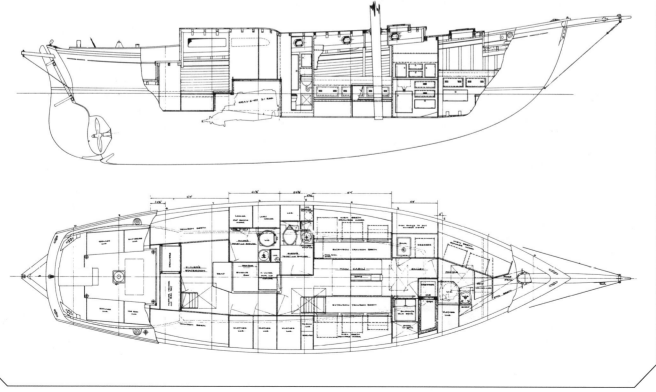

CHARLOTTE, A UTILITY LAUNCH OF 1936
25'9" x 8'3"

When John Elton needed a boat to shuttle back and forth between his Thimble Island summer home and the Connecticut mainland, he had Warner design, and the Dauntless Shipyard build, this gasoline-powered launch. Normally she steers by means of a stick on the port side of the big open cockpit that is connected to the tiller lines; but for long runs, or when the weather is bad, there's wheel steering and seating available in the cabin. And if the desire or need arises, the two 6'3" cabin settees can be used for sleeping. With teak cabin sides and coamings, a mahogany transom, and laid teak decks, this little craft, with varnished trim, would have been a real yacht. But even with a plainer finish she'd be good to look at as well as being practical and useful. Catalog Nos. 46.125 & .249

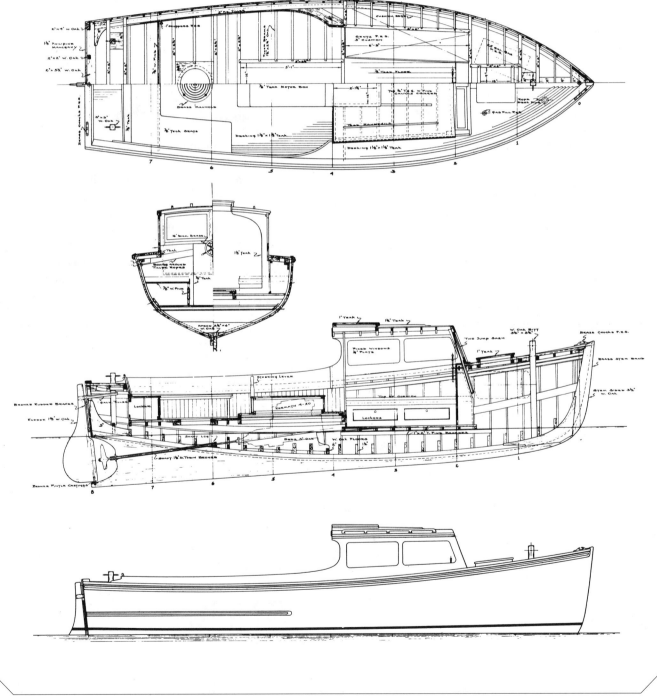

EARLY BIRD, A COMMUTER OF 1951
29'6" x 9'9"

Early Bird was purposely built for daily runs across Boston's outer harbor between Cohasset on the South Shore, where owner Sherman Thayer lived, and Lynn on the North Shore where he worked. Twin 145-hp Chris-Craft gas engines enabled cruising at 20 mph for a 45-minute commute, compared to at least twice that time by auto during the rush hour. With relatively high freeboard, an enclosed steering shelter where the engine boxes could serve as seats, and a self-bailing cockpit, *Early Bird* could make the run safely in all but the worst weather, and be quite comfortable, too. But, for those stormy nights when prudence called for staying at Lynn, *Early Bird*'s Spartan cabin offered the sought-after snugness.

Early Bird's finish was mostly paint, for low upkeep; and one of the drawings indicates full-length spray rails, which the boatbuilders at Wharton's Shipyard in Jamestown, Rhode Island, who built her in 1951, must have installed. With them, no doubt she'd be a good deal drier.

Catalog No. 46.69

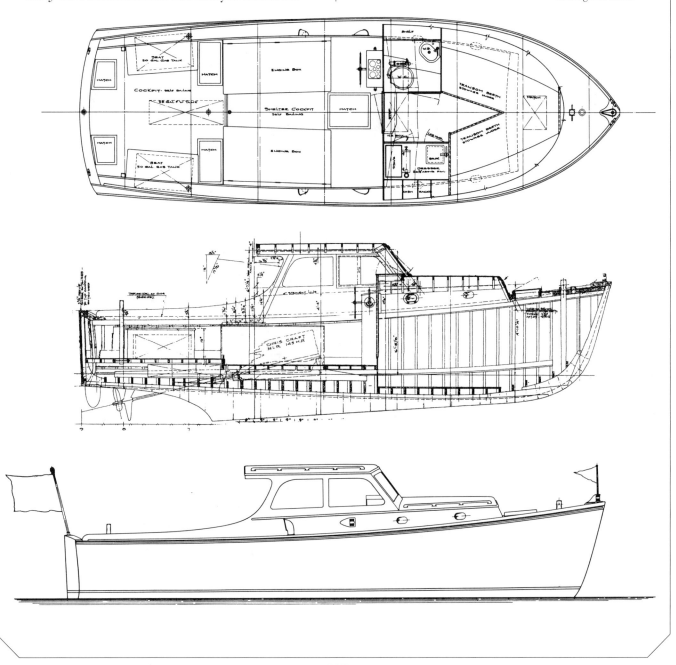

Here you can choose between two versions of the same design, just as the owners did back in 1950 when the pair were built at Portland Boat Works, just across the river from Warner's Middletown, Connecticut, office. *Sting Ray* was the first, the fastest, and the nicest looking, but you couldn't stand up in her cabin as you could in *Gulnare*'s. With her eight-cylinder Packard gasoline engine, *Sting Ray* did better than 20 mph, while the less-powerful Chrysler Crown drove *Gulnare* only 17.

Because of her higher trunk cabin, Warner fitted *Gulnare* with a raised steering platform, so the helmsman could see out ahead. The full-width platform also served to cover the engine. *Sting Ray*'s engine was boxed in, and her platform was all at one low level; she also had a seat across its aft end. *Sting Ray* (built for yard owner Wallace Kimball) and *Gulnare* are like overgrown bass-boats, a type that always seems to have endured among changing styles.   Catalog No. 46.56

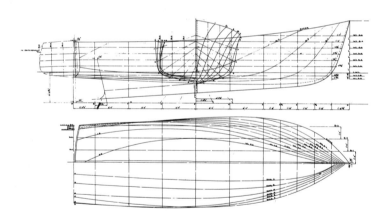

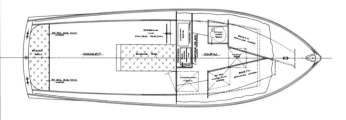
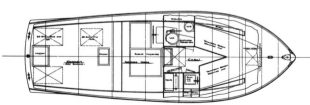

A POWER CRUISER OF 1953
32'1" x 10'6"

Indications are that the idea for Portland Boat Works to build stock boats to this design was abandoned before any were built. But a few years later, in 1955, after Warner made this one of his standard offerings, a couple of these power cruisers were completed. The design is conservative, especially so by today's standards, but the options of single or twin screw, an enclosed pilothouse or an open steering station with windshield, plus several variations on window styles, gave the design unusual flexibility to meet a variety of tastes and needs. Warner figured she'd do 22 mph with twin Chrysler Crowns, while a single engine would push her along at about 14 and use only a fraction of the fuel. For all the alternatives, Warner held to the same belowdeck arrangement. There's sleeping for four in the one space after the seatbacks have been hinged upward to form the upper berths. Daytime, the lowers become settees where folks can sit facing each other with a hinged-leaf table between them. A matched pair of generous hanging lockers have been worked in way forward, while aft against the bulkhead are the galley to starboard and the enclosed head to port, separated by the centrally located companionway. The power plant, no matter whether it's one engine or two, hides below the raised platform amidships, and you step down to a lower, but still self-bailing, level as you walk aft. In appearance, this cruiser of Warner's looks a lot like one of the Pacemaker power cruisers of which C.P. Leek, of Lower Bank, New Jersey, built so many. Catalog No.46.67

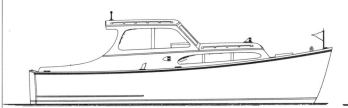

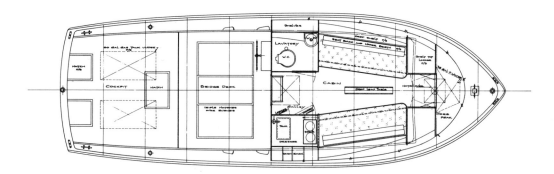

WALRUS, A POWER CRUISER OF 1956

35'2" x 10'7"

Leroy Wallace, partner in the Thomaston, Maine, Newbert & Wallace yard, had had his fill of yacht building when Warner asked him to consider building this boat. He planned to return to and stick with the commercial fishing craft that had always been the yard's specialty; but Warner persisted, complimenting him on the recently built Warner 33, *Coracle*, and Wallace relented, agreeing to build *Walrus* with an all-paint, no-varnish, finish.

Designed as a combination boat for both coastal cruising and sportfishing, *Walrus*'s layout shows ample accommodation for two or three, but can sleep four in a pinch by pulling out the settee opposite the galley so it is wide enough for sleeping. Outside under the open-backed steering shelter is a full-width bridge deck over the matched pair of 175-hp Chris-Craft gasoline engines.

Walking aft, you step down a little to the cockpit platform, but that platform is still high enough to be reliably self-bailing. The sailboat-like lifelines and bow pulpit make the passage forward along the side decks a safe one and allow confident, secure anchor handling on the foredeck.

Lansing Carpenter, who had had earlier experience with Warner's *Sting Ray*, commissioned the design and building of *Walrus*. Although Carpenter lived in Haddam, Connecticut, not far from Warner's office, he ran *Walrus* out to Martha's Vineyard and Nantucket for fishing during the summer and cruised to Florida for the winter. On those kinds of long-distance runs, *Walrus*'s 17-knot cruising speed (20 knots tops) kept the running times reasonable, and her seakindly hull could take bad weather in perfect safety, albeit at slower speeds.   Catalog No. 46.76

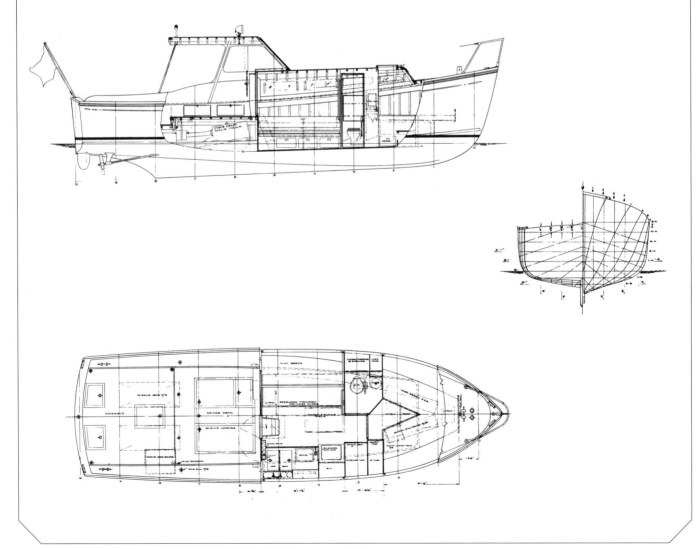

SHANG WHEELER, A RESEARCH VESSEL OF 1951
50'10" x 14'9"

Reminiscent of the Stonington dragger hull shape, but smaller, proportionally shallower, wider in the stern, and more lightly built, *Shang Wheeler* replaced the Fish & Wildlife Service's *Phalarope II* as a floating laboratory for its Milford, Connecticut, marine biology station. With a towing post on the aft deck centerline, rollers at the rails, and a mast and boom, she's fitted for dragging oysters and analyzing the catch in the laboratory which occupies the entire 'midship deckhouse. The GM 6-71 diesel that powers both the propeller and the deck winches is under the lab, while just forward, under the pilothouse and foredeck, are the living quarters for four with a full-width galley and enclosed toilet room.

As is always to be expected when dealing with a government agency, red tape and paperwork abounded, beginning with detailed drawings, lengthy written specifications, and sealed bids. West Haven Shipyard, West Haven, Connecticut, at $44,480 was low bidder and got the job. For his efforts, which were considerable all during the vessel's construction, Warner eventually received $3,200. While few today would have much interest in duplicating *Shang Wheeler*'s special-purpose layout, maybe someone could become inspired by the alternate configurations shown here that Warner developed for this same hull. One is for a party fishing boat, and the other shows a sunken deckhouse forward of a raised pilothouse—a better-looking profile by far than *Shang Wheeler*'s.   Catalog No. 46.60

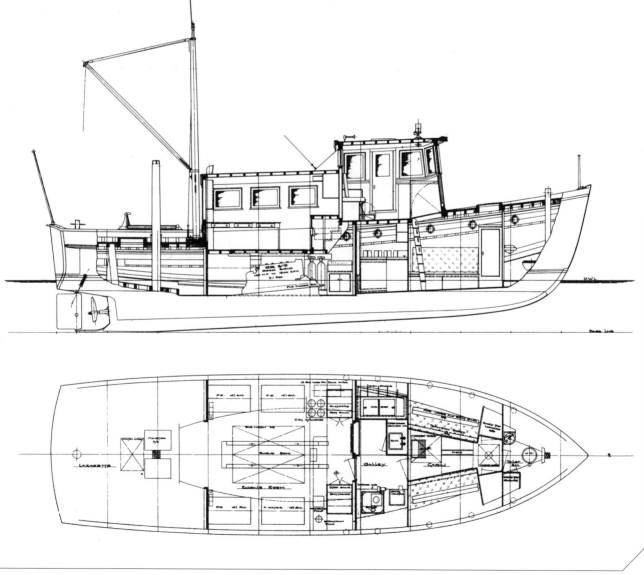

FISHING DRAGGERS AND THE NEW ENGLAND 57
54'8" - 58'0" x 15'8"

A few months before war was declared in 1941, Wink Warner and Henry R. (Hank) Palmer, Jr. collaborated on a 55' Western-rigged dragger for the Stonington, Connecticut, fishing fleet, with the idea of Palmer building them in his Stonington Boat Works shop. *Carl J* was the first boat— to be followed by the nearly identical *Tip Top*, *Nathaniel B. Palmer*, and *William Chesebrough* of 1941 and '42. These were all framed with 2 x 3" bent oak, planked with 1½" yellow pine, and decked with 2 x 4" fir. The fo'c's'le, just forward of the engineroom, contained living space and

galley for four under the raised foredeck. The fish hold ran from amidships aft to the lazarette, which contained the chipped ice for preserving the catch. Power was by a single 100-hp Caterpillar diesel which gave a cruising speed of 10½ knots. Not only are the drawings done to Warner's usual high standards, but there are some 17 pages of written specifications that reveal much about the commercial construction, in wood, of that size vessel in that era. A comparison between these and the plans and specifications of Albert Condon for Eastern-rigged, sawn-frame draggers would give

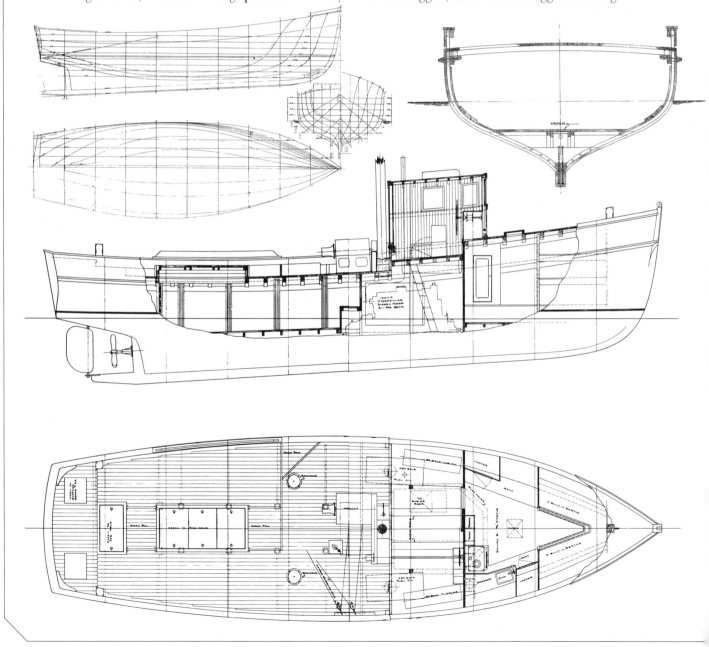

122

one a good deal of understanding. In 1943 and '44 came a second batch of boats, designs Nos. 118 and 120, having outboard rudders, a larger pilothouse, a floor timber on every frame instead of every other one, and some other fairly minor changes. Three boats, *Portugal*, *S.M. Murtosa*, and *America*, sprang from this new design, having all been built by West Haven Shipyard of West Haven, Connecticut. Warner drew a new set of plans for this second generation, resulting in craft that were 3' longer overall and an inch narrower. After the War, Warner amended the 55-footers' lines plan

by raking the stem, and using this drawing which resulted in a 57' hull, Willis Reid of Boothbay Harbor, Maine, built the dragger *Rose Marie* in 1946. After more than two decades, Warner designed what he termed the New England 57, a trawler-type power cruiser utilizing *Rose Marie*'s shape, but with the cabins and layout for pleasure rather than for commercial fishing. Only two NE 57s were built, both in Rockland, Maine, by O. Lie-Nielsen: *Blue Star* of 1969 and *Janie C.*

Catalog Nos. 46.41, 46.46 & 46.92

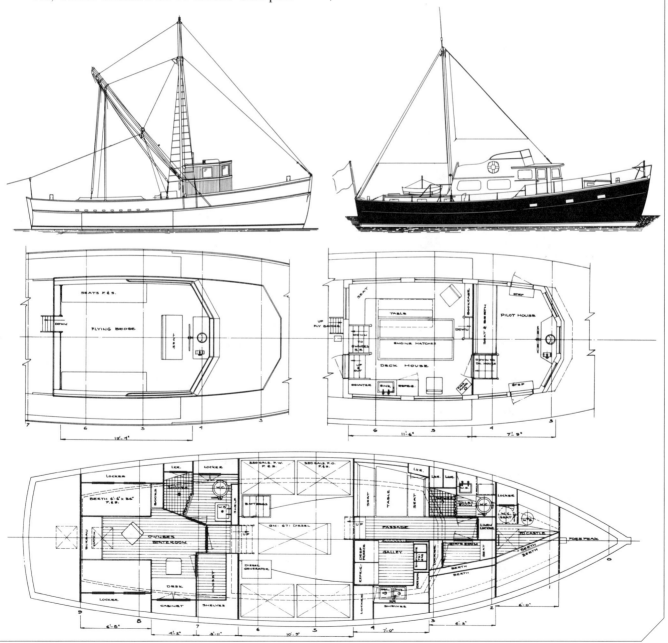

FREDERICK C. GEIGER
1910 – 1982

Fred Geiger was born just outside Philadelphia in Overbrook, December 23, 1910, and became involved with boats as a child during summers at the family's vacation retreat at Eastern Point, at the mouth of the Thames River in Connecticut. There he raced his Cape Cod knockabout *Boreas* and helped establish the Shennecossett Yacht Club in 1928. Further stimulus leading to a career in yacht design came from his brother-in-law, John Wilford, in whose cutter *Windrush* Geiger often sailed from a base in Oxford, Maryland.

After his 1932 graduation from Culver Military Academy, he signed up for and completed the Westlawn School's correspondence course in yacht design, immediately after which, in 1935, he and yacht broker Frank Harris started Philadelphia-based Yacht Sales and Service—an impressive name for a two-person business. Design after design, all of them well-proportioned and beautifully depicted, came out under the "Frederick C. Geiger of Yacht Sales and Service" moniker until 1955 when, with the death of her husband, Mrs. Harris liquidated the company.

Fred Geiger then became the resident designer for John Trumpy's Annapolis yard where big, elegant motoryachts were the specialty. These designs came out under the Trumpy rather than the Geiger name. He retired from Trumpy's in 1972.

Fred and his wife Mimi had two children, Tina and Fred Jr. Although there was never a family yacht, the Geigers sailed in Dyer Dhows during vacations at Eastern Point, and they got to cruise in a lot of clients' boats, mostly on Chesapeake Bay. Fred did a good deal of racing there as well. He was a member of the Annapolis Yacht Club, where there is now a large silver trophy with Geiger's name on it that members vie for each Wednesday evening, a gift of Geiger's sister.

As a Naval Reserve officer, Fred Geiger put in two stints on active duty in the Philadelphia Naval Shipyard's design department, once during World War II, and again during the Korean campaign.

THE GEIGER COLLECTION

Rod Stephens arranged for Mystic Seaport to receive the Geiger drawings, which were donated by Geiger's widow, Miriam, in 1987. They consist of 662 sheets and represent 84 different Geiger designs as well as drawings by others that were collected by the designer over the years. The collection includes no drawings made while Geiger was in Trumpy's employ.

Geiger's designs were always welcomed by the editors of *Yachting* and *The Rudder*, and it was always a treat for the readers to see them published. Because of the Geiger designs in those magazines, it is apparent that a good deal of Geiger's work has disappeared, for there are some 50 published designs for which Mystic Seaport does not hold the plans.

Although no complete list of Geiger designs has yet surfaced, the published designs leave little doubt that most of the boats Geiger designed were actually built. He seemed reluctant to do work on speculation as, say, Louis Kromholz did.

THE FREDERICK C. GEIGER PLANS

SAILING YACHTS

LOA	Beam	Description	Date	Plan Codes	Cat.No.
18'0"	6'4"	Sailing dinghy *Sally S* w/sloop rig & centerboard	1939	LCSADhDr	75.10
20'0"	6'4"	Cruising cutter *Wee One*, short-ended	1934	LOCSADh	75.1
26'4"	8'4"	Cruising ketch *Blue Water*, short-ended	1939	LOCSADhDr	75.9
29'8"	7'3"	Keel-centerboard one-design sloop	1947	CSA	75.21
29'8"	7'3"	Cruising sloop *Sea Star*	1951	SDr	75.34
31'3"	9'6"	Cruising ketch *Sorceress*, short-ended	1945	CA	75.46
33'0"	7'9"	One-design flush-decked sloop for Southern Yacht Club		S	75.45
33'2"	7'9"	Flush-decked cruising sloop *Avalon*	1950	LOCSADr	75.26
33'6"	7'9"	Cruising sloop *Lady Anne*	1953	SDh	75.28
34'6"	9'0"	Cruising ketch *Chinook*	1960	SDhDr	75.35
35'0"	9'0"	Keel-centerboard cruising sloop *Vigilant*	1946	CSDr	75.20
35'3"	8'8"	Cruising sloop *Lapwing* w/doghouse	1955	LOCSADhDr	75.32
35'6"	9'4"	V-bottomed cruising cutter *Ycla* w/doghouse	1938	LCSADr	75.5
35'9"	8'7"	Flush-decked cruising sloop *Candida*	1954	LOCSADhDr	75.29
36'0"	9'3"	Cruising cutter	1934	L	75.79
36'3"	9'11"	Cruising cutter *Deep Water*, short-ended	1935	LOCSADhDr	75.2
36'8"	10'3"	Keel-centerboard sloop *Veronica*	1950	LOCSADr	75.27
38'0"	10'6"	Keel-centerboard cruising sloop or yawl *Ranger*	1940	LOCSADhDr	75.11, .48, .58
38'0"	10'6"	Keel-centerboard cruising sloop *New Ranger*	1944	LOCSADhDr	75.11A
43'1"	11'0"	Keel-centerboard cruising sloop *Teal*	1940	LOCSADr	75.6
43'2"	10'9"	Cruising yawl *Tar Baby*	1937	LSPDHDr	75.4
43'3"	11'9"	Keel-centerboard sloop, steel construction	1961	LOCSADhDr	75.36
46'1"	10'8"	Cruising cutter *Egret* w/alternate yawl rig	1937	CSAPDhDr	75.3
46'3"	12'0"	Cruising ketch *Marjoly* w/shallow-draft keel	1940	LCSAPDr	75.8
46'5"	11'10"	Keel-centerboard yawl w/low doghouse	1955	CSA	75.31
46'7"	11'6"	Cruising sloop	1957	CSADh	75.42
47'0"	13'0"	Clipper-bowed keel-centerboard ketch *Sanban*	1958	LCSADH DR	75.33
48'0"	12'3"	Keel-centerboard cruising ketch *Windy Day*	1946	LOCSADhDr	75.13
48'2"	12'3"	Keel-centerboard cruising ketch *Stardust*	1945	LOCSADhDr	75.14

POWER YACHTS

LOA	Beam	Description	Date	Plan Codes	Cat.No.
23'0"	7'0"	Inboard powered garvey w/tunnel stern	1950	CP	75.16
32'1"	10'6"	V-bottomed sedan-type power cruiser *Loligo*	1949	LOCAPDh	75.25
50'0"	14'5"	V-bottomed sedan-type power cruiser *Coline*	1948	LOCAPDh	75.23
51'0"	13'10"	Power cruiser		C	75.71
54'0"	15'0"	Power cruiser	1965	LDh	75.63
60'0"	15'9"	Power cruiser w/twin screws	1959	L	75.50

PLAN CODES: L=lines; O=offsets; C=construction; S=sail; A=arrangement; P=profile; Dh=hull detail; Dr=rigging detail

LOA	Beam	Description	Date	Plan Codes	Cat.No.
60'2"	15'0"	Power cruiser *Sirius*	1963	LDh	75.59
60'5"	15'1"	Sport fisherman *Paranda*, twin-screw w/rig	1949	LOCAPDhDr	75.24
61'3"	16'2"	Power cruiser *Malova V* w/aft cabin under deck	1946	LOCAPDr	75.17
62'0"	13'2"	Power cruiser *Aquila*, sedan-type w/twin screws	1939	LOSAP	75.7
62'7"	15'4"	Sedan-type power cruiser w/twin screws	1950	AP	75.43
64'0"	16'0"	Power cruiser *Admiral Blake*	1956	LDh	75.60
64'10"	13'5"	Power cruiser *Alcy* w/twin screws & dinghy on deck	1940	LOCAPDh	75.18
65'4"	15'4"	Power cruiser *Makaira* w/twin screws & dinghy on deck	1945	LOCAPDh	75.19
67'0"	15'6"	Power cruiser w/twin screws	1960	L	75.49
68'0"	15'8"	Power cruiser *Visitor IV* w/canopied after deck	1954	LOCAPDh	75.30
77'6"	17'0"	Power cruiser w/raised pilothouse & stack	1947	ADh	75.22
83'0"	16'5"	Power cruiser, converted from USCG cutter	1948	CAPDh	75.15
84'0"	17'0"	Power cruiser *Aquila* w/raised pilothouse	1945	LOCAPDhDr	75.12
94'1"	18'3"	Motoryacht w/'midship pilothouse & stack	1954	LAP	75.40

MISCELLANEOUS DETAILS

Description	Date	Cat.No.
Diagram showing fish trawling setup		75.72
Weight summary for power cruiser	1963	75.61
Hydrostatic curves for retriever boat *Bon Jean*	1941	75.51
"TruLoc" terminal fittings		75.76
Displacement data sheet	1944	75.77
Boom gooseneck & outhaul		75.74
Headstay takeup gear		75.84
Description of reefing procedure	1948	75.78
Deck ventilator	1949	75.73

PLANS BY OTHER DESIGNERS

LOA	Description	Date	Plan Codes	Cat.No.
60'1"	Eastern-rigged dragger w/round stern by Albert Condon	1944	LCP	75.56
62'0"	Eastern-rigged dragger *Priscilla V.* by Albert Condon	1943	LDh	75.54
62'7"	Sloop-rigged motorsailer *Egret* w/aft pilothouse by Trumpy	1971	LOCAPDhDr	75.37
67'3"	Eastern-rigged dragger w/round stern by Albert Condon	1943	LA	75.55
76'3"	Western-rigged seiner w/round stern by J.M. Martinac	1936	LOCAP	75.57
81'5"	Eastern-rigged dragger w/transom stern by EWR	1955	C	75.53
173'8"	Submarine chaser w/twin screws by Allen, Adler, Major & Mooney	1940	LODh	75.52

© Mystic Seaport, Rosenfeld Collection, Mystic, Connecticut. Negative 115699F

Aquila in 1947

© Mystic Seaport, Rosenfeld Collection, Mystic, Connecticut. Negative 129346F

Paranda in 1951

WEE ONE, A SHORT-ENDED CUTTER OF 1934
20'0" x 6'4"

The tough economic times of the 1930s gave talented designers ample time to create beautifully detailed drawings for equally handsome small cruisers such as this one, which Frederick Geiger produced in 1934 as a kind of rite of passage upon his entry in the field of yacht design. (That the 126' J-class sloop *Weetamoe* immediately follows *Wee One* in *Lloyd's Register of American Yachts* makes for an astonishing contrast.) In spite of being only 20' long, *Wee One* has standing headroom under her trunk cabin, sleeping for two, a reasonable galley, a toilet, an inboard engine, and plenty of stowage space. She was carefully built by Ralph Wiley of Oxford, Maryland, for James England; and, largely because the fastenings were copper and bronze instead of steel and iron, she is with us still, having been recently purchased by a friend of mine who plans to sail her in Maine waters. In 1938, when owned by Harry Young, *Wee One* sailed from Chesapeake Bay to Bermuda and back, heaving-to a couple of times when the wind piped up. Young's engaging yarn was published in the December 1938 issue of *Yachting*.

Catalog No. 75.1

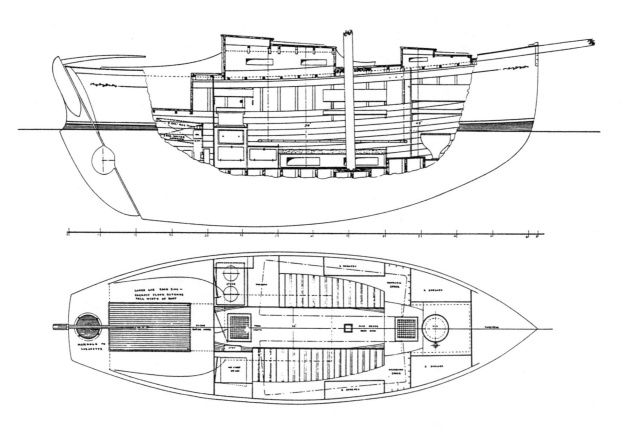

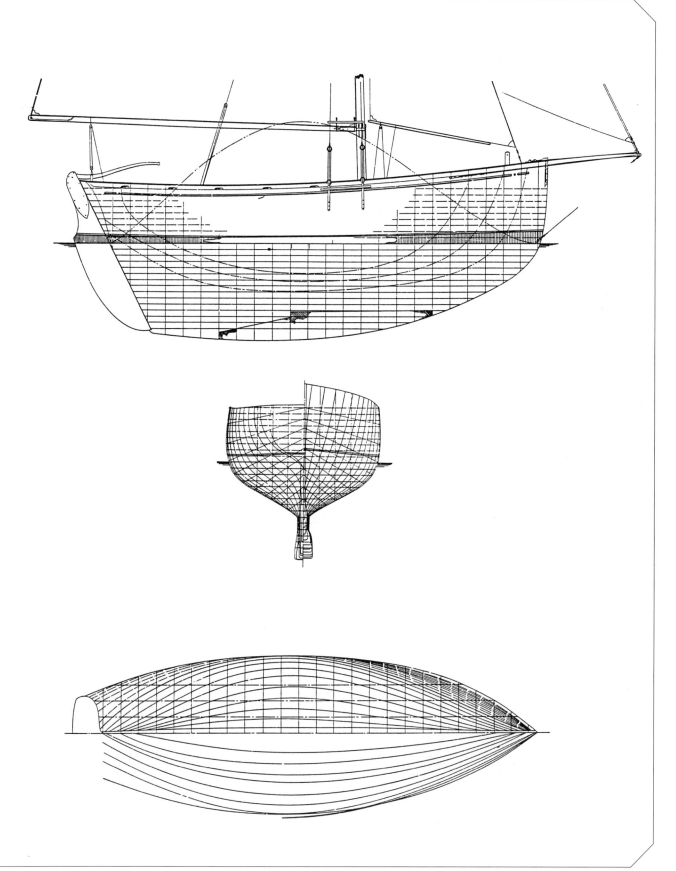

DEEP WATER, A SHORT-ENDED CRUISING CUTTER OF 1935
36'3" x 9'11"

Of a similar type to *Wee One*, but larger by good
measure, is this lovely flush-decker. In her there is
standing headroom throughout, and a private
stateroom aft for the owner with a single berth and
chart table. As with many such arrangements
where privacy is paramount, the companionway
leading below deck is separated from the cockpit—
a compromise not to everyone's liking. There is
another companionway ahead of the mast leading
to the galley where the paid hand's pipe berth is
located. Another version of the arrangement drawing, published in *The Rudder* (July 1935), shows a
winding staircase leading to the main cabin rather
than a simple ladder shown here, as well as some
other minor differences. The Mathis Yacht Building
Co., in Camden, New Jersey, built *Deep Water* for
Charles Welch.   Catalog No. 75.2

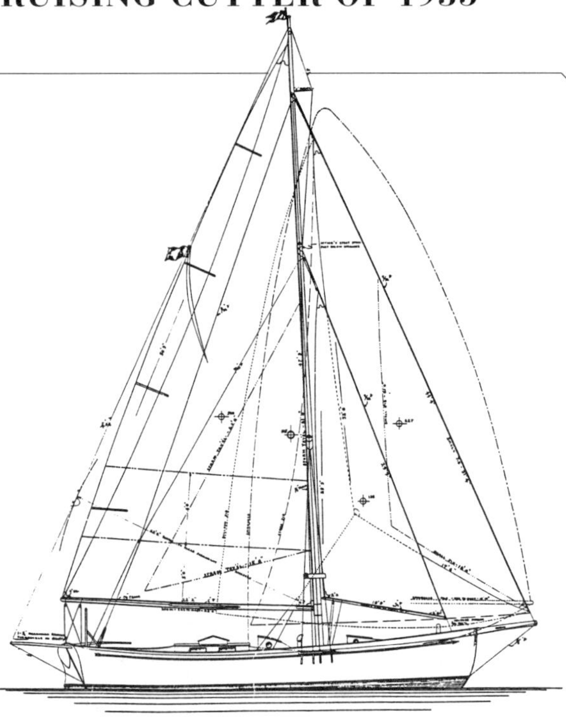

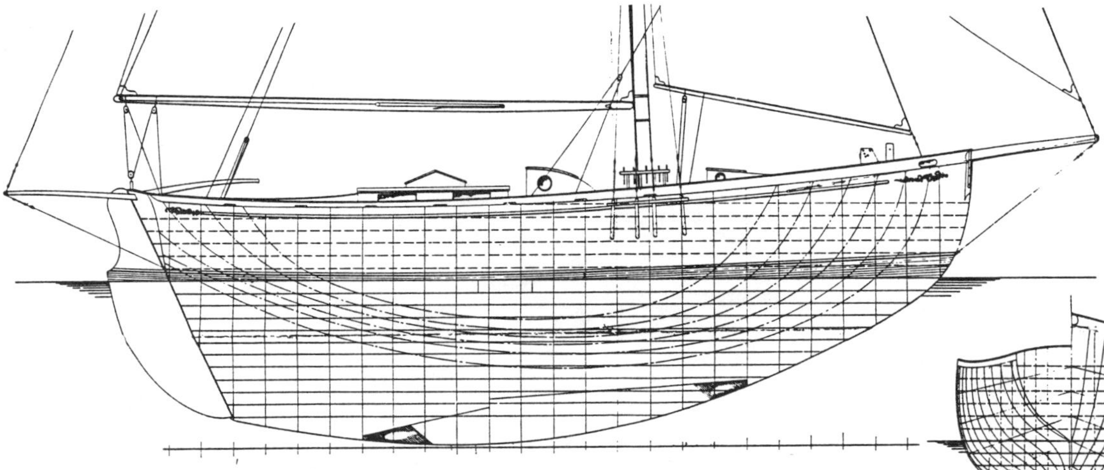

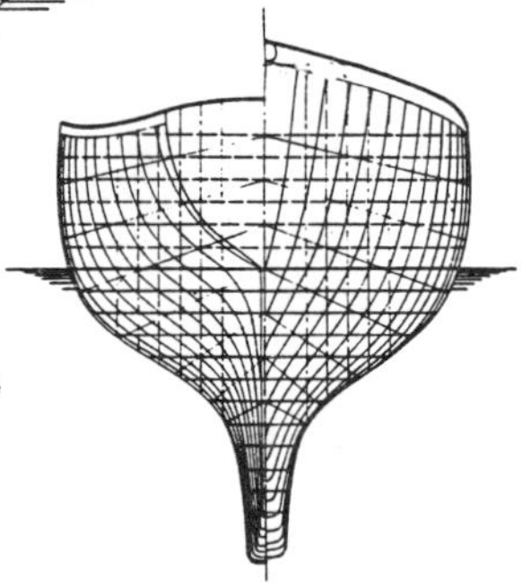

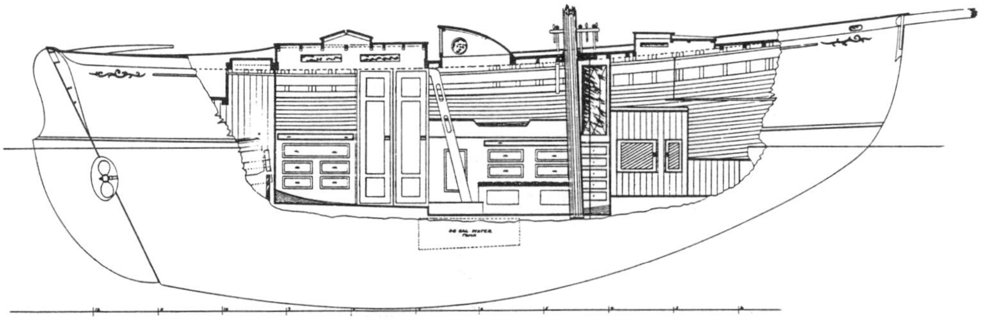

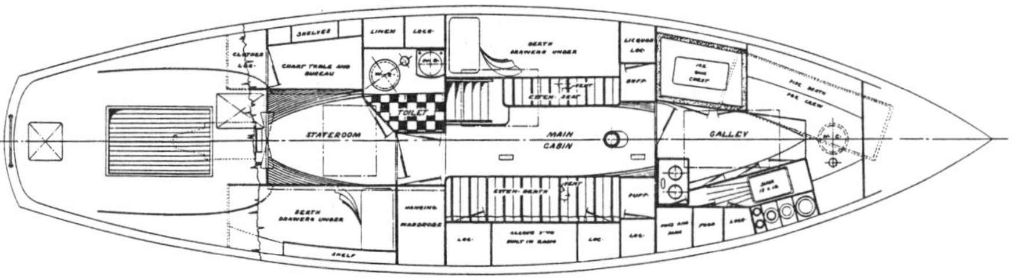

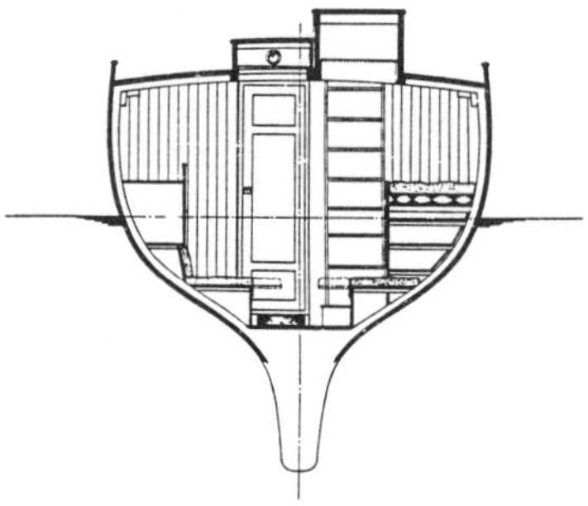

BLUE WATER, A SHORT-ENDED CRUISING KETCH OF 1941
26'4" x 8'4"

When Harry Young returned to Baltimore from Bermuda in *Wee One*, he commissioned *Blue Water*'s design, larger with a divided rig, but still accommodating only two persons—a sure indication of his firsthand sea experience. Although *Blue Water* has a transom stern, that stern is narrow with good deadrise, giving the hull the balanced ends needed for comfort and security at sea. Young built the boat himself and ended up with a fine little ship capable of cruising anywhere.

Catalog No. 75.9

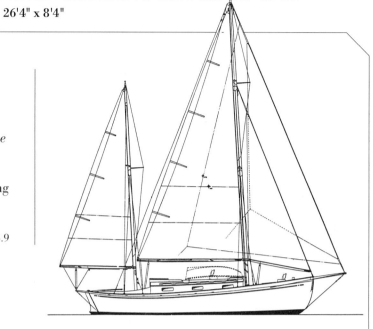

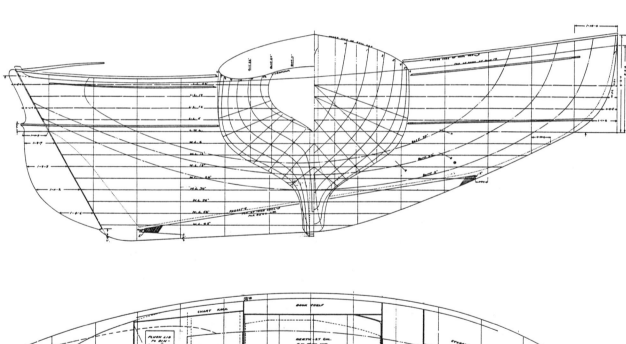

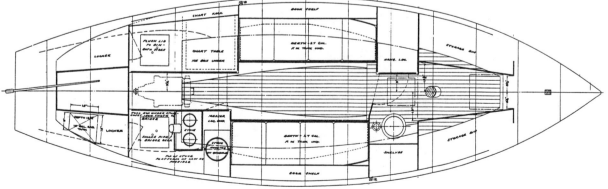

RANGER AND *NEW RANGER*, CRUISERS OF 1940–44
38'0" x 10'6"

Chesapeake Bay offers many more cruising possibilities to a shallow-draft boat than to a deep one; thus many of Geiger's designs are of the combination keel/centerboard type. The pre-war and post-war *Ranger*, both offered as stock boats by Morton Johnson & Co. of Bay Head, New Jersey, were nearly identical and about as nice a craft as one could ask for. The draft was less than 4' with the centerboard raised, the rig was self-tending to make tacking quick and easy, and the below-deck arrangement was the accepted standard for a four-berth auxiliary of this size (although I'd have placed the toilet room in its proper port-side location). There was, of course, the centerboard trunk projecting above the cabin sole, but this was almost an asset in that it formed the middle part of the cabin table. How interesting that Geiger designed *Ranger* almost 15 years before the famous and very similarly shaped *Finisterre* type by Sparkman & Stephens became so popular! Catalog No. 75.11, 11A, .48, and .58

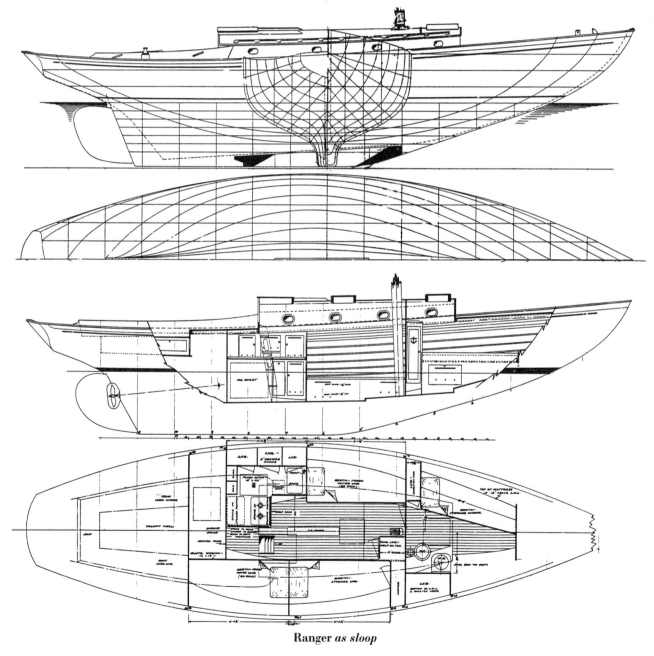

Ranger *as sloop*

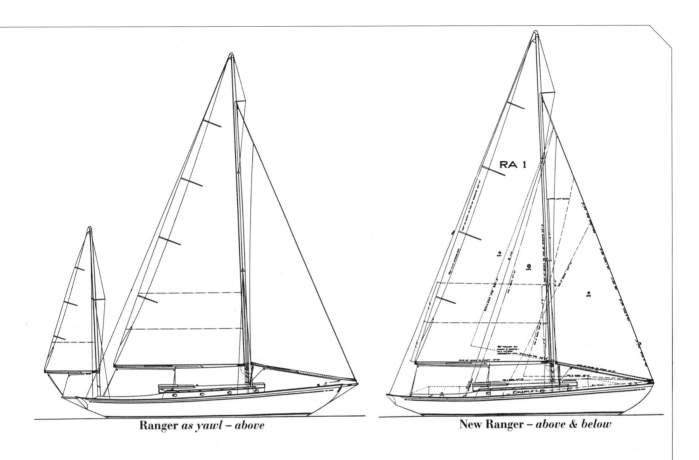

Ranger *as yawl – above*   New Ranger – *above & below*

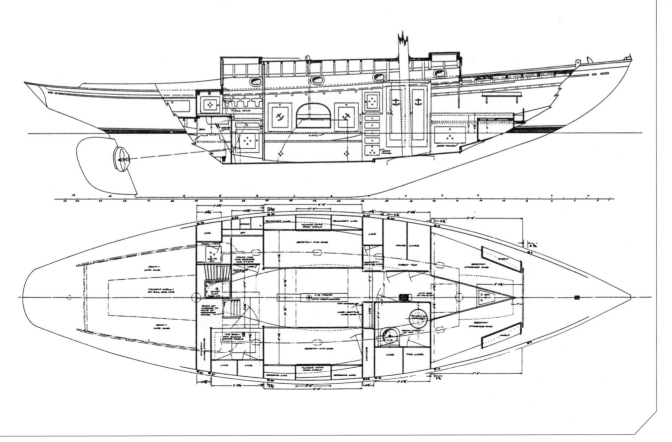

STARDUST AND WINDY DAY, CRUISING KETCHES OF 1947
48'2" x 12'3"

Although of similar length, beam, and draft, and carrying identical sailplans, the lines of this pair of shallow-draft ketches indicate somewhat different hull shapes. *Stardust*, whose drawings are dated a few months earlier, has firmer bilges than *Windy Day* (perhaps because she has an iron ballast keel). Although both boats were built in the same yard (Morton Johnson's) at almost the same time, it appears that *Windy Day* was the fancier of the two, with a double-planked hull, teak-over-plywood decks, a lead ballast keel, and five pairs of steam-bent belt frames installed inside the hull after it was ceiled and before the joinerwork went in. The difference in layout below deck shows that Mr. Cawthorne's *Windy Day* would sail with a paid crew who would prepare the meals in the forward-placed galley; while, for *Stardust*, Mr. Booth preferred a more open and democratic galley-aft arrangement, sacrificing Cawthorne's private stateroom in the process. Catalog Nos. 75.13 & 75.14

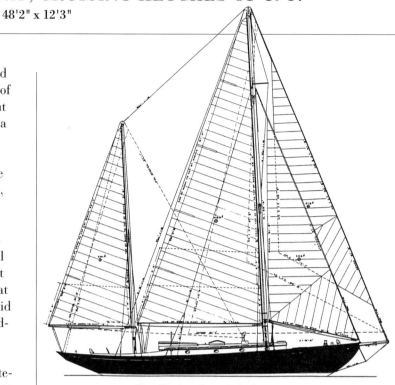

Stardust – *above & below*

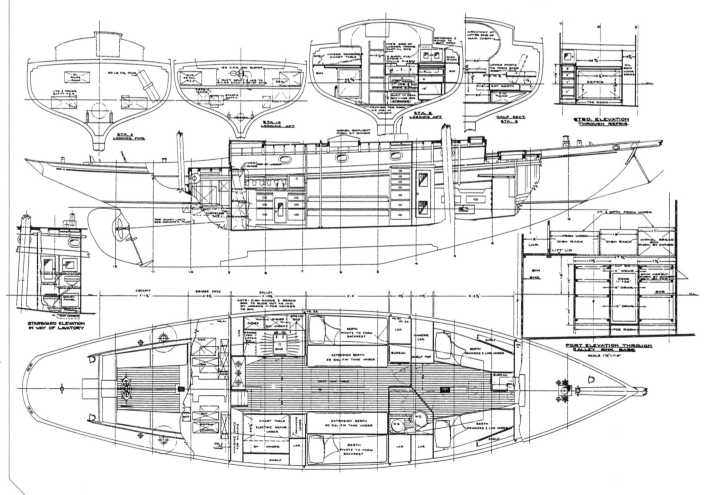

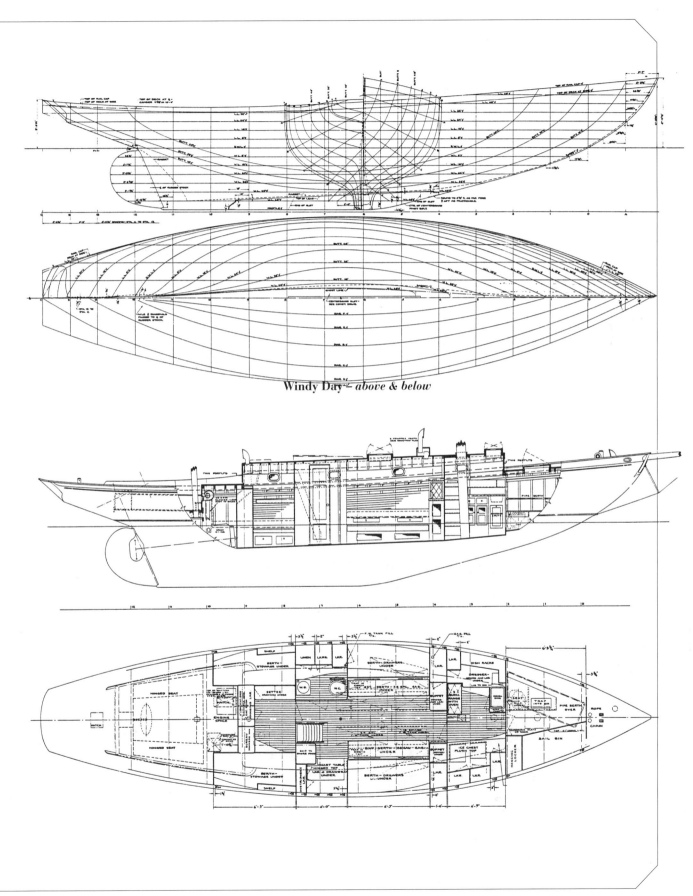

Windy Day – *above & below*

AVALON, A FLUSH-DECKED SLOOP OF 1952
33'2" x 7'9"

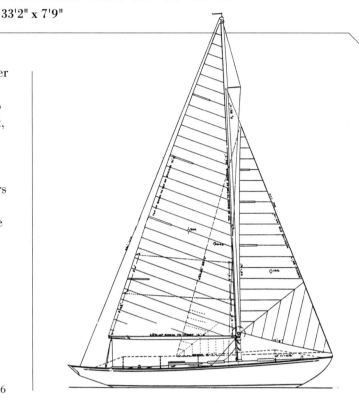

Racing yachts were neither what Frederick Geiger specialized in nor was known for, but in *Avalon* he produced a winner, for she showed her heels to the entire Tampa Bay fleet during her 1952 debut, winning the six-race series and the Egmont Key race that same year. Owner Francis Crow wrote that "this has turned out to be the best sailing boat anyone in this area has ever seen. In light airs she has beaten every boat around here boat for boat. In heavy weather and rough seas, she is able to knife through and keep going far longer than other boats anywhere near her size. She has an easy motion and is exceptionally dry. As to balance, she is perfect." *Avalon* is also an exceptionally strong and simple craft, an advantage, of course, of the flush deck. Subsequently, for full headroom, a doghouse version was built in Nova Scotia for Melville Grosvenor, named *Lady Anne*. (*Avalon* was built by Clark Mills in Dunedin, Florida.)   Catalog No. 75.26

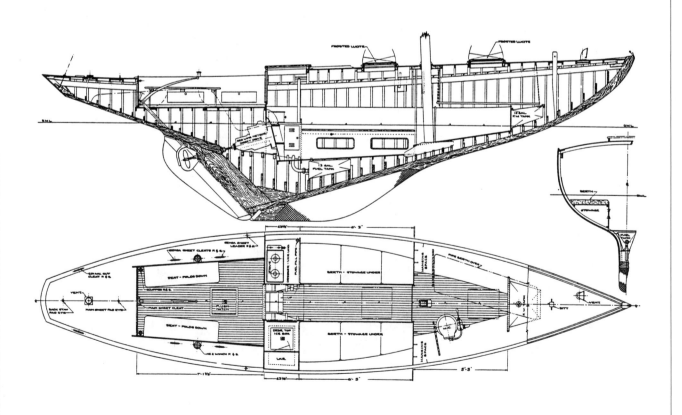

CANDIDA, A FLUSH-DECKED SLOOP OF 1955
35'9" x 8'7"

A variation on the same theme as *Avalon* is *Candida*, a boat designed for my friend John Streeter and built for him by Oxford Boat Yard in Oxford, Maryland. She, too, is flush-decked with a seven-eighths rig, and sleeps two, but differs from *Avalon* and from most other sailboats in the layout of her cockpit—an arrangement that Streeter and Geiger worked out together, and one that provided unusual comfort and convenience. The helmsman, with tiller and mainsheet within easy reach, sat way aft on a transverse bench, with sloping back-rest, enough higher than the crews' seats that visibility was virtually unobstructed. Construction is light, with ¾" cedar for planking, a 2"-thick sprung keel timber, and a ⅜" plywood deck supported by spruce beams. Inside, the 1¼" x 1¼" oak frames are mostly exposed, with only a little ceiling in way of the berths. The mast steps on deck and is supported below by a ½" plywood structural bulkhead. Of canoe-type hull form, similar to the modern fin-keeled IOR boats, *Candida* has no deep bilge, as does *Avalon*, in which water can collect and not slosh around when heeled. This construction was a necessary economy move on John Streeter's part, and he recommended against it if a wineglass shape is economically feasible.

Catalog No. 75.29

LAPWING, A RACING/CRUISING SLOOP OF 1955
35'3" x 8'8"

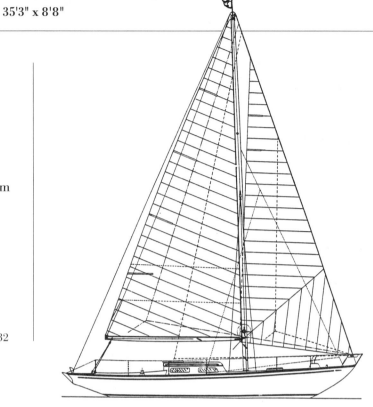

Lapwing, built by the Heidtmann yard in
Germany for Harold Wilcox, can be considered a
masthead-rigged big sister of *Avalon*, and a more
sophisticated one as well. Like *Avalon*, she only
sleeps three, although both boats have cockpits
that are long enough for sleeping. *Lapwing*'s
interior is made more habitable by the doghouse
which, although small, allows one to stand up from
the 'midship galley all the way aft to the cockpit.
Living is still wonderfully basic below, where the
third crew member sleeps in a canvas-bottomed
Root berth and a cedar bucket takes the place of
the usual toilet. Before arriving in the states,
Lapwing sailed from Germany to England where
she placed fourth in the 220-mile Channel Race
and participated in the Plymouth–LaRochelle as
well as the famed Fastnet.   Catalog No. 75.32

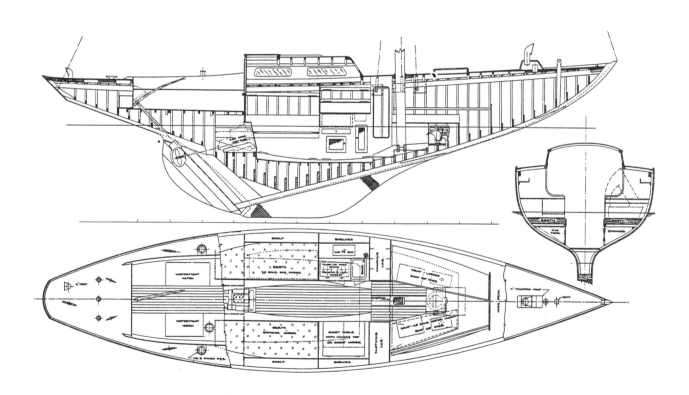

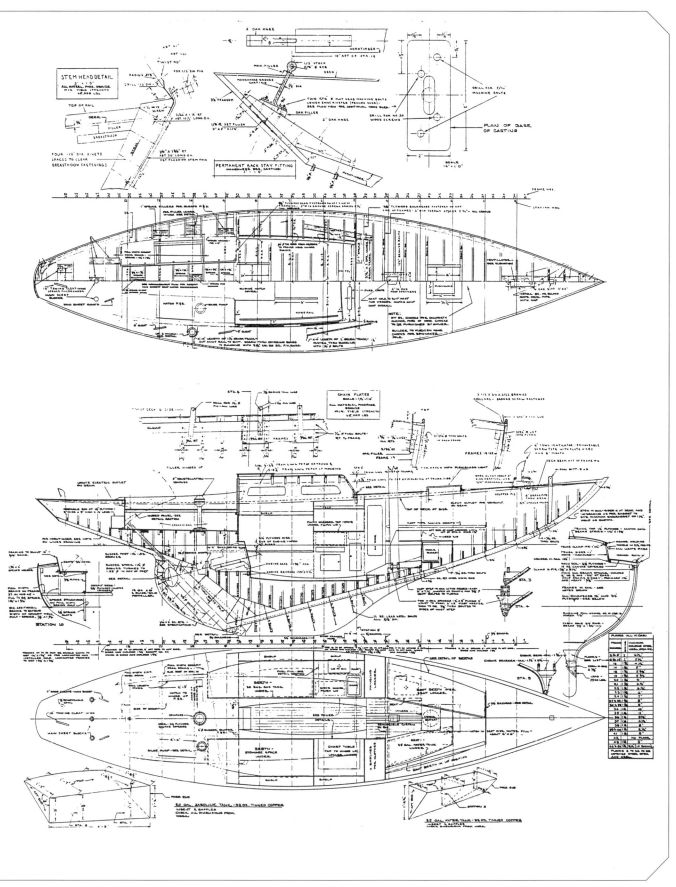

AQUILA, A POWER CRUISER OF 1940
62'0" x 13'2"

*A*quila, as big a sedan cruiser as you're ever likely to see, is like a split-level house. From the living/dining/patio (in the aft part of the boat), you go down half a flight of stairs to the kitchen, the two bathrooms, and the three bedrooms, all of which are on the same level. (Way forward the crew lives in relatively cramped quarters, sleeping in folding pipe berths and climbing in and out through a fore-deck hatch.) Owner Philemon Dickinson insisted that the cockpit, or patio as I've called it, adjoin and be on the same level as the deckhouse (the living/dining area)—thus the "sedan" configuration. *Aquila* was built by the Hubert Johnson yard of Bay Head, New Jersey.

Catalog No. 75.7

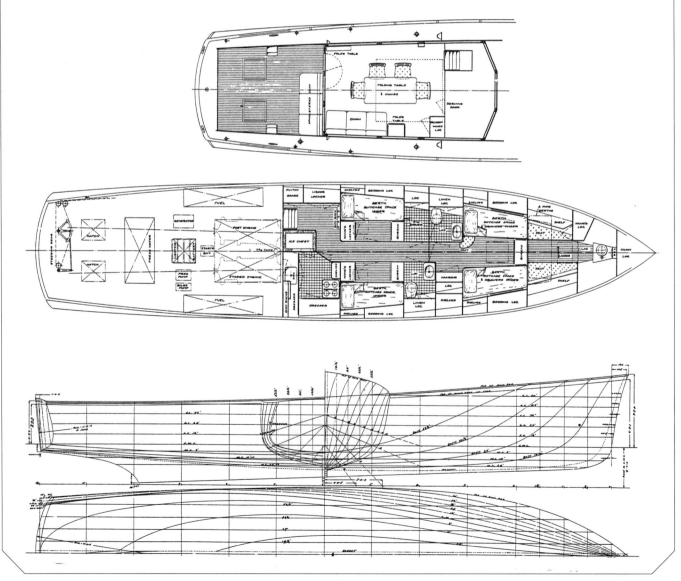

AQUILA, A POWER CRUISER OF 1946
84'0" x 17'0"

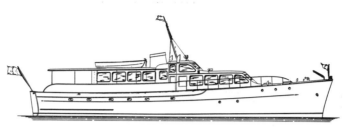

Not only was Philemon Dickinson attached to the name *Aquila*, but he also utilized Fred Geiger as repeat designer for his post-war yacht. This second *Aquila*, larger than her predecessor by 22', was also built in Bay Head, but by Morton Johnson & Co. instead of the Hubert Johnson yard, which was by then set up for the building of stock sport-fishing boats. In hull shape, the new boat echoed the old, being round-bottomed with a slightly con-cave bow profile, and having considerable flare forward, a skeg aft, and twin screws. In arrangement and profile, however, the new boat is quite different and, as befits her greater size, far more complex. Those familiar with the big yachts for which builder John Trumpy of Annapolis became well-known, can see through this *Aquila* why Frederick Geiger became Trumpy's in-house designer in later years.   Catalog No. 75.12

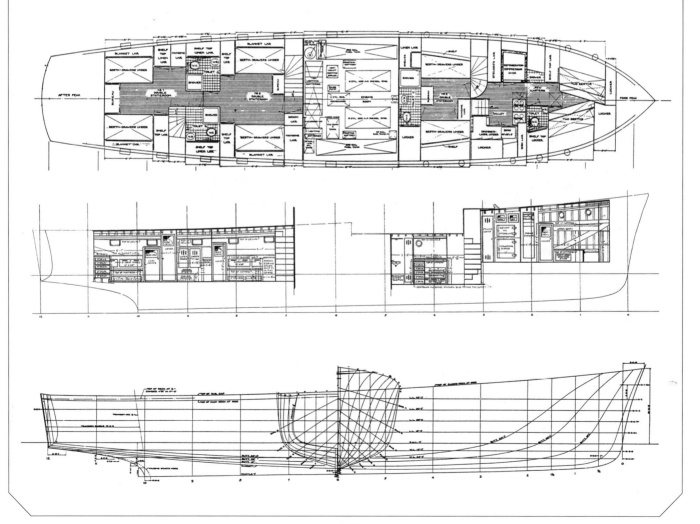

COLINE, A V-BOTTOMED SPORTFISHERMAN OF 1949
50'0" x 14'5"

This is an early version of what has become the accepted Florida-based sportfisherman—that is, a V-bottomed, twin-screw craft with a flush foredeck, a deckhouse placed well aft on which is mounted a flying bridge—and, of course, a cockpit that runs to the transom and contains fighting chairs, fishboxes, and lockers for tackle. In her day, *Coline* was right in the thick of the Gulf Stream fishing scene. She was based at the Cat Cay Club in the Bahamas, where her owner, George Collier, was manager. More than four decades have passed since Morton Johnson of Bay Head, New Jersey, built *Coline*, and nowadays she'd have to have a far larger flying bridge (enclosed by the usual "elephant oxygen tent" see-through curtains) and a tower perched above it after the fashion.

Catalog No. 75.23

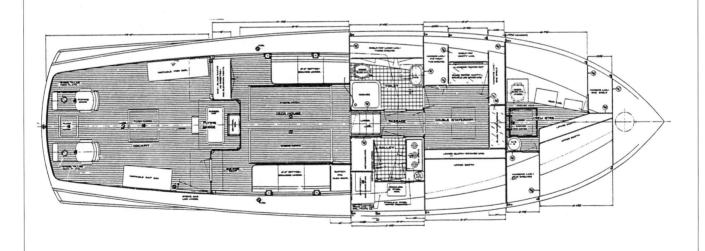

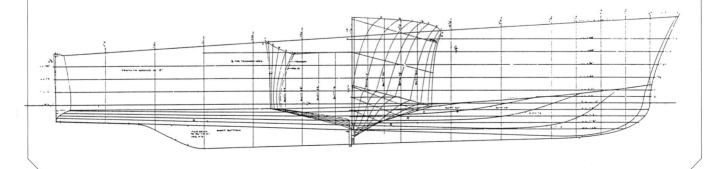

PARANDA, A SPORT FISHERMAN OF 1951
60'5" x 15'1"

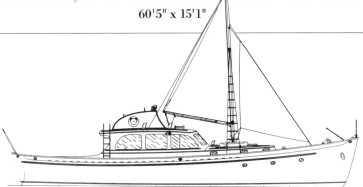

While a sportfishing machine of the "sedan" configuration, *Paranda* looks, and indeed is, more seaworthy than most. The springy sheerline, the stanchion-supported rail, the jib-and-mainsail steadying rig, and the deep hull all speak of capability and comfort at sea. Some might argue that she'd have been better with a single propeller on centerline (for which she certainly has sufficient draft) instead of twins which are unprotected and tend to roll out, trap air, and allow the engines to race when the boat rolls heavily in a beam sea. The unusually handsome *Paranda* was built by the Jacobsen Shipyard at Oyster Bay, New York, for Daniel Braman's use in Gulf of Mexico waters.

Catalog No. 75.24

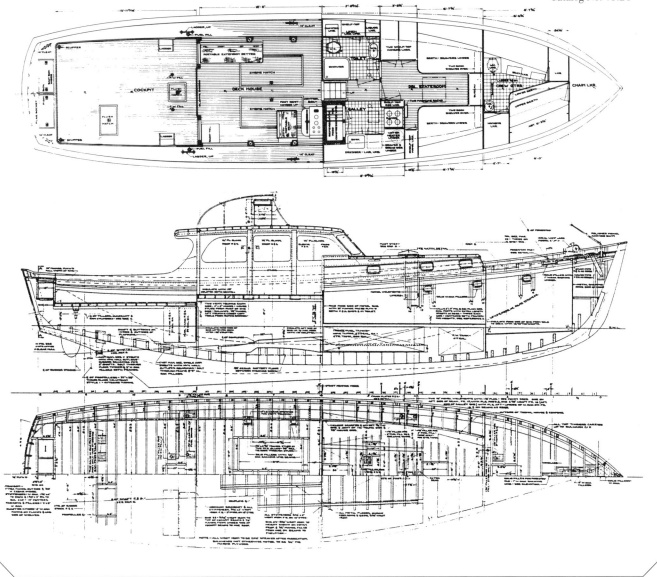

LOUIS L. KROMHOLZ
1890 – 1965

As the least-known of the six featured designers, Louis Kromholz nevertheless produced some exceptionally lovely yacht drawings. A lifelong bachelor who continued to live with his parents while they were alive (his mother lived into her 90s), and afterwards alone, he never set up a formal design office, but did his work in a spare bedroom at home. He was largely self-taught, and is said to have, at times, worked as a designer or draftsman in established naval architectural firms such as Sparkman & Stephens. Both his mother and father were immigrants from Lithuania and, after arriving in about 1890, continued to live in the New York City area, first in the Bronx and later in White Plains. Louis had three brothers, but, according to a nephew, Frank Kromholz, the family's demise is imminent, he being its only living member still carrying the name. Frank remembers his Uncle Louis as a handsome man who was a loner and very much a perfectionist.

Louis Kromholz's artistically rendered drawings have an engaging quality, and several of his designs were published in *Yachting* and *The Rudder*. He left no list of designs nor any indication of which of his designs resulted in actual boats being built. His love of teak led him to design teak furniture as well as yachts. Taking photographs and processing the pictures was one of his hobbies. He never had a boat of his own.

THE KROMHOLZ COLLECTION

Louis Kromholz willed his drawings to Mystic Seaport, and they arrived in 1965, shortly after his death. Besides original plans drawn by him, there are prints of other designers' work that Kromholz had accumulated over the years for reference. Of his own work, there are less than two dozen complete designs, but there are numerous preliminaries that apparently never came to fruition. Deserving special mention are Kromholz's beautiful colored renderings (catalog nos. 10.12 and 10.46), not to be missed by anyone interested in his work.

Kromholz's career spanned more than a half century, with his earliest drawings made in 1909 and his last in 1961. As full-time professional yacht designers go, Kromholz seems not to have been especially prolific. The entire collection consists of only 268 sheets, including the reference prints, that represent 80 different designs. But we know he drew more plans than were contained in his bequest, because at least 16 of his designs, for which Mystic Seaport has no drawings, were published in *Yachting* or *The Rudder*, some of the more interesting ones being a 100' motoryacht (*Yachting*, September 1911); a 40' double-ended, sloop-rigged motorsailer with an extensive description written by Kromholz himself (*Yachting*, February 1913); a 45' fast power cruiser, again with the designer's detailed description (*Yachting*, November 1913); and a 30-mph 71' power cruiser designed near the end of his career (*Yachting*, April, 1952).

Except where noted, all plans listed on the following pages were drawn by Louis Kromholz.

THE LOUIS L. KROMHOLZ PLANS

SMALL CRAFT

LOA	Beam	Description	Date	Plan Codes	Cat. No.
8'0"	3'4"	Flat-bottomed pram for outboard motor	1961	LOC	10.44
10'0"	3'8"	Lapstrake yacht tender	1912	LOC	10.32
10'0"	4'1"	Lapstrake tender for the motorsailer *Yarra*	1934	LOC	10.16
11'6"	4'4"	Lapstrake tender for the power cruiser *Audlee*	1930	LOC	10.14A

SAILING YACHTS

LOA	Beam	Description	Date	Plan Codes	Cat. No.
32'6"	8'9"	Cruising cutter with small deckhouse	1959	LSAP	10.43
56'2"	15'0"	Clipper-bowed ketch *Eva R. Martin*, gaff main	1934	LCS	10.40
75'5"	16'6"	Flush-decked cruising ketch	1935	LSAP	10.21

POWER YACHTS & MOTORSAILERS

LOA	Beam	Description	Date	Plan Codes	Cat. No.
28'5"	7'6"	Launch w/double cockpits & aft shelter cabin	1930	AP	10.76
30'0"		Power cruiser, double-ended w/raised foredeck	1909	P	10.2
37'6"	11'0"	Launch w/three cockpits & tunnel stern	1935	LCP	10.19
38'7"	11'3"	Power cruiser w/stack & tender atop trunk cabin	1934	LAP	10.25
40'0"	9'4"	Power cruiser w/raised foredeck & aft cabin	1919	LOCAP	10.7
40'0"	9'6"	V-bottomed power cruiser *May M* w/raised foredeck	1924	LO	10.9
40'0"	9'9"	Power cruiser w/raised foredeck	1915	LOCAP	10.3
41'0"	10'6"	Power cruiser w/raised foredeck	1926	LO	10.10
40'0"	10'6"	Power cruiser, sedan-type (beautiful renderings)	1935	AP	10.46
40'0"	10'9"	Double-ended power cruiser *Loon* w/raised foredeck	1937	LAP	10.41
40'0"	12'2"	Ketch-rigged motorsailer *Margie* w/outboard rudder	1935	LOCSA	10.18
40'9"	10'6"	Power cruiser w/cut-down waist, aft cabin & stack	1935	LOAP	10.26
41'0"	13'0"	Power cruiser (tugboat configuration) w/pilothouse & stack	1953	AP	10.28
41'0"	14'4"	Power cruiser w/steadying sails	1952	LAP	10.30
41'0"	14'4"	Power cruiser w/steadying sail (jib)	1951	LAP	10.80
43'0"	11'6"	Power cruiser w/aft cabin & steadying sail (jib)	1959	AP	10.24
46'0"	12'0"	Power cruiser *Randa* w/raised foredeck & aft cabin	1929	LOCAP	10.11

PLAN CODES: L=lines; O=offsets; C=construction; S=sail; A=arrangement; P=profile; Dh=hull detail; Dr=rigging detail

LOA	Beam	Description	Date	Plan Codes	Cat. No.
50'0"	10'7"	Power cruiser *Rainbow* w/raised foredeck & aft cabin	1916	LOAP	10.6
50'8"	14'3"	Ketch-rigged motorsailer *Yarra* w/outboard rudder	1934	LCSADh	10.17
52'0"	11'4"	Power cruiser w/raised foredeck & aft cabin	1919	LOCAP	10.8
53'6"	15'0"	Sloop-rigged motorsailer w/outboard rudder	1951	SA	10.22
55'10"	13'2"	Power cruiser *Cygnus II* w/raised foredeck & aft cabin	1930	LOCAP	10.13
58'6"	13'0"	Power cruiser w/twin screws, raised foredeck & aft cabin	1928	AP	10.37
58'9"	13'9"	Power cruiser w/twin screws, raised foredeck & aft cabin	1929	AP	10.38
59'0"	16'5"	Sloop-rigged motorsailer	1951	SA	10.27
60'9"	11'6"	Power cruiser, triple screw w/V-bottom	1923	L	10.35
62'0"	13'9"	Power cruiser *Audlee* w/raised foredeck & aft cabin	1930	LOCAP	10.14
66'0"	16'6"	Flush-decked, ketch-rigged motorsailer	1934	SA	10.20
68'6"	14'0"	Power cruiser w/raised foredeck & stack	1928	LAP	10.12
70'0"	14'9"	Power cruiser, streamlined w/snub-nosed bow	1935	AP	10.53
82'0"	18'0"	Houseboat w/twin screws & steel hull	1932	AP	10.5
83'0"	20'0"	Motoryacht profiles for PT-boat conversion	1946	AP	10.48
84'3"	20'7"	Motoryacht *Thunderbird* (PT-boat conversion)	1946	AP	10.50
88'0"	12'0"	Fast motoryacht w/twin screws & stack	1919	AP	10.33
88'10"	16'0"	Motoryacht, twin screws & raised foredeck	1932	AP	10.4
89'0"	16'0"	Power cruiser w/raised deck & stack	1929	AP	10.39
97'0"	23'0"	Flush-decked motorsailer w/big 'midship house	1952	LAP	10.31
99'10"	17'0"	Motoryacht w/two deckhouses & stack between	1923	LAP	10.36
122'7"	24'0"	Power cruiser w/streamlined cabins	1948	AP	10.1
124'0"		Motoryacht w/round stern & stack amidships	1942	AP	10.42
132'0"		Motor yacht w/long deckhouse & stack amidships	1930	LP	10.45
138'0"	28'6"	Motoryacht w/round stern & streamlined cabin	1949	AP	10.79
139'8"	23'7"	Motoryacht w/round stern & big stack	1929	AP	10.34
170'0"	26'0"	Steam yacht w/ plumb stern		AP	10.74

COMMERCIAL & MILITARY

LOA	Beam	Description	Date	Plan Codes	Cat. No.
55'9"	13'2"	Dispatch boat w/firefighting nozzle on after deck	1936	AP	10.23
60'0"		Air-sea rescue boat w/V-bottom & twin screws		AP	10.73
61'0"	13'8"	Survey boat w/ raised deck & V-bottom	1930	LOCAPDh	10.15
78'0"		USCG patrol boat w/small pilothouse & dory on deck	1930	AP	10.49
80'0"		Steel-hulled tugboat	1953	P	10.29

PLANS BY OTHER DESIGNERS

LOA	Beam	Description	Date	Plan Codes	Cat. No.
24'0"	6'0"	Launch w/double cockpit & canvas shelters by Tams & King	1923	LOCAP	10.69
30'0"		Launch w/double cockpit by Tams & King	1922	LOCAP	10.66
36'8"	10'8"	Motorsailer *Dutchess* w/outboard rudder by Taylor Newell	1954	LOS	10.62
39'6"		Power cruiser w/forward cockpit by Tams & King	1923	LOCAP	10.68
37'0"	10'6"	One-design cruising sloop by Francis S. Kinney	1960	LS	10.61
45'4"	12'6"	Cruising yawl w/round cabin front by Tams & King	1922	LOCAP	10.65
68'3"	17'0"	Cruising ketch *Pandora IV* by Sparkman & Stephens	1958	LS	10.63
72'0"	14'6"	New York 50-class sloop by N.G. Herreshoff	1913	CSP	10.60
76'3"	15'6"	Cruising ketch by Sparkman & Stephens	1956	SA	10.64
90'0"	12'0"	Double-ended motoryacht *Grayling* by Tams, Lemoine & Crane	1907	LS	10.77
113'0"	22'10"	Coastal cargo vessel w/deckhouses amidships by Cox & Stevens	1942	AP	10.75
120'0"	20'0"	Inspection boat w/two deckhouses & stack between by Cox & Stevens	1913	AP	10.55
141'6"	26'0"	Steel freighter w/deckhouse & stack amidships by Cox & Stevens	1942	LCAP	10.58
157'0"	30'0"	Steel freighter w/stack & deckhouse aft by Cox & Stevens	1942	LAP	10.59
178'0"	23'4"	Steam yacht *Rambler* by Tams, Lemoine & Crane	1910	P	10.72
180'7"	24'0"	Motoryacht w/round stern by Cox & Stevens	1921	LO	10.57
200'		Motoryacht w/long deckhouse & stack amidships		A	10.47
214'0"		Three-masted topsail schooner		SP	10.78
256'		Ship-rigged, steel-hulled yacht *Valhalla* by Tams, Lemoine & Crane	1907	SP	10.71
256'0"		Motoryacht profiles by Tams & King	1923	P	10.67
277'6"	32'8"	Steam yacht *Vanadis* w/clipper bow by Tams, Lemoine & Crane	1908	LAP	10.70
262'8"	28'6"	Steam yacht w/plumb stem, 2 deckhouses, & 2 stacks by Cox & Stevens	1914	P	10.56
		Steam yacht w/clipper bow & stack by Cox & Stevens	1909		10.54

MISCELLANEOUS DETAILS

Description	Date	Cat. No.
Yacht joinery	1947	10.52
Yacht furniture	1936	10.51

A RAISED FOREDECK POWER CRUISER OF 1915
40'0" x 9'9"

How styles in powerboats have changed since Louis Kromholz designed this raised-decker to the fashion of 1915! The plan shows the big Wisconsin gasoline ("gasolene" back then) engine sharing the space below deck with the people who slept and cooked and ate there, and how those same people had almost no shelter from wind and spray when they were on deck, since there was only a pipe-frame canvas awning over the otherwise open cockpit. Riding in one of these craft was as close to sailing as powerboating ever got, for soon trunk cabins and deckhouses became commonplace and open-air cruising was left to the sailing fraternity. Forgoing some of what would today be considered necessities for a power cruiser, however, had some advantages. For example, the exposed engine was often a shined and polished showpiece which, because of the care lavished upon it, became almost a part of the family and thus far more reliable than one that was hidden away in its own space and hard to get at. This boat's round-bottomed hull, taken alone, is not especially light, but, because the interior is unburdened by "extras," the boat sits light on her lines. Records show that *Tarpon II*, a near sister also by Kromholz, reached 20 mph with only 90 horsepower.

Catalog No. 10.3

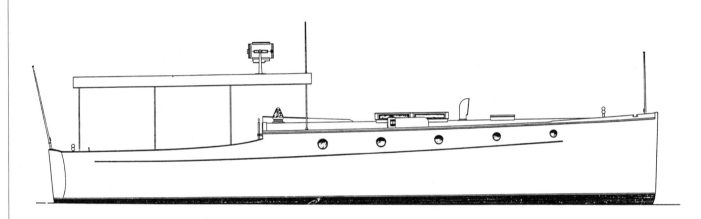

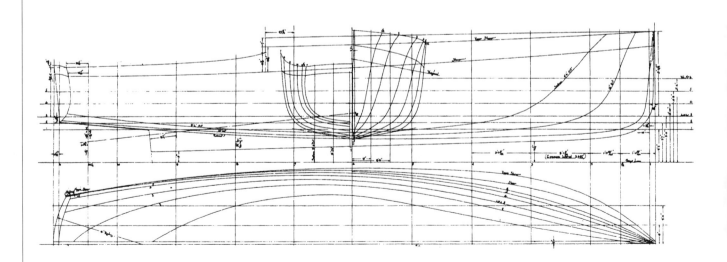

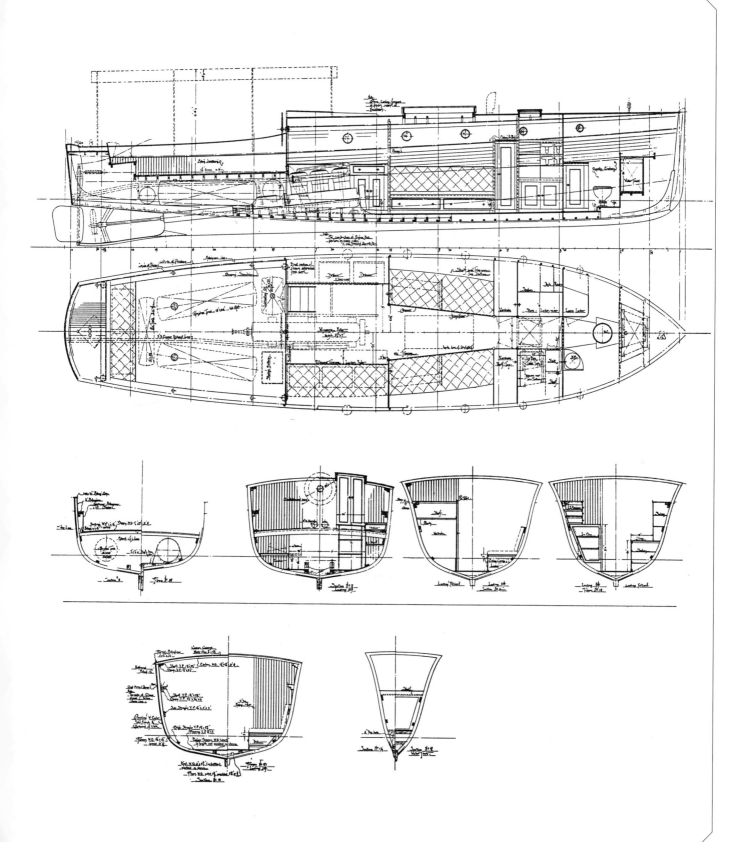

RANDA II, AN AFT CABIN POWER CRUISER OF 1929
47'0" x 12'0"

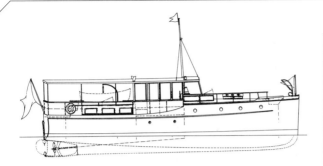

Imagine how you might feel as owner of this aft-cabin cruiser. Your stateroom is in that aft cabin; the entrance, the only one, is down from the after deck, where on each side of the companionway is a comfortable seat built into the cabin structure. Below, there's a 4'-wide double berth on one side and a 3' day bed on the other, both projecting outboard and aft under the deck. Ahead of you as you descend the stairs is a dresser against the bulkhead (no doubt with a mirror above), while outboard on each side is a pair of hanging lockers (called wardrobes on the drawing). There's a doorway to the right of the dresser which leads to your private bath, where you'll find a toilet, a lavatory, and a bathtub with shower. Chances are that you'll be taking your meals forward in the main cabin, which you get to by climbing up on the after deck, passing through the enclosed wheelhouse, then decending into the galley and on forward. Here the table has been set and your guests (as many as four) await. There's not a trace that this is where they slept last night, as now, for dining, the bedding has been stripped and stowed, the upper berths have hinged down to become backrests, and the lowers are doing double duty as settees. All around in this and the other cabins are beautiful, paneled bulkheads, partitions, and doors finished in natural mahogany, and you silently give thanks to designer Louis Kromholz and builder Emil Meyer. And you've a whole year to enjoy this life before "Black Tuesday" and the Great Depression which followed it.

Catalog No. 10.11

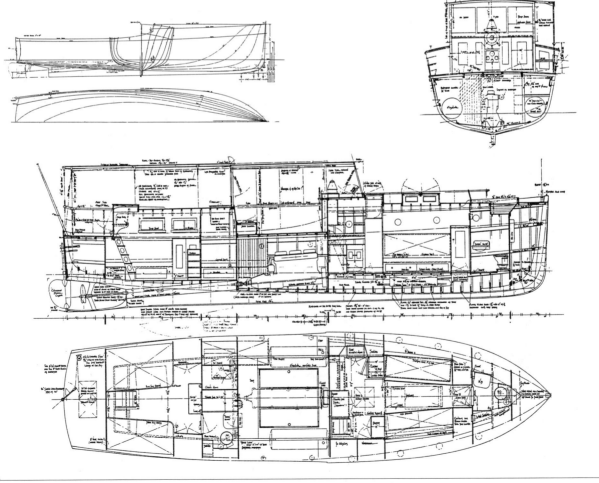

CYGNUS II, AN AFT CABIN POWER CRUISER OF 1930
55'10" x 13'2"

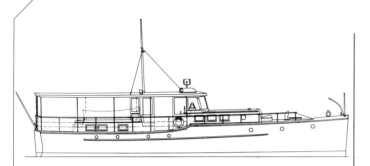

Cygnus's 10 additional feet allow more space for living, but most of the space here has been used for crew's quarters forward. The increased size aside, I prefer some of *Cygnus*'s features over

Randa's. For starters, access to the owner's aft cabin is improved, at least in my opinion, leading as it does from the pilothouse rather than the after deck. It's also nice that there's no galley between the pilothouse and main cabin—an advantage, I guess, of putting the crew's quarters forward where the galley could logically be adjacent to it. Kromholz thoughtfully provided on-deck seating forward and aft as well as along the back of the open-sided pilothouse. *Cygnus* shows just a touch of early streamlining in that her cabin fronts are raked aft and the pilothouse front windows are in knuckled panels. The Brooklyn, New York yard of Jakobson & Peterson built *Cygnus* for Clifford Swan of the Larchmont Yacht Club.   Catalog No. 10.13

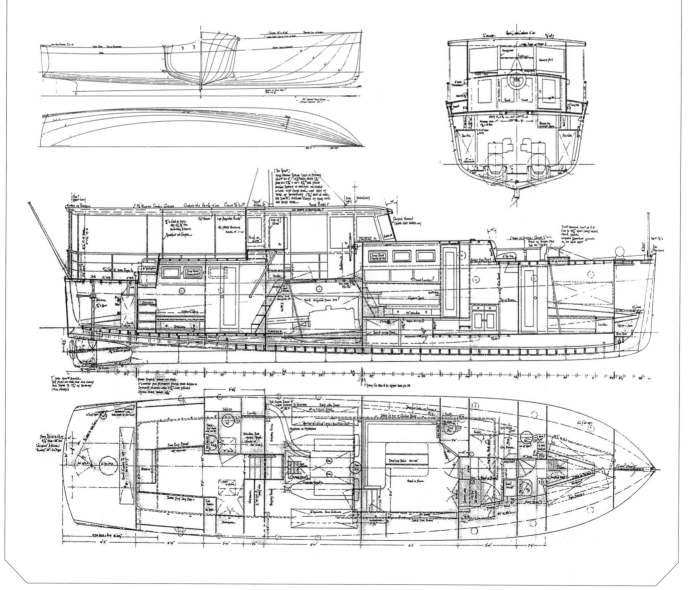

Louis Kromholz, as the skilled illustrator, is evident in these stylish and evocative profiles. One might ask how a prospective client could resist saying yes after looking at this kind of work, but that well may have been the case; for, although both designs were published in *Yachting* magazine (as black-and-white line work, unfortunately, and not the renderings shown here), it appears that neither boat was built. Too bad, because they're both really fine yachts that would look every bit as good in real life as they appear here. The prevailing style has changed markedly in the seven years between the two designs. The larger one, of course, is the older and carries the formal exterior appearance and interior arrangement of big money and a full professional crew. The sedan cruiser, on the other hand, although intended as a custom design, is a Depression-era craft having lots of berths arranged without regard for class, and a minimal galley located right smack in the center of things. And she shows some of the streamlining that was to prevail in powerboat design from the mid-1930s onward.

Catalog Nos. 10.12 & 10.46

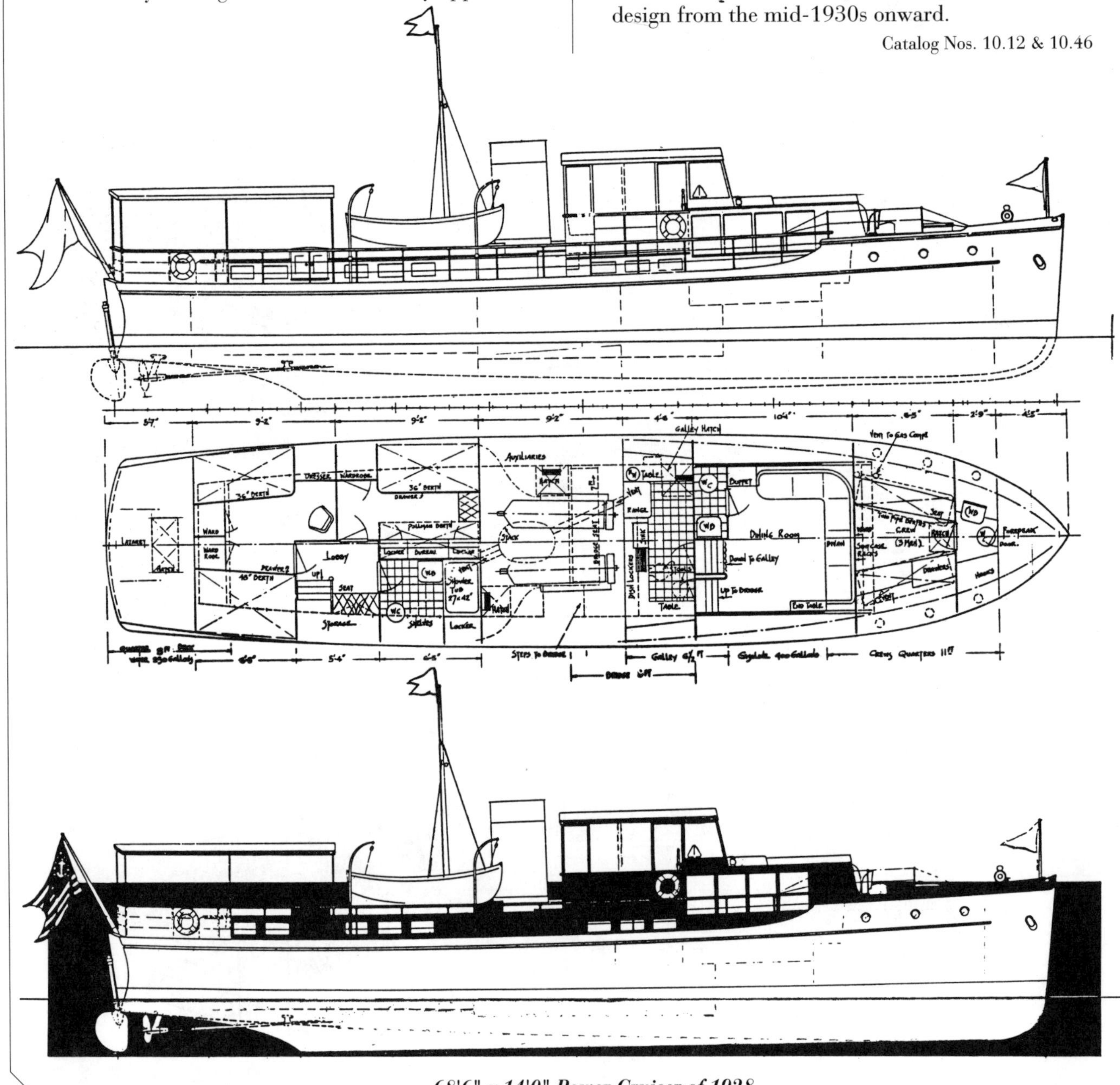

68'6" x 14'0" Power Cruiser of 1928

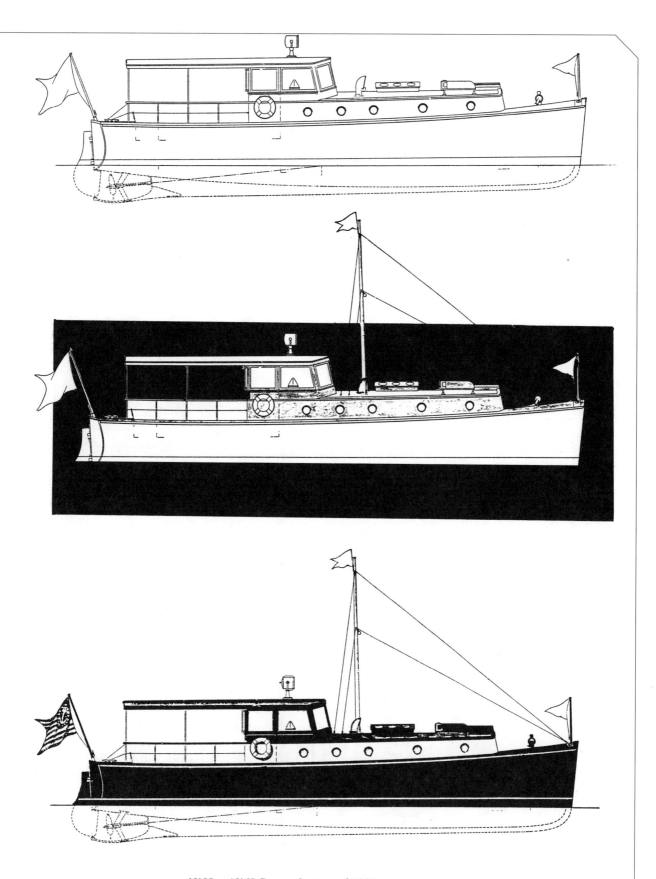

40'0" x 10'6" Power Cruiser of 1935

YARRA, A KETCH-RIGGED MOTORSAILER OF 1934
50'8" x 14'3"

My favorite Kromholz design is this, one of his few motorsailers—a vessel on which one could live and go to sea in comfort and safety, a craft not too big to be cared for and handled by one person, and, certainly, a hull shape of exceptional beauty. She was built for New York photographer Anton Bruehl by Robert Jacob, one of the finest yacht builders on City Island, and at the time caused quite a stir. Perhaps it was because of the hard times and the all too few new building contracts that both *The Rudder* and *Yachting* devoted an entire page to her design when it came out. But I like to believe that this design had unusual appeal and that, like me, the editors fancied themselves heading off for parts unknown, secure in the knowledge that this handsome vessel would handle whatever the sea offered up.   Catalog No. 10.17

YARRA'S TENDER OF 1934
10'0" x 4'1"

Quite a match for *Yarra* herself is this lovely lap-strake dinghy which has a touch of flare forward as well as some hollow to the waterline near the bow. She can be rowed from either or both of two positions; and with the center section of the stern seat removed, a small outboard motor can be fitted. The hull was planked with 5/16" Peruvian cedar, a wood used also for the transom, floorboards, and seats. Her weight was calculated at 135 pounds. Earlier, in 1930, Kromholz had designed a slightly larger tender much like this one for the 62' power cruiser *Audlee*, so it should be safe to assume that this 10-footer benefited somehow from the designer's experience with the earlier boat.

Catalog No. 10.16

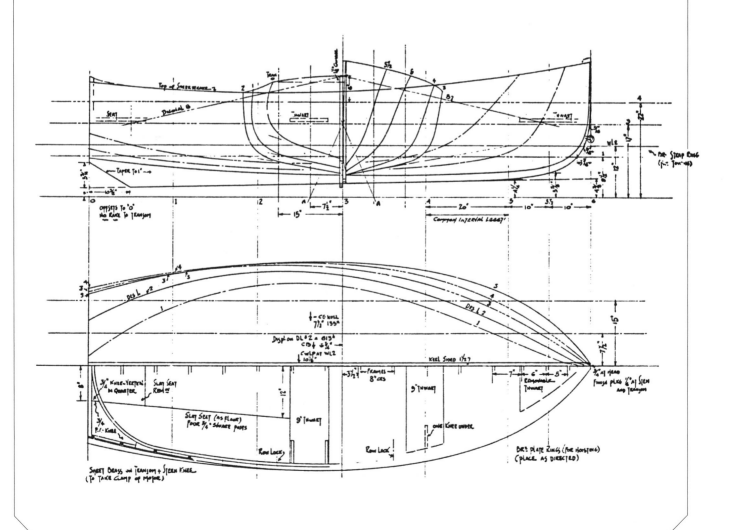

A PT BOAT CONVERSION OF 1946
83'0' x 20'0'

Louis Kromholz and a number of other designers undertook to draw up modifications for the military hulls that became surplus at the end of the war so they could be used for pleasure. The idea had some merit and some conversions were made, but, having seen some of the results, I'm quite certain the final cost was far greater than anticipated. The new interiors, systems, exterior trim, deckhouses, and power plants made up a large part of the total cost, as these items invariably do in any new yacht. Then there was the ripout and the inevitable structural repairs. This is one of several design studies that Louis Kromholz drew around 1946, doing what he was able to do with an existing hull shape.

Catalog No. 10.48

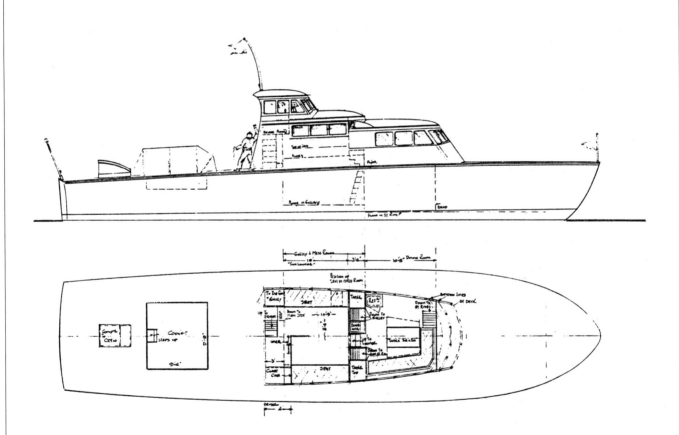

A YACHT OF THE FUTURE, 1949
138'0" x 28'6"

One gets the feeling that producing renderings like this was a source of great pleasure for Louis Kromholz, even though there wasn't much chance of the yacht itself ever seeing fruition. As inspiration for this ultra-streamlined craft, Kromholz may well have used Anthony Fokker's pre-war Consolidated-built yacht of equally bizarre profile, a vessel named *Q.E.D.* which caused a sensation when she appeared and left a lasting impression on those who saw her published plans and photographs. Given his eye for this kind of styling, were he at work in the 1980s, Louis Kromholz would have been a successful designer of modern megayachts.

Catalog No. 10.79

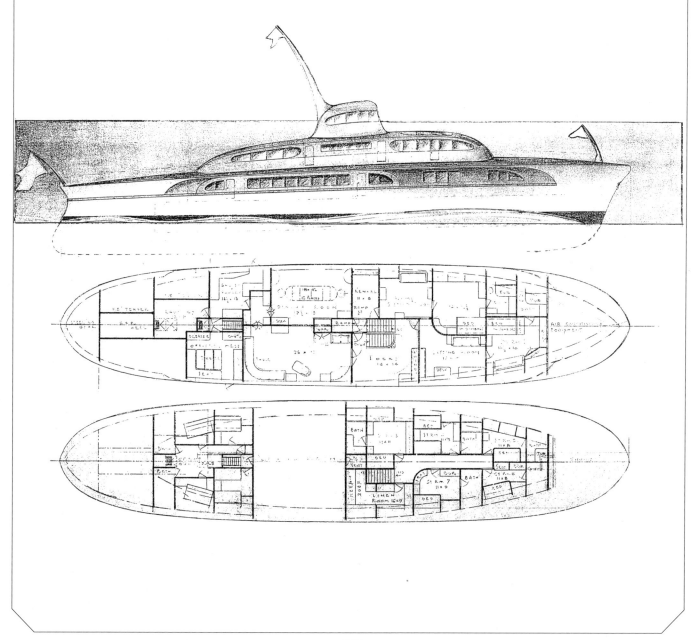

ALBERT E. CONDON
1887 – 1963

Although Albert Condon had moved away from his native mid-coast Maine by the time I was old enough for boats to become my absorbing interest, his reputation as an exceptional designer, a master builder, and, in general, a very fine man lingered behind, and I can remember hearing the Condon name whenever good locally built boats were talked about. Just down Mechanic Street, only a little more than a stone's throw from our Rockland home, was the I.L. Snow Co. shipyard where Condon had served as designer and master builder during most of the 1930s. Snow's was generally a commercial yard with a couple of big railways where coasting schooners and fishing draggers were built and repaired, but the shops occasionally turned out new Condon-designed yachts—fine craft which photos show to have been beautifully built, with lovely brightwork, carved and gilded coves and scrolls, and hull forms whose proportions were timeless.

Condon moved to Fairhaven, Massachusetts, on the eve of World War II, but he left behind a team of ship carpenters and boatbuilders ready to enter the wartime shipbuilding program with a flying start. One of those builders was another Friendship, Maine, native named Leroy Wallace whose careful workmanship and unquestioned integrity gave the Newbert & Wallace yard at Thomaston such a fine reputation for dragger building—Condon designs, naturally—after the war was over.

The Condon name should be better known than it is, for not only were his designs executed with precision and a refined aesthetic sense, but Albert Condon was one of those rare designers who was a hands-on builder as well and was equally at home with yachts or commercial craft and with power or sail. And I believe he was always one who personally drew everything he designed, running a one-man design office, often while supervising construction.

Formal education was spread out and intermingled with practical boat and ship building, so Condon was nearly 30 years old when he stopped attending classes, graduating in March 1916 from a two-year night course in naval architecture at Boston's Franklin Union. Earlier, he had been tutored for a couple of winters in the same subject by an MIT graduate, and earlier still, in 1908, had graduated from Hebron Academy in Maine, where he specialized in mathematics, physics, and chemistry. He had, in all, a pretty sound technical background.

As for the on-the-job-training part of Condon's education, that, too, was strong and well-rounded. As a teenager in Friendship, Albert Condon worked—apprenticed, actually—for Rufus Condon, a local boatbuilder who later had this to say about his young nephew: "Albert E. Condon, when a boy, showed so much interest in my shop and the boats I built, that when he was not at school I had him work for me. Because he was more interested in his work and in having our boats a success than anything else, I gave him the best or most difficult work to do, and it was always done right. He worked for me until he thought it might be to his advantage to go to another place. I believe that his character and ability are such that he will make good on anything he undertakes to do."

Charles A. Morse of Thomaston, who later became John G. Alden's favored builder (Malabar schooners, etc.), was Condon's next employer following graduation from Hebron. He was with Morse from June 1908 to October 1909. Morse had this to say: "I have known Albert E. Condon from a small boy, during the time he worked his way through school, and up to the present time. He worked about one-and-a-half years for me as a first-class builder, and I considered him one of the most capable and trustworthy men that I ever employed.... I would not know where to find a better man than Mr. Condon."

The famed Lawley yard at Neponset, Massachusetts, was Condon's next stop (October 1909 to January 1912, age 22 to 25), a yard where some of the country's highest-grade yachts were built. George Lawley himself, when later asked for a recommendation, recorded as his final thought, "We only regret that he [Condon] is not with us at the present time." And John Harvey, Lawley's cantankerous, Scottish head of the small-boat shop, had similar praise, which he expressed in part as, "Having been under my jurisdiction for three years, I can faithfully say that he [Condon] is a good worker, steady, and very fit in handling men placed under his charge. I will gladly recommend his ability to anyone who may seek it."

For the decade before, during, and after World War I until 1921, Condon worked first as a draftsman for Portsmouth Naval Shipyard and Bath Iron Works, drawing plans for ships being built in those yards for the Navy. He then moved to Boston to work as a machine draftsman, drawing general and detailed plans for mechanical devices such as tools and carburetors at the Webber Mfg. Co. In 1921 he returned to Rufus Condon's shop in Friendship, and married May Leland that same year. Two years later, in 1923, he moved on to Gray Boats in Thomaston where he worked as superintendent and resident designer until 1931; he then worked for the I.L. Snow yard in Rockland in the same capacity. Shortly after that yard reorganized as Snow Shipyards, Inc., Albert left (in the fall of 1939) to become superintendent of the Peirce & Kilburn yard at Fairhaven, Massachusetts. (Most of Condon's fishing draggers were designed during the Fairhaven era.)

During his time at Snow's, Condon inspired a young Snow named Bertram to take up designing, which he did. Snow, now Rockland's retired chief of police, but before that a successful naval architect, remembers Albert telling him to "watch your corners," meaning that whether it was dirt being swept off the floor, or wood being put together, or two lines joining on paper, well-fitting corners were a sure sign of good workmanship. Another memory was of Condon saying that he measured his workday by what he accomplished, not by how many hours he put in.

Condon's health had already begun to fail when he returned to Maine in 1948. A few designs were produced at home in Thomaston during his retirement years, as and when he was able to work. Albert E. Condon died on July 15, 1963, at age 76, leaving a wife, three grown sons (Everett, William, and Clinton), and a magnificent body of work that, through good fortune and the generosity of those sons, subsequently found its way to Mystic Seaport, where it will available for many years to come.

THE ALBERT E. CONDON COLLECTION

The drawings prepared by Albert Condon make up the largest part of this collection, numbering 598 sheets and representing the designs shown on the accompanying list. Power yachts, which range from 16' to just under 100' in overall length, come mostly from Condon's early career while he was with Gray Boats. The corresponding sailing yachts were generally designed during the 1930s while Condon was working at the Snow yard. And the draggers—the designs for which Albert Condon is justifiably best known—were nearly all drawn in the 1940s when he was in Fairhaven, Massachusetts, with Peirce & Kilburn.

As with any designer, there is a reference file of drawings from other designers, machinery manufacturers, and such, which are grouped together in the list that follows. Significant among these are complete plans for a dory-skiff by Ben Dobson and several drawings, presumably measured from the existing vessels by Condon and drawn by him as well, of the steamer *Vinalhaven* (built in 1892) and the steamer *W.S. White*, which was built just downriver from Mystic Seaport, in Noank, at the Palmer yard in 1906.

Most of Condon's dragger designs (about three dozen in number, ranging between 56' and 110') have extensive written specifications which describe the major timbers, their joints and fastenings, and in general give a pretty good understanding of how each vessel was constructed. The evolution of the Eastern-rigged dragger is a task well worth the research, and in due course I'm confident that these Albert Condon designs will play a key role in that study.

Condon kept notebooks which contain random data and sketches as well as some financial records, both personal and professional. Anyone interested in learning everything possible about a given design, or about the man himself, should check this source.

The drafting tools and the drawing board were also part of the donation, and although normally in storage because of lack of exhibit space, are viewable by appointment.

THE ALBERT E. CONDON PLANS

COMMERCIAL VESSELS

LOA	Beam	Description	Date	Plan Codes	Cat. No.
		Eastern-rigged draggers for Sample's Shipyard	1940s	AP	35.126
50'0"	11'6"	Round-sterned towboat for Maine Central Power Co.	1931	LCAPDh	35.61
51'6"	16'1"	Dragger, transom stern		L	35.29
53'1"	14'9"	Eastern-rigged dragger w/round stern	1954	LP	35.31
55'11"	15'3"	Eastern-rigged dragger *Christine & Dan*, transom stern	1944	LCAP	35.30
60'0"	14'6"	Proposed patrol boat for U.S. Customs	1933	L	35.96
60'0"	16'0"	Eastern-rigged dragger *Capt. Bill*, round stern	1942	LOCAP	35.5
60'0"	16'2"	Coastal oil tanker for Gulf Refining Co., round stern	1933	LCAPDh	35.62
60'1"	16'9"	Eastern-rigged dragger *Roann*, round stern	1944	LCAP	35.22
62'0"	16'10"	Eastern-rigged dragger *Priscilla V*, transom stern	1943	LOCAPDhDr	35.21
63'0"	16'0"	Eastern-rigged dragger *Sea Hawk*, round stern	1943	L	35.25
65'2"	17'6"	Eastern-rigged dragger *C R & M*, round stern	1946	LOC	35.7
67'3"	17'9"	Eastern-rigged dragger, round stern	1943	LOA	35.28
67'6"	17'0"	Eastern-rigged dragger *Annie M. Jackson*, transom stern	1940	CAPDh	35.2
68'0"	17'0"	Eastern-rigged scalloper *Nancy Jane*, round stern	1949	LOCAP	35.17
69'6"	19'0"	Coastal oil tanker for Gulf Refining Co., round stern	1933	LDh	35.63
70'3"	17'2"	Eastern-rigged dragger *Growler*, transom stern	1941	LOCAP	35.10
70'7"	17'6"	Eastern-rigged dragger *Bobby & Harvey*, transom stern	1941	LOCAP	35.3
70'8"	17'6"	Eastern-rigged dragger, transom stern	1943	LO	35.33
71'0"	17'6"	Eastern-rigged dragger *Carol & Estelle*, round stern	1943	LOC	35.6
71'4"	17'10"	Eastern-rigged dragger, round stern	1944	LOCAP	35.34
72'0"	18'0"	Eastern-rigged dragger *Muskegon*, round stern	1937	LAP	35.16
72'4"	17'5"	Eastern-rigged dragger, round stern	1950	L	35.35
73'7"	17'0"	Eastern-rigged dragger *Mari Gale Barbara*, round stern	1960	LOCA	35.37
73'10"	18'3"	Eastern-rigged dragger, round stern		LA	35.36
75'0"	18'3"	Eastern-rigged dragger, round stern		LA	35.38
75'4"	18'0"	Eastern-rigged dragger, round stern	1945	LA	35.39
76'1"	17'6"	Eastern-rigged dragger *Vivian Fay*, round stern	1950	LOCAP	35.24
77'0"	18'9"	Eastern-rigged dragger *Ethel C*, transom stern	1942	LOCAP	35.8
77'0"	18'9"	Eastern-rigged dragger *Eugene H*, transom stern	1942	LOCAP	35.9
77'10"	17'6"	Eastern-rigged dragger *Ruth Moses*, round stern	1952	LCAP	35.23
78'10"	19'0"	Eastern-rigged dragger *Pelican*, round stern	1943	LOCAP	35.18
78'10"	19'0"	Eastern-rigged dragger *Jerry & Jimmy*, transom stern	1943	LOCAPDh	35.11
78'10"	19'4"	Eastern-rigged dragger, round stern	1946	LOCAP	35.40
80'0"	19'4"	Eastern-rigged dragger *Buzz & Billy*, round stern	1943	LO	35.4
80'4"	16'6"	Maine Seacoast Mission Society boat *Sunbeam II*	1926	LOCAP	35.57
84'0"	20'0"	Eastern-rigged dragger, round stern	1943	LOA	35.41
84'1"	19'6"	Eastern-rigged dragger, round stern	1945	LOAP	35.42
84'11"	16'6"	Eastern-rigged dragger *Pomander*, round stern		LDh	35.19
85'0"	20'0"	Eastern-rigged dragger, round stern		LA	35.43
86'0"	18'0"	Ketch-rigged seiner *Mary Grace*, transom stern	1936	LAPDr	35.14
86'0"	20'0"	Proposed passenger ferry *Vinalhaven III*	1949	LODh	35.59
87'4"	19'8"	Eastern-rigged dragger, round stern	1946	LAP	35.44
87'4"	19'8"	Eastern-rigged dragger, round stern	1945	LOAP	35.45

PLAN CODES: L =lines; O=offsets; C=construction; S=sail; A=arrangement; P=profile; Dh=hull detail; Dr=rigging detail

LOA	Beam	Description	Date	Plan Codes	Cat. No.
89'0"	20'0"	Eastern-rigged dragger, round stern		L	35.46
90'0"	20'0"	Eastern-rigged dragger *Julia Eleanor*, round stern	1936	LAPDh	35.12
90'0"	20'0"	Eastern-rigged dragger *Mary Jane*, round stern	1936	LDhDr	35.15
91'8"	19'4"	Eastern-rigged dragger, round stern		LAP	35.48
92'0"	20'11"	Eastern-rigged dragger *Aloha*, round stern	1944	LOCAPDhDr	35.1
93'1"	20'0"	Eastern-rigged dragger, round stern	1940	L	35.47
95'0"	21'0"	Proposed fireboat for Portland, Maine	1930	CAP	35.97
96'7"	20'7"	Eastern-rigged dragger *Thomas D*, round stern	1943	LOCAPDh	35.32
96'7"	21'7"	Eastern-rigged dragger *Junojaes*, round stern	1943	LOCAPDh	35.13
98'0"	23'0"	Eastern-rigged dragger, transom stern, alternate arrangements	1942	LAPDh	35.49
98'4"	21'9"	Eastern-rigged dragger *Sylvester F. Whalen*, round stern	1946	LOCAPDh	35.27
99'0"	22'0"	Eastern-rigged dragger, round stern	1944	LO	35.50
100'0"	16'0"	Passenger steamer *Vinalhaven* (delineation by AEC)	1892	L	35.58
100'0"	22'6"	Eastern-rigged dragger, round stern	1944	LOCAP	35.51
103'0"	24'3"	Passenger steamer *W.S. White* (delineation by AEC)	1906	LA	35.60
110'0"	23'0"	Eastern-rigged dragger *St. George*, round stern	1939	LAPDhDr	35.26
111'0"	23'0"	Eastern-rigged dragger, round stern	1943	LOCAP	35.52
121'0"	26'0"	Eastern-rigged dragger *Moby*, round stern	1940	P	35.53
159'2"	31'9"	Four-masted codfishing schooner	1935	LCSA	35.77
170'0"	32'0"	Three-masted auxiliary coasting schooner	1920	CSA	35.76

POWER YACHTS

LOA	Beam	Description	Date	Plan Codes	Cat. No.
		Power cruisers—various offerings by Gray Boats	1920s	AP	35.129
16'5"	4'7"	Outboard-powered dinghy	1929	LAP	35.93
23'0"	6'6"	Power cruiser		L	35.81
28'0"	6'6"	Runabout	1937	LAP	35.86
32'0"	9'6"	Power cruiser w/alt. cabin arrangements	1937	LCAP	35.79
36'0"		Power cruiser	1937	AP	35.94
36'10"		Power cruiser *Caroline III*, raised deck	1929	AP	35.88
40'0"	10'6"	Power cruiser	1936	AP	35.92
40'0"	10'8"	Twin-screw power cruiser w/raised deck	1928	AP	35.82
42'4"	11'0"	Twin-screw power cruiser	1930	AP	35.89
50'0"	13'0"	Power cruiser with aft cabin		AP	35.84
54'0"	14'0"	Twin-screw power cruiser	1930	P	35.83
56'0"	14'0"	Power cruiser w/'midship pilothouse & aft cabin	1930	LAP	35.95
60'0"	14'6"	Twin-screw power cruiser	1930	AP	35.90
64'0"	14'6"	Power cruiser w/stack, aft cabin, & rig	1928	LOAP	35.85
85'0"	11'1"	Twin-screw power cruiser w/raised deck		L	35.19A
85'0"	16'9"	Twin-screw motoryacht	1928	AP	35.91
95'0"	20'0"	Twin-screw motoryacht	1930	LOAPDh	35.65
98'0"		Twin-screw power cruiser w/round stern, *Pony Express*	1916	LP	35.56
107'0"	19'1"	Motoryacht *Fantasy*		LO	35.99

SAILING YACHTS

LOA	Beam	Description	Date	Plan Codes	Cat. No.
21'9"	7'6"	Gaff-rigged cruising sloop		A	35.127
28'3"	9'6"	Cruising sloop	1933	LSA	35.68
30'0"	7'6"	Proposed knockabout sloop	1934	S	35.69
33'0"	10'5"	Cruising sloop or yawl *Mac*	1934	LCSA	35.55
33'2"	10'0"	Cruising sloop	1933	L	35.67
37'6"	11'9"	Friendship sloop	1931	L	35.70
39'0"	11'0"	Cruising sloop or yawl	1938	LSA	35.66
39'3"	11'5"	Cruising sloop or yawl *Flying Yankee*		A	35.128
45'0"	14'0"	Cruising yawl	1933	LSA	35.64
48'0"		Schooner-yacht, gaff foresail		S	35.73
67'7"	16'0"	Schooner-yacht, gaff foresail	1937	LSA	35.78
67'10"	16'0"	Schooner-yacht, gaff foresail	1934	LSA	35.74
74'2"	17'2"	Schooner-yacht, gaff foresail	1931	LSADh	35.75
96'0"	24'0"	Staysail schooner w/launch on deck	1937	S	35.72

MISCELLANEOUS DRAWINGS

Description	Cat. No.
Cost curves for wooden draggers at 1941-44 prices	35.135
Various engine outline drawings	35.130
Atlas engine outline drawings	35.131
Superior engine outline drawings	35.133
Engine installation drawing	35.136
Fairbanks-Morse engine outline drawings	35.132
Various deck machinery	35.134
Elevation drawings for Peirce & Kilburn shipyard	35.137

PLANS BY OTHER DESIGNERS

LOA	Beam	Description	Date	Plan Codes	Cat. No.
11'0"		Dory skiff for 60' patrol boat by Dobson	1943	LCAP	35.111
16'0"	5'7"	Metal lifeboat	1941	A	35.114
16'1"	5'0"	Launch w/tunnel stern by Eldredge-McInnis	1944	L	35.112
21'9"	7'6"	Penobscot Bay Class gaff-rigged cruising sloop by Gray	1932	LSA	35.71
24'0"	6'0"	"Marinette" power cruiser by Elco.	1929	AP	35.110
28'0"	8'8"	Raised-deck power cruiser by Deed	1921	L	35.116
30'0"	7'0"	Double-cockpit runabout by Gray	1932	AP	35.80
32'0"	9'5"	"Cruisette" by Elco. w/various layouts	1928	AP	35.109
37'8"	10'0"	Runabout		L	35.87
43'3"	10'8"	Re-rig of Fishers Island 31 Class sloop by Alden	1930	S	35.124

LOA	Beam	Description	Date	Plan Codes	Cat. No.
46'8"	12'0"	Ketch *Malabar XII* by Alden	1939	C	35.121
53'9"	14'3"	Ketch *Malabar XIII* by Alden	1944	C	35.122
54'9"	12'5"	Re-rig of cruising ketch *Vagabond* by Alden	1928	S	35.119
57'0"	13'1"	Clipper-bowed ketch *Paradise Bird* by L.F. Herreshoff	1932	CSA	35.123
60'6"	16'0"	Eastern-rigged dragger, round stern, by Eldredge-McInnis	1944	CAP	35.125
63'4"	13'10"	Aircraft rescue boat, V-bottom	1953	LCDh	35.103
63'7"		Power vessel *Radiant*		L	35.102
65'0"	17'4"	Ketch-rigged motorsailer	1958	LS	35.113
75'0"	13'8"	Power cruiser *Korana* (as *YP 273*)	1928	LDh	35.104
76'4"		Eastern-rigged dragger *Acushnet*, transom stern	1946	P	35.54
84'3"	18'7"	Eastern-rigged dragger *Wamsutta*, round stern	1942	L	35.100
86'5"	20'3"	Eastern-rigged dragger *Newfoundland*, round stern	1942	L	35.101
87'0"	21'0"	Eastern-rigged dragger, round stern, by Alden	1944	LAP	35.120
87'2"	16'8"	Motoryacht *Lochinvar* (as *YP 210*)	1942	LDh	35.105
88'4"	21'1"	Eastern-rigged dragger *Dolphin*, round stern		A	35.98
94'0"		Eastern-rigged dragger *Noreen*, round stern	1936		35.108
96'4"	21'6"	Eastern-rigged dragger, round stern	1943	L	35.117
98'4"	23'2"	Eastern-rigged dragger *Potomska*, transom stern	1941	LOA	35.20
126'0"	22'6"	J-class sloop *Yankee* by Paine	1935	L	35.106
146'0"	26'0"	Steel trawler *Wave*, double-ended, by Alden	1941	LP	35.118
174'5"	40'0"	Passenger ferry *Noodle Island*	1921		35.107
205'2"	32'6"	Steam-powered side-wheeler *Mary Chilton*	1916	P	35.115

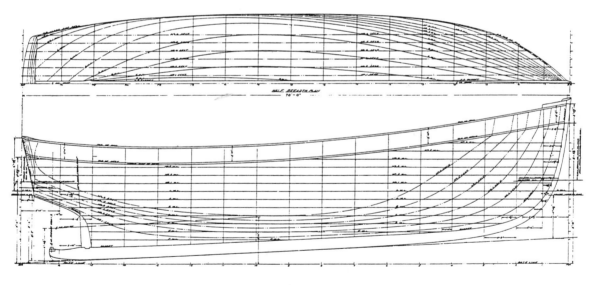

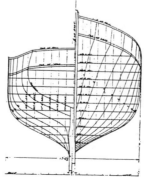

PONY EXPRESS, AN EXPRESS CRUISER OF 1916
98'0"

As far as we know, this long, lean, fantail-sterned cruiser was never built, the 1916 date being a good indication that Condon drew her for one of the courses he was taking at the time at Franklin Union.

Catalog No. 35.56

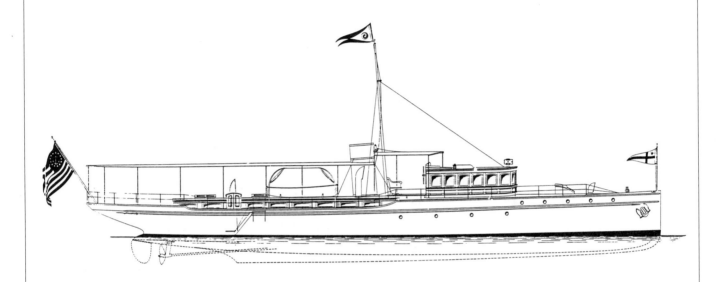

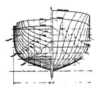

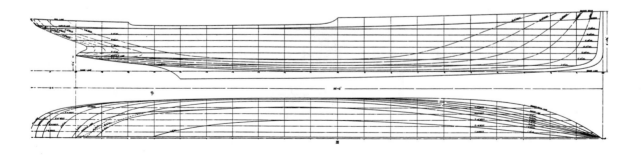

SUNBEAM II, MAINE SEACOAST MISSION SOCIETY BOAT OF 1926
80'4' x 16'6"

This second of the Maine Coast Missionary Society's *Sunbeam*s (there have been five to date) was designed while Condon was connected with Gray Boats, which was basically a yacht yard and doubtless had plenty of that kind of work in 1926, so this vessel was built elsewhere—at Jonah Morse's yard in nearby Friendship. Until she was replaced in 1940, *Sunbeam II* carried on God's work, winter and summer, among the islands of Maine. Church services were held just outside the pastor's stateroom in the deckhouse "saloon," a strange name at best for any main cabin, but an even less appropriate one for this floating missionary. Below deck, five staterooms, a big galley and adjoining dining room, along with a hospital room, take up most of the space not occupied by the engine and fuel oil tanks. *Sunbeam* is ruggedly built with double-sawn frames, a proper keelson in three layers, and a rudderpost that penetrates the hull and bolts to the deck frame.   Catalog No. 35.57

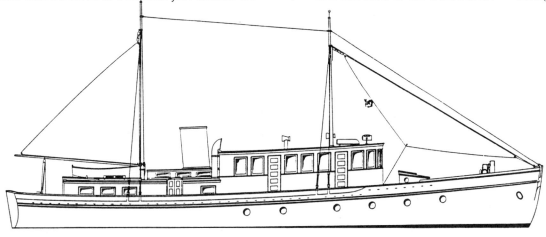

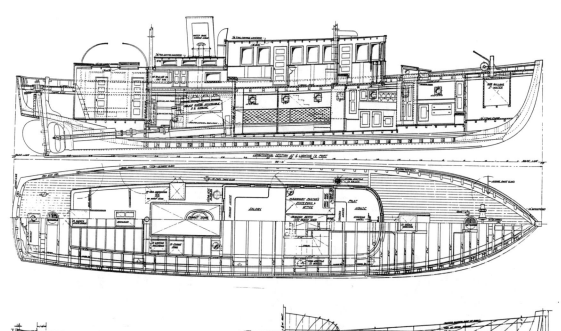

A CRUISING SLOOP OF 1933

28'3" x 9'6"

As one of his last designs for Gray Boats, Albert Condon drew up this lovely little cruiser which, presumably, would be offered as a stock model—an oft-employed promotional technique during the depressed 1930s when custom commissions for both designers and builders were scarce. She's cute as a button, and even today would be finestkind for two-person cruising. The hull has the powerful sections of a Friendship sloop, and her sailplan has plenty of area for ghosting in light weather—although it looks a bit old-fashioned in this day of tall, narrow, handkerchief-sized mainsails and masthead jibs.

Catalog No. 35.68

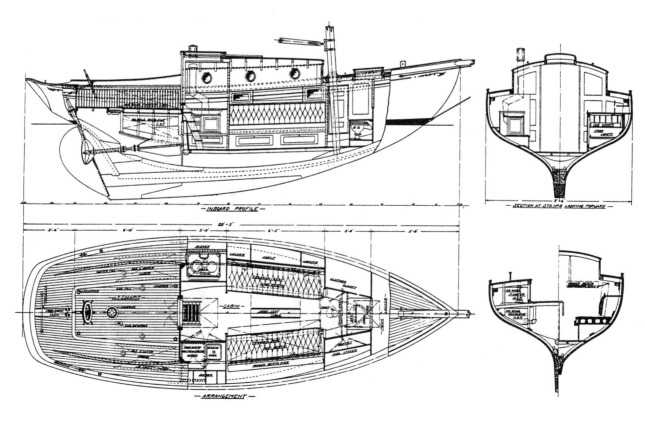

—INBOARD PROFILE—

—ARRANGEMENT—

—SECTION AT STA. N°8 LOOKING FORWARD—

A SCHOONER-YACHT OF 1934 WITH GAFF FORESAIL
67'10" x 16'0"

Another Depression design, probably done on speculation and probably never built, this, at least to my eye, is as graceful and perfectly proportioned as anything similar turned out by Alden, Crocker, or Crowninshield. Curiously for the times, she's not carrying an auxiliary-propulsion engine, only an engine-driven generator for the electric lights. There's a fine big owner's stateroom aft with its own toilet room, a double stateroom between the masts just aft of the crew's quarters and galley, and a good-sized main cabin space for eating and sitting with a skylight overhead.   Catalog No. 35.74

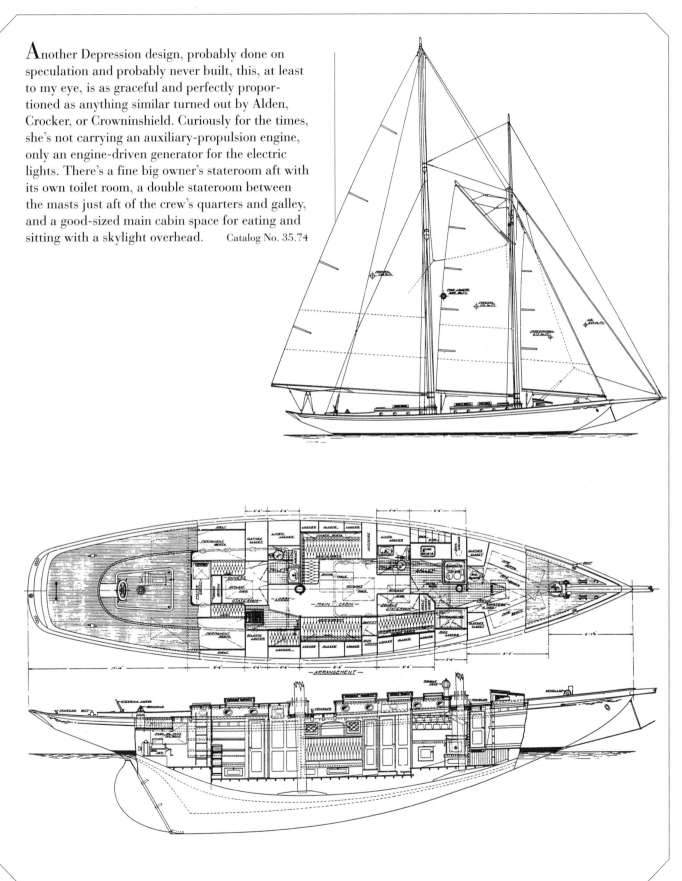

A CODFISHING SCHOONER AND COASTING SCHOONER OF 1935 AND 1920
159'2" & 170'0"

I believe these two commercial vessels were designed while Condon was connected with Snow's yard, which was very much a commercial operation (at least in the days before Albert Condon), and quite a change from Gray Boats. For the present, the background of both designs remains a mystery, although schooner-building had been Snow's stock-in-trade at earlier times and these designs may have been an attempt to revive that aspect of the business. Neither design appears to have been completed, although there is more detail on the cod-fisherman than on the coaster.

Catalog Nos. 35.77 & .76

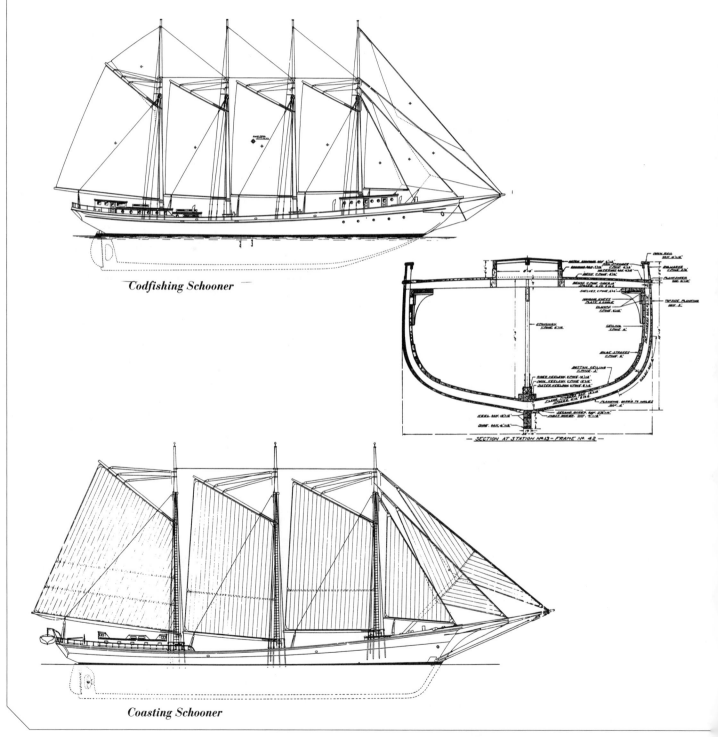

Codfishing Schooner

Coasting Schooner

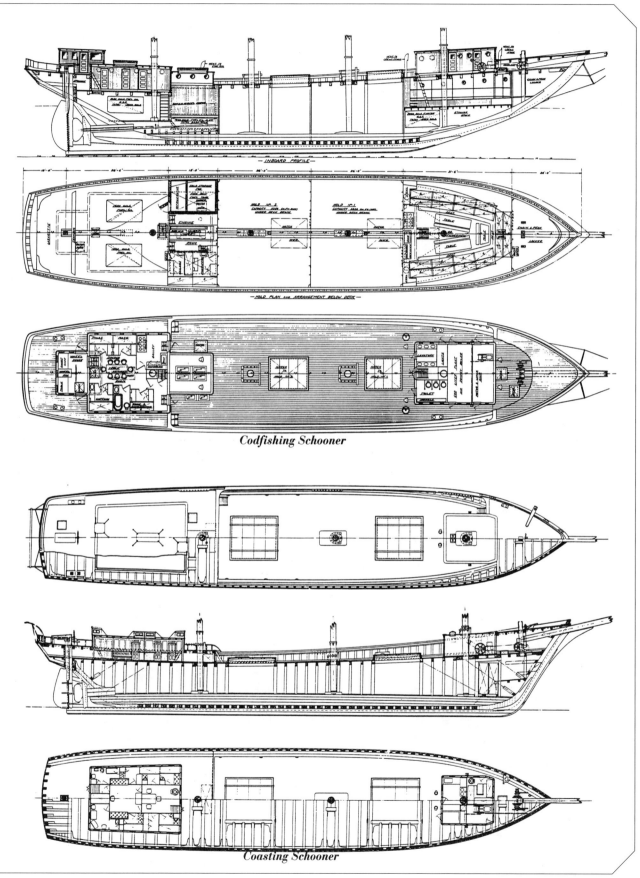

Codfishing Schooner

Coasting Schooner

ST. GEORGE, AN EASTERN-RIGGED DRAGGER OF 1940
110'0" x 23'0"

Owner Capt. Clyson Coffin named this big wooden vessel after his native town, a village only a few miles from the Snow yard in Rockland where she was built. Coffin kept his vessels painted white, making them stand out from the green and/or black hulls of the rest of the fleet. Both his *St. George* and the later *Ethel C* when freshly painted looked like yachts, but it only took a single trip for the rust from their steel sheathing to spoil that fine appearance. *St. George*'s plans, probably because her building cost was subsidized by the U.S. Maritime Commission, were drawn by Condon in ink instead of his usual pencil. They show the typical arrangement, with berths and galley in the fo'c's'le with water tanks under, a fish hold more or less amidships so as not to put the vessel out of trim when filled, followed by an engineroom with pilothouse aft above it. Since *St. George* is larger by at least 20' than the usual Eastern dragger, she has additional space aft of her Fairbanks-Morse diesel engine for four single staterooms. Where 10 men were usual for the 80-to-90-footers, *St. George* could carry as many as 15. The two booms rigged from the mainmast are for hoisting the baskets of fish up out of the hold through either of the two deck hatches. Snow's launched two more draggers, *North Star* and *Belmont*, on the heels of *St. George*. These were based on this Condon design but lengthened to 120' and 122', respectively, making them at the time the largest draggers ever built in wood.

Catalog No. 35.26

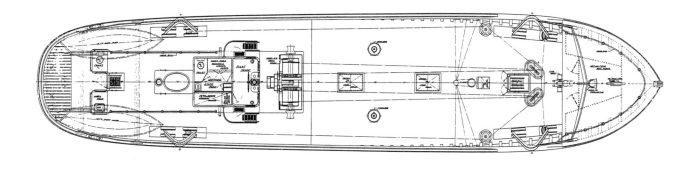

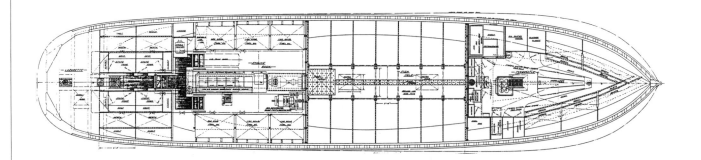

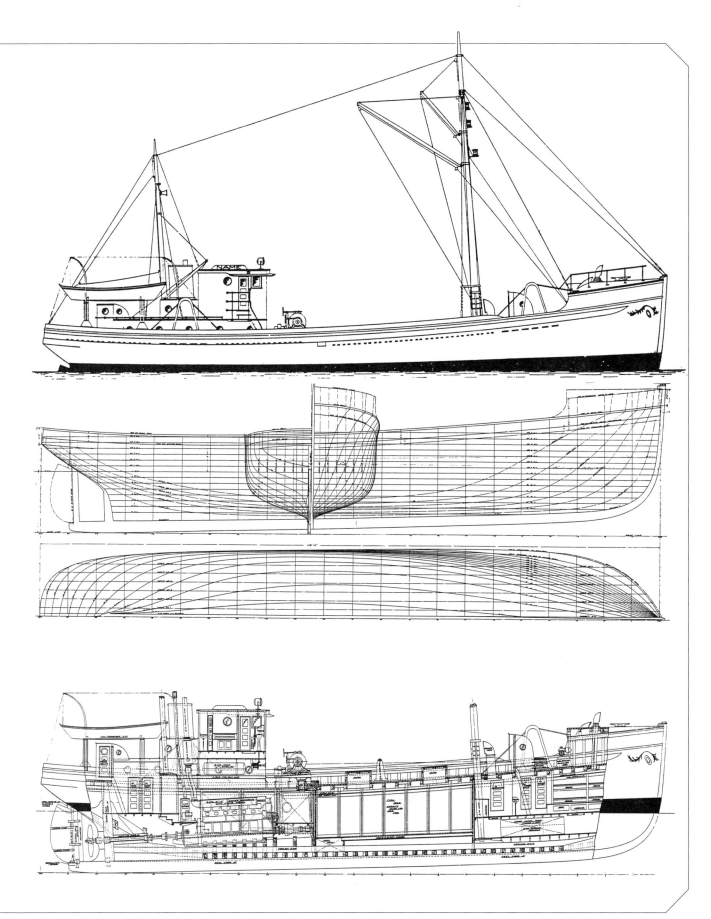

GROWLER, AN EASTERN-RIGGED DRAGGER OF 1942
70'3" x 17'2"

Condon was living in Fairhaven when he designed most of the draggers, and *Growler* was one of the early ones—about as far toward the other end of the scale from *St. George* as possible. She's smaller, of course, and simpler in both layout and construction. Her deck is unbroken (*St. George* had a raised quarterdeck) and is open all the way to the bow. Her hull is of bent rather than sawn frames; there is a transom rather than round stern; and she's powered with a little six-cylinder Buda diesel. Although her basic arrangement, like *St. George*'s, is typical, there is less volume—resulting in about half the capacity and berthing for only 11. Three steadying sails are shown, but generally only the forward and after ones (the jib and trysail) were rigged—these to reduce the rolling in a beam sea. *Growler* was built in Thomaston by Newbert & Wallace.

Catalog No. 35.10

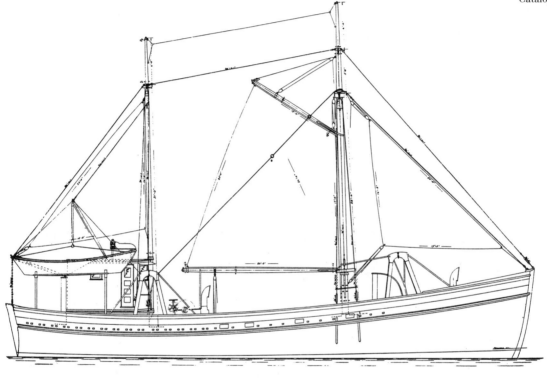

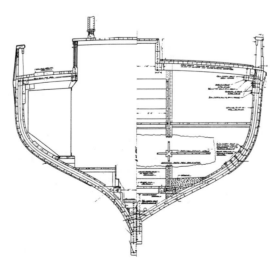

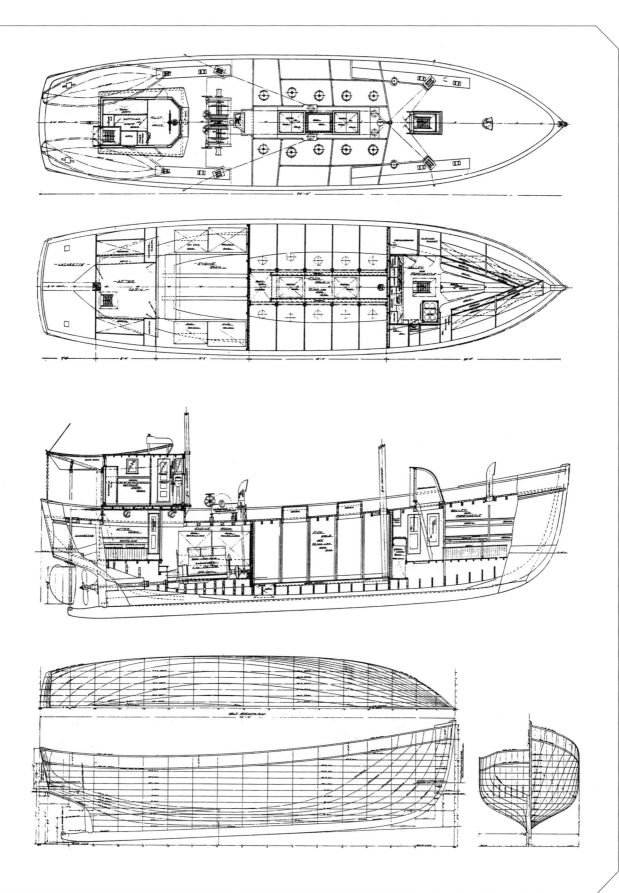

PELICAN, AN EASTERN-RIGGED, ROUND-STERNED DRAGGER OF 1944

78'10" x 19'0"

If one had to pick a single design that epitomized Condon-designed Eastern-rigged draggers of the World War II era, it would probably be this one from which several vessels were built. On deck forward, the decked-over fo'c's'le head provided sheltered stowage for fishing gear as well as gave the working deck aft of it some protection. The vessel is laid out to fish from either side, the towing cables coming aboard at the gallows frames and leading through deck-mounted lead blocks to a double-drum, engine-driven winch located just forward of the pilothouse. A raised quarterdeck starting at the fish hold/engineroom bulkhead tends to keep the fish and seawater forward of it on the main deck where they belong. The pilot-house is raised for visibility, with a sleeping cabin for the skipper adjoining aft of it. A pair of dories serve as lifeboats in this pre-liferaft, pre-survival-suit era. And the vessel has a round stern, preferred for its strength and seaworthiness.

Catalog No. 35.18

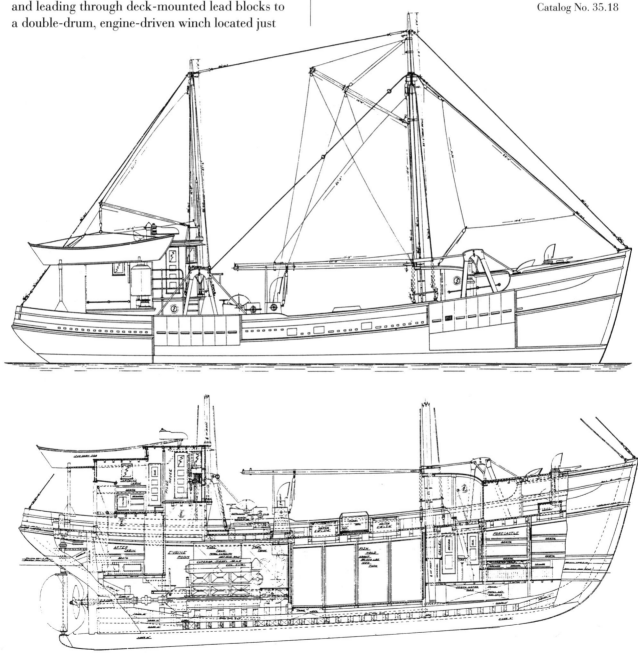

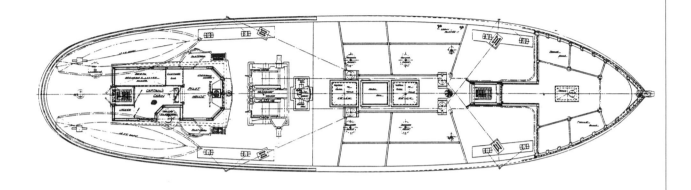

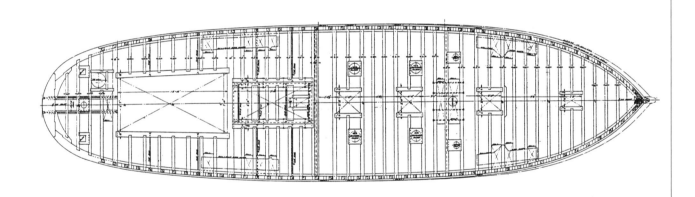

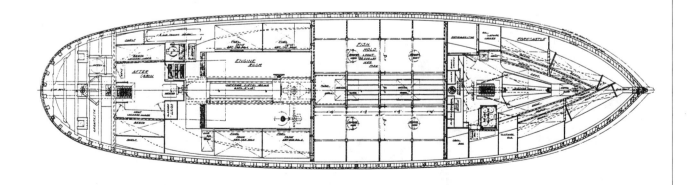

PRISCILLA V. & ROANN, EASTERN-RIGGED DRAGGERS OF 1943
60'1" x 16'9" (ROANN), 62'0" x 16'10" (PRISCILLA V.)

Here are a couple of little ones, about as small as is practical, one designed with a transom stern, the other with a round one. While, with the exception of the different stern configuratons, their shape is almost identical, there is a marked contrast in hull construction. *Pricilla V.* has the heavy sawn frames (average cross-section about 6 x 6") with which the larger draggers are built, while *Roann*'s frames are steam-bent and more closely spaced (10" vs. 16"). This is a somewhat lighter (cross-section about 4 x 4") and more yacht-like type of construction,

having deep plank-type floor timbers joining together every other frame pair side-to-side across the keel. Both boats carry the same amount— 45,000 pounds of fish—but, because of the greater internal volume afforded by her bent-frame construction, *Roann*'s fish hold is shorter fore-and-aft, giving a little additional space in the fo'c's'le and engineroom. Both boats were built by Newbert & Wallace in Thomaston, and *Roann* has now taken a well-deserved place in Mystic Seaport's Watercraft Collection.　Catalog Nos. 35.21 & .22

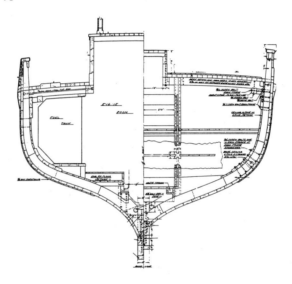

Priscilla V. – above and below

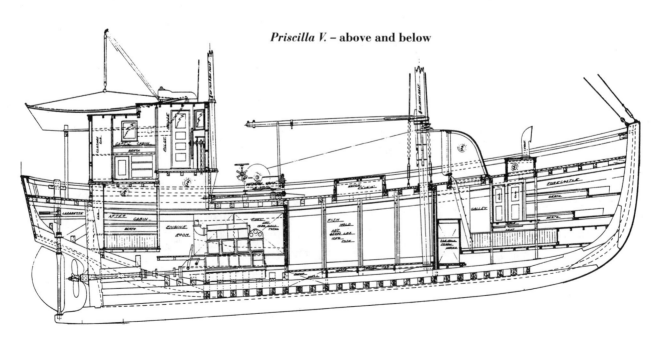

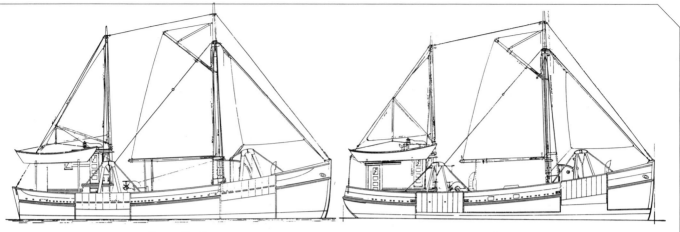

Priscilla V.   *Roann*

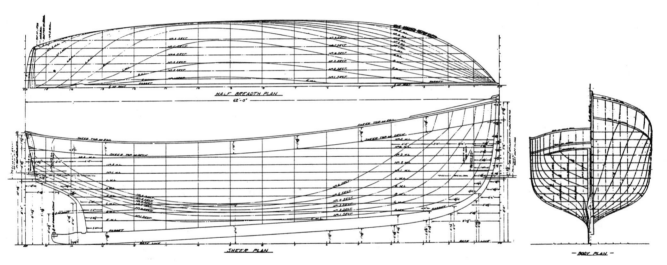

Priscilla V.

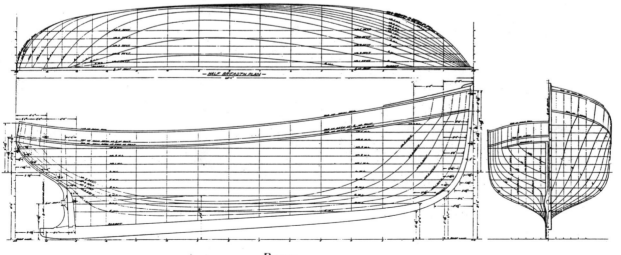

Roann

MYSTIC SEAPORT VESSELS
AND SMALL CRAFT

(COLLECTION NO. 7)

The drawings in this chapter for the most part depict watercraft that are in the museum's collection which range in size from the 9'3" Lawley-built yacht tender *Madelon* to the 114' whaleship *Charles W. Morgan*. Unlike the previous chapters which represent finite collections of plans, this chapter's collection is open-ended to accept newly-prepared drawings as watercraft get measured and delineated. Mystic Seaport's goal is to measure, record, and develop drawings of every watercraft in its collection for which drawings don't exist, and since so few of the early builders drew plans—they worked from carved, wooden half models instead—it's an enormous task. (Two guides for this kind of work have been recently published, one for ships and another on boats: *Guidelines for Recording Historic Ships* by Richard K. Anderson, Jr., available from the U.S. Government Printing Office, and *Boats, A Manual for Their Documentation*, published by The Museum Small Craft Association and available from Mystic Seaport Publications.)

Besides the drawings of the museum's own watercraft, there are a few others depicting closely related objects such as oars, and a few more of non-museum boats, which, because of their special historical or technical interest, have been documented by measured drawings. Presently this collection contains approximately 625 individual plans representing some 125 different designs.

Drawings in this collection find considerable use by the Seaport staff in preserving and restoring various watercraft, and from time to time undergo revision as additional information becomes available, either through research in the field or when opportunities for further examination occur, as they frequently do during a major restoration.

These drawings are also popular with model-makers and boatbuilders; some drawings are sufficiently detailed for this purpose, while others are basically pictorial representations, but for nearly every design the watercraft itself is here at the museum and available for reference.

Since the drawings in this chapter were not prepared by the designer but by various draftsmen through measuring the completed small boat or larger vessel, they are listed differently from those in the previous chapters. The sequence brings together like types so that, for example, all the Cape Cod catboats show up in one grouping for easy reference. Following the organization of the published catalog of the watercraft collection (*Mystic Seaport Museum Watercraft* by Maynard Bray), the various types are further grouped under major headings such as Sloops and Cutters, Ketches and Yawls, or Power Craft.

Column headings differ a bit as well and, for the most part, are self-explanatory. There is an additional indication (by the letter R) of boats that are recommended for amateur construction, a listing of the number of sheets that make up each design (from which the price is determined), and, for boats belonging to the museum, the accession number is included for more positive identification. (Numerals to the left in the accession number indicate the year of acquisition and those to the right, which begin anew each year, tell where an object is in the sequence of a year's acquisitions. For example, 60.196 means that the boat came into the collection in 1960 and that there were 195 objects—not necessarily boats—that came earlier that year). Boats without accession numbers are not owned by the museum and the drawings represented by this category are identified by "Misc." to the left of the catalog number.

Plans for Mystic Seaport's Watercraft

Cats

LOA	Beam	Description	Designer/Builder	Codes	Sheets	Acc.No.	Cat.No.
14'4"	6'7"	Cape Cod catboat *Sanshee*	Charles A. Anderson	LCS	1	70.646	7.50
14'10"	6'8"	Cape Cod catboat *Trio*	Wilton Crosby	LOC	3	60.499	7.53
16'10"	7'10"	Cape Cod catboat *Edith*	Crosby	LOCS	5		Misc.10
18'7"	9'4"	Cape Cod catboat *Sarah*		LO	1		Misc. 36
20'0"	9'8"	Cape Cod cat reconstr. *Breck Marshall*	Crosby/MSM	LOCS	6	86.10	7.125
20'10"	9'8"	Cape Cod catboat *Frances*	Wilton Crosby	LOCS	3	59.1221	7.7
21'		Great South Bay catboat *Pauline*	Gil Smith	LOCS	5		Misc. 40
21'5"	7'0"	Great South Bay catboat	Gil Smith	LOCS	2	60.4	7.52
12'3"	5'4"	Newport catboat *Button Swan*	Button Swan	LOCS	3	49.145	7.59
17'6"	8'10"	Newport catboat *Peggotty*		LOCS	3		Misc. 15
13'6"	6'0"	Woods Hole spritsail boat *Susie*	E.E. Swift	LOCS	3	86.32	7.121
13'		Woods Hole spritsail boat *Spy*		LOCS	4		Misc. 35
13'3"	5'11"	Woods Hole spritsail boat *Explorer*	Crosby	LOCS	3	60.196	7.54
13'6"	6'0"	Woods Hole spritsail boat	E.E. Swift	LOCS	3	68.2	7.122
12'7"	4'2"	Seaford skiff *Brownie*	Charles Verity attr.	LOC	1	62.674	7.58
13'6"	4'4"	Seaford skiff *Ro Ro*		LOCS	2	76.149	7.100
14'7"	4'3"	Seaford skiff reproduction	Gritman/Ketcham	LOS	3	72.264	7.119
13'10"	4'9"	Melonseed skiff		LOS	3		Misc. 5
14'11"	3'8"	Cat-rigged cutter *Snarleyow*	Harvey/Smith	LO	1	52.498	7.51
16'7"	4'5"	Norwegian Bindals boat		LC	2	50.1103	7.67
12'1"	4'2"	Sneakbox from Barnegat Bay	Perrine	LOCR	1	61.915	7.57
14'10"	3'10"	Delaware ducker for oars		LOC	2	69.98	7.103
14'10"	4'5"	Delaware tuckup *Spider*		LOCS	6		Misc. 25
15'		Delaware tuckup *Thomas M. Seeds*		LCS	4		MIsc. 24
15'0"	4'0"	Delaware ducker		LOCS	5	69.821	7.123

Sloops and Cutters

LOA	Beam	Description	Designer/Builder	Codes	Sheets	Acc.No.	Cat.No.
13'11"	3'9"	Half-decked, double-ended sailboat		LOS	3	75.22	7.107
15'10"	5'10"	Buzzards Bay 12½ sloop *Nettle*	Herreshoff/HMCo.	LCS	2	63.595	7.75
18'9"	6'5"	Cutter *Galena*	Purdon/Graves	LS	2	57.537	7.71
21'11"	5'1"	Chesapeake Bay sailing log canoe *Fly*		LOC	1	51.4205	7.60
24'9"	6'9"	Buzzards Bay 15 sloop *Fiddler*	Herreshoff/HMCo.	LCS	2	59.1286	7.70
26'0"	7'7"	Cabin daysailer *Alerion*	Herreshoff/HMCo.	LCS	3	64.631	7.1
24'7"	12'1"	Noank sloop *Breeze*	Morgan	LS	2	79.15	7.89
32'7"	12'9"	Oyster sloop *Nellie*		LS	1	64.1551	7.14
34'5"	11'9"	Friendship sloop *Estella A*	R.E. McLain	LCS	3	57.498	7.22
45'2"	13'6"	Carryaway boat *Regina M*		LOCS	4	40.338	7.66
45'9"	14'8"	Noank well smack *Emma C. Berry*	Latham/Palmer	LS	3	69.231	7.6

PLAN CODES: L=lines; **O**=offsets; **C**=construction; **S**=sail; **P**=profile; **Dh**=hull detail; **Dr**=rigging detail; **R**=recommended for amateurs

179

KETCHES AND YAWLS

LOA	Beam	Description	Designer/Builder	Codes	Sheets	Acc.No.	Cat.No.
17'4"	6'0"	Square-sterned Hampton boat *Cuspidor*	Capt. D. Perry Sinnett	LOCS	4	61.916	7.61
23'4"	6'6"	Double-ended Hampton boat *Cadet*	E. Durgin attr.	LC	1	55.318	7.8
15'8"	5'5"	Kingston lobsterboat *Annie A. Fuller*	Arthur Rogers	LC	1	63.818	7.55
19'0"	6'3"	Kingston lobsterboat, strip-planked	William Bates	LCS	3	56.1544	7.63
20'		Kingston lobsterboat *Solitaire*	E. A. Ransom	LCS	4		Misc. 19
15'9"	5'1"	New Haven sharpie-skiff *WB*		LOCSR	1	51.4206	7.65
35'4"	6'11"	New Haven sharpie		LOCS	1	47.597	7.64
23'0"	9'0"	Block Island cowhorn *Glory Anna II*	Howard	LS	2	70.763	7.23
19'9"	6'5"	Nomans Land boat *Orca*	Delano	LOCS	3	63.592	7.12
19'9"	6'2"	Nomans Land boat	Josiah Cleveland	LOCS	3	52.1115	7.13
18'3"	5'5"	Canoe yawl *Half Moon*	Akester/Barlow et al.	LCS	3	59.1209	7.72

LARGE VESSELS

LOA	Beam	Description	Designer/Builder	Codes	Sheets	Acc.No.	Cat.No.
111'0"	25'2"	Ship-rigged training vessel *Joseph Conrad*	Burmeister & Wain	LS	1	47.1948	7.9
113'11"	27'8"	Whaleship *Charles W. Morgan*	Hillman Bros.	LOCSDhDr	7	41.761	7.5
123'0"	24'11"	Gloucester fishing schooner *L.A. Dunton*	McManus/Story	LCSDr	4	63.1705	7.11

FLAT-BOTTOMED ROWBOATS AND DORIES

LOA	Beam	Description	Designer/Builder	Codes	Sheets	Acc.No.	Cat.No.
10'3"	3'9"	Flatiron skiff *Wilbur*	MSM	LOCSR	3	78.121	7.92
11'2"	4'3"	Skiff	Asa Thomson	LOCR	1	76.148	7.95
12'7"	4'6"	Noank sharpie-skiff		LCR	2		Misc. 8
13'9"	4'0"	Sharpie-skiff (20 pg. instr. book $5.00)		LOC	3		Misc. 38
14'1"	4'5"	Marblehead skiff		LOCSR	2		Misc. 18
12'7"	5'0"	Swampscott dory skiff *Fat Boat*		LOC	2		Misc. 23
13'5"	4'0"	Dory-skiff reproduction	Chamberlain/MSM	LOCSR	2	71.238	7.32
14'0"	4'0"	Dory-skiff from Amesbury, Mass.		LCR	1	57.290	7.24
14'5"	4'4"	Decked dory skiff	George Chaisson	LOCR	1		Misc. 27
16'5"	4'1"	Piscataqua River wherry		LOCR	2	73.236	7.91
17'3"	4'6"	Swampscott sailing dory reproduction	MSM	LOCSR	2	74.1025	7.108
17'4"	4'8"	Dory from Mass. Humane Society		LC	1	63.1517	7.33
18'0"	4'6"	Gunning dory (McGee Island)		LOC	1		Misc. 3
18'3"	5'1"	Banks dory from schooner *Black Hawk*		LC	1	55.320	7.31
19'8"	5'8"	Banks dory from Lunenburg, N.S.		C	1	70.686	7.68
13'0"		Amesbury dory-skiff		LCR	2	89.94.1	
21'4"	4'6"	Dory (McGee Island)	George Chaisson	LOC	2		Misc. 28

ROUND-BOTTOMED TENDERS AND PULLING BOATS

LOA	Beam	Description	Designer/Builder	Codes	Sheets	Acc.No.	Cat.No.
11'11"	3'10"	Whitehall-type pulling boat *Capt. Hook*		LOC	3	74.472	7.102
13'2"	4'10"	Boston Whitehall		LOC	3	69.584	7.78
13'7"	3'8"	Pulling boat for livery use		LOC	3	73.728	7.118
14'0"	3'10"	Whitehall	Partelow	LOC	5	73.39	7.96
14'0"	4'6"	Pulling boat	Wardwell	LOC	2	49.323	7.44
14'1"	3'3"	Pulling boat *A.L. Rotch*	J.H. Rushton	LOC	3	60.261	7.115
14'7"	3'3"	Rangeley Lake boat	Barrett attr.	LOCR	2	74.1007	7.45
14'10"	4'2"	Whitehall reproduction	Rice Bros./MSM	LOC	4	74.94	7.80
15'0"	4'1"	Whitehall	Sheldon	LOC	3	80.5	7.111
15'6"	3'10"	Lennox-model pulling boat		LOC	2	73.235	7.94
15'8"	3'6"	Pulling boat for lake use		LOC	3	73.25	7.86
16'0"	4'2"	Lake George rowboat *Winona*		LOC	2	79.70	7.113
16'4"	4'4"	Whitehall	Paddlefast	LO	2		Misc. 1
16'9"	3'7"	Fancy Whitehall w/sliding seat		LOC	3	54.211	7.21
17'		Pulling boat		LOC	2	76.78	7.93
20'1"	5'1"	Whitehall		LOC	3		Misc. 2
20'6"	4'6"	Gig	G.F. Lawley & Sons	LO	2		Misc. 4
24'10"	5'1"	Gig from the steam yacht *Noma*		LC	1	59.967	7.40
9'3"	3'8"	Lapstrake yacht tender *Madelon*	G.F. Lawley & Sons	LOC	3	77.254	7.90
11'6"	4'1"	Lapstrake yacht tender	Herreshoff/HMCo.	LOCSR	4	74.930	7.112
11'9"	4'0"	Strip-planked pulling boat *Favorite*		LOC	3	40.504	7.35
11'10"	4'3"	Tender	Dion	LOC	3		Misc. 34
16'2"	4'2"	Gig from the schooner-yacht *Dauntless*		LC	1	38.570	7.30

ADIRONDACK GUIDEBOATS, ST. LAWRENCE SKIFFS, AND PEAPODS

LOA	Beam	Description	Designer/Builder	Codes	Sheets	Acc.No.	Cat.No.
13'0"	3'1"	Adirondack guideboat	B. & I. Parsons	LOC	3	AD64.170	Misc. 33
13'1"	3'1"	Adirondack guideboat	Blanchard	LOC	3		Misc. 17
16'3"	3'1"	Adirondack guideboat	Warren W. Cole	LOC	4	AD57192.2	Misc. 30
16'5"	3'1"	Adirondack guideboat *The Ghost*	H. Dwight Grant	LOC	4	AD71.141	Misc. 31
14'0"	3'2"	St. Lawrence River skiff	Sheldon	LO	2	75.177	7.88
17'9"	3'3"	St. Lawrence River skiff *Annie*	A. Bain & Co.	LOC	2	80.76	7.116
18'1"	3'7"	St. Lawrence River skiff *Clotilde*		LOC	2		Misc. 14
18'2"	3'6"	St. Lawrence River skiff		LOC	2		Misc. 6
20'5"	3'6"	St. Lawrence River skiff *Bobby*		LOC	2		Misc. 7
14'2"	4'5"	Peapod reproduction	Whitmore/MSM	LOR	1	71.237	7.42
14'2"	4'4"	Peapod from North Haven, Maine	Whitmore	LOC	3	85.135	7.124
14'11"	4'5"	Peapod *Red Star*	Nate Eaton	LOCS	2	70.638	7.120
16'0"	4'5"	Maine peapod		LOC	2	59.1472	7.41
16'2"	4'2"	Peapod from Cape Split, Maine		LOC	2	67.302	7.109

LIFEBOATS, SURFBOATS, AND WHALEBOATS

LOA	Beam	Description	Designer/Builder	Codes	Sheets	Acc.No.	Cat.No.
21'4"	6'6"	Lifeboat reprod. for the *Joseph Conrad*	(Denmark)/MSM	LO	1	80.149	7.101
24'7"	6'1"	Race Point surf boat	USCG Curtis Bay	LC	1	47.1982	7.46
28'6"	6'4"	Whaleboat replica	Beetle	LOCS	3		Misc. 21
28'11"	6'6"	Whaleboat from the *Charles W. Morgan*	Beetle	LCS	3	68.60	7.48

ROWING WORKBOATS

LOA	Beam	Description	Designer/Builder	Codes	Sheets	Acc.No.	Cat.No.
11'0"	4'1"	Sailing Whitehall-type		LOCS	4	73.22	7.79
11'4"	4'8"	Newport shore boat		LOC	3	54.1482	7.15
13'9"	2'7"	Planked pirogue		LOC	1	59.1426	7.29
14'3"	4'3"	Maine Wherry		LOC	3		Misc. 16
15'7"	5'9"	Connecticut River shad boat		LOCS	3	59.808	7.49
15'9"	5'6"	Rhode Island hook boat	Steve Peckham	LC	1	67.201	7.36
17'10"	6'5"	Connecticut River shad boat *Dorothy D.*		LO	1		Misc. 29
18'6"	4'11"	Hudson River shad boat		LOC	3		Misc. 9
20'4"	6'10"	Seabright skiff		LC	1	63.248	7.43
10'3"	4'7"	Duck boat *Brant*	Charles Ferguson	LOCR	1	57.917	7.25
12'5"	3'5"	Duck boat from the Connecticut River		LC	1	59.208	7.62
14'8"	3'4"	Duck boat from Great Bay, N.H.		LOC	1	61.559	7.34

POWER CRAFT

LOA	Beam	Description	Designer/Builder	Codes	Sheets	Acc.No.	Cat.No.
14'9"	3'1"	Autoboat launch *Papoose*	Clark	LC	1	63.879	7.77
21'3"	5'1"	Naphtha launch *Lillian Russell*	Gas Engine & Power Co.	LOC	2	53.3071	7.73
21'11"	5'6"	Lozier launch *Yankee*	Miller/Lozier Motor Co.	LOC	1	61.1167	7.83
25'7"	7'11"	Yawlboat from the *Mertie B. Crowley*		LC	2	56.1137	7.84
30'10"	5'1"	Steam launch *Nellie*	The Atlantic Works	LOC	3	56.1085	7.74
31'2"	4'7"	Raceboat *Panhard I*	Electric Launch Co.	LOC	2	53.3072	7.76
57'1"	23'0"	Passenger ferry *Sabino*	H. Irving Adams	LCP	3	73.187	7.85

CANOES FOR PADDLING

LOA	Beam	Description	Designer/Builder	Codes	Sheets	Acc.No.	Cat.No.
12'0"	2'4"	Rob Roy-type decked canoe	MacGregor	LOC	1	58.1286	7.104
15'		Canoe	J.R. Robertson	LOC	2		Misc. 39
15'11"	2'6"	Canoe with flush lap planking	J.H. Rushton	LOC	2		Misc. 37
16'0"	2'4"	Arkansas Traveler canoe	J.H. Rushton	LOC	2	AD60.44	Misc. 32
16'10"	2'5"	Decked double-paddle canoe *Chic*		LOC	1	61.262	7.110

CANOES FOR SAILING

LOA	Beam	Description	Designer/Builder	Codes	Sheets	Acc.No.	Cat.No.
11'6"	2'2"	Vaux Junior sailing canoe	J.H. Rushton	LOC	1		Misc. 26
14'6"	2'4"	Sailing canoe	Wisner	LOCS	3		Misc. 20
15'0"	2'8"	Sailing canoe *Kestrel*	W.P. Stephens attr.	S	1	47.1508	7.10
16'0"	2'7"	Vesper sailing canoe *Argonaut*	J.H. Rushton	S	1	69.207	7.3

DUGOUTS AND KAYAKS

LOA	Beam	Description	Codes	Sheets	Acc.No.	Cat.No.
15'1"	2'4"	Eskimo kayak	LC	1	65.903	7.37
27'1"	3'2"	Oyster tonging dugout	LOC	1	46.643	7.27
30'8"	3'7"	Oyster tonging dugout	LC	1	46.644	7.28

CHARLES W. MORGAN, A WHALESHIP OF 1841
113'11" x 27'8"

The venerable *Morgan*, the only surviving wooden whaleship in the world and the symbol of Mystic Seaport, celebrates her 150th year as I write this. Built in New Bedford, Massachusetts, at the Hillman Bros. shipyard to what by then had become pretty much the standard whaleship in terms of size, construction, rig, and layout, the *Charles W. Morgan* served longer (80 years) and earned more money ($1,400,000) than any of her near sisters. Clearly an anachronism when she returned from her last voyage in 1921, she spent the next two decades laid up in the New Bedford area—outfitted briefly for a couple of movies, but hard aground for most of the time as an exhibit ship in a sand berth in nearby South Dartmouth. Only weeks before World War II, the *Morgan* came to Mystic under tow where, once again placed in sand, she became the centerpiece of the Seaport and where, after she was refloated in 1973, she has gradually been restored and outfitted in a most genuine manner. She was built stout and built to last and, in spite of the replacement of rotted timber, still retains almost half of her original wood. Insofar as possible, these drawings were prepared from measurements taken directly from the ship, since the practice of 1841 was generally to build without plans. Where the ship herself didn't contain complete or accurate information, photographs and other records were used to produce a complete set of drawings that are as accurate as this kind of research enabled. Research is ongoing, however, and as more material comes to light, the drawings are revised or, as necessary, new sheets are added.

Catalog No. 7.5

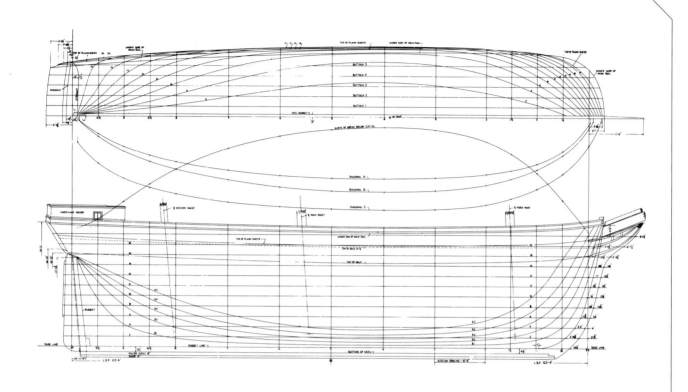

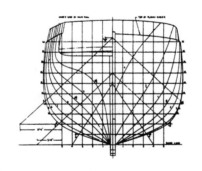

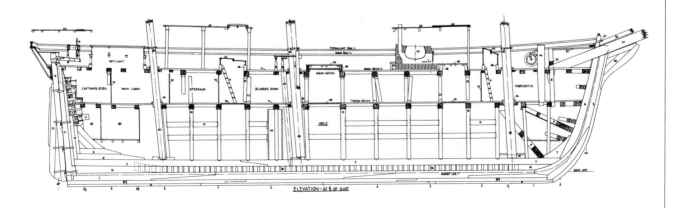

ELEVATION—AT ℄ OF SHIP

L.A. DUNTON, A GLOUCESTER FISHING SCHOONER OF 1921
123'0" x 24'11"

About as different from the *Morgan* as a sailing vessel could be, the *Dunton* is nevertheless just as representative of the great dory-fishing schooners homeported at Gloucester, Massachusetts, as the *Morgan* is of whaleships from New Bedford. The *Dunton* and her sister vessels sailed from Boston or Gloucester to the fishing banks and returned after a few weeks with fish that had been cleaned and salted. Competition, including some racing, was inevitable, and, perhaps mirroring some of yacht racing's quest for speed under sail, these fishing schooners evolved into sleek-lined craft (especially when compared with whaleships) and set great spreads of sail. The *Dunton* was launched from the Essex, Massachusetts, yard of Arthur D. Story in 1921, the same year as the *Morgan*'s last whaling voyage. In her and others of her type, the fish were caught by means of baited hook-and-trawl line set from the ten dories she carried on deck, nested five deep in two stacks. Dory fishing was notoriously dangerous work in foggy weather and rough seas, and the fishing went on in winter as well as summer. Hundreds of men and dozens of vessels were lost—and today, as one of only a handful of survivors, the *Dunton* is a reminder of that kind of risk-taking, hard-working heritage. As with the *Morgan*, plans were drawn from the vessel herself after she was acquired by the museum, and are subject to the same modifications that result from ongoing research.　Catalog No. 7.11

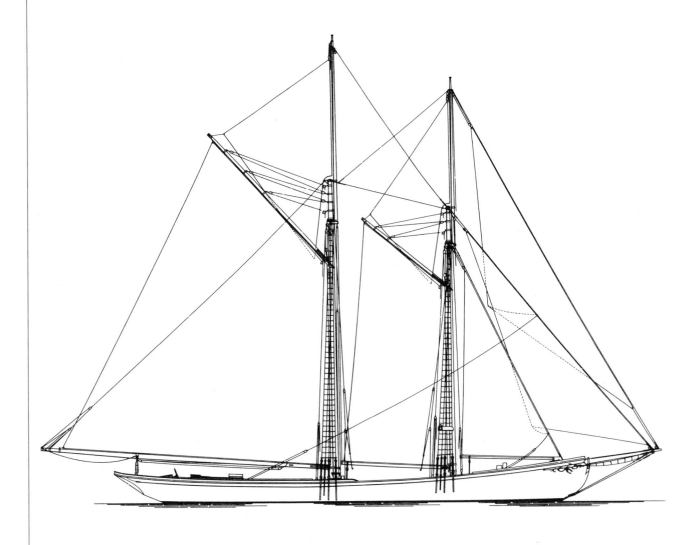

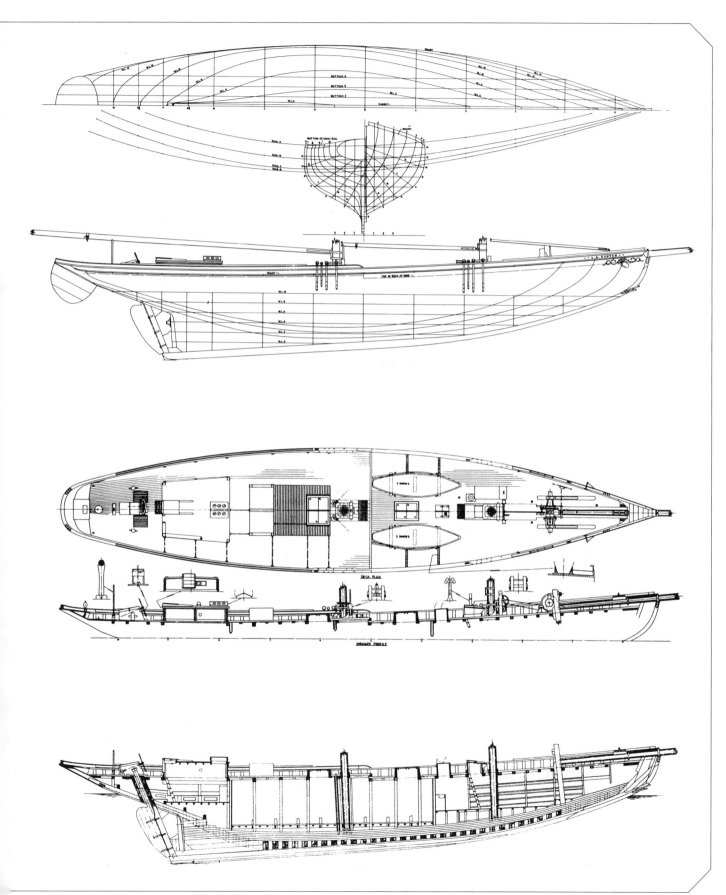

EMMA C. BERRY, A NOANK WELL SMACK OF 1866
45'9" x 14'8"

The *Berry* came to Mystic Seaport in 1969 as a two-masted schooner, the rig she'd carried for much of her life—although she was a sloop when launched, and had been extensively rebuilt as well as re-rigged during her century as a fishing vessel, cargo carrier, and, ultimately, a yacht. While a less-altered Noank sloop would have been preferable, there were none still extant. The *Berry's* model was a fine one, and, because Noank lies only three miles away from the museum at the mouth of the river, research in support of a restoration was convenient. Thus it was that she took on her original appearance as a gaff sloop, was given back her wet well (an open-to-the-sea compartment for fish, built into the hull amidships), and recently had her deck replaced with the deck frame configuration of the period. At least one vessel has been built to the *Berry's* drawings to be used for pleasure. Hopefully, there will be others.   Catalog No. 7.6

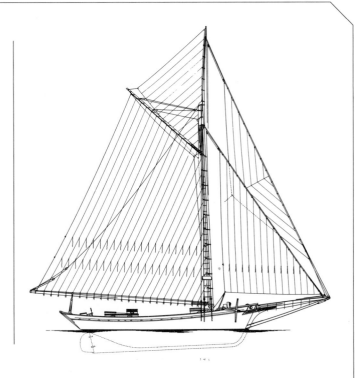

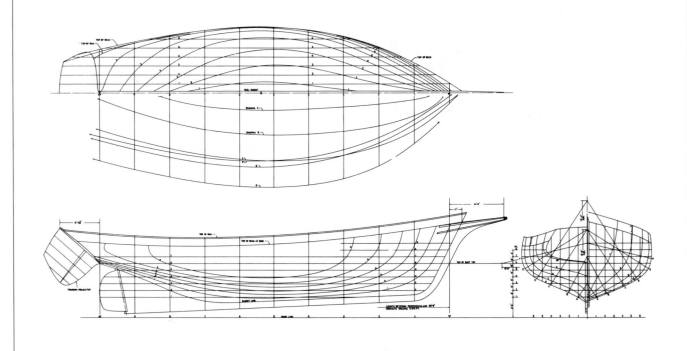

BREEZE, A NOANK SLOOP OF 1898
24'7" x 12'1"

Breeze is a little sister of the *Emma C. Berry*, having some characteristics in common like the hollow
entrance, a deep-bodied hull with noticeable drag
to the keel, and a rabbet line that runs parallel to
the keel until well aft so as to accommodate the
wet well which both boats originally had. And, of
course, she shares the "Noank sloop" name. But to
my eye *Breeze* relates more strongly to the working
catboats of Newport and Cape Cod, in spite of her
mast being farther aft, carrying a sloop rig, and
not having a "barn door" rudder. Compare her
lines with those of *Breck Marshall*, for example.
As of this writing, *Breeze* has not been fully
researched, nor has a decision been made on how,
or even whether, she'll be restored. Thus, the only
drawings that have been prepared are the lines and
sailplan shown here.   Catalog No. 7.89

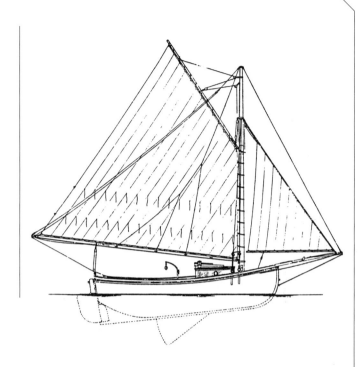

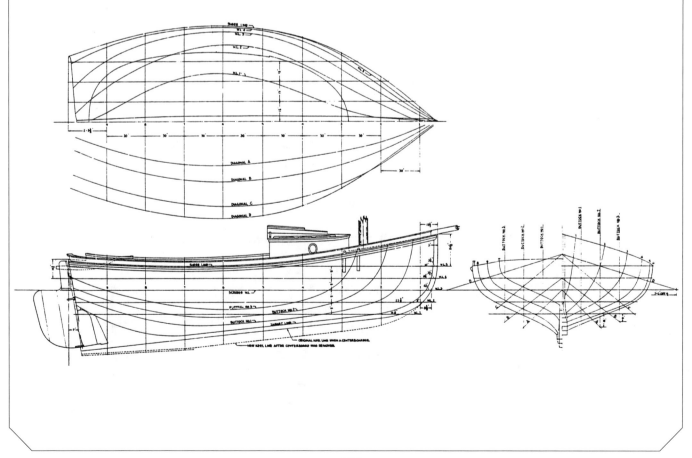

BRECK MARSHALL, A CAPE COD CATBOAT OF 1986
20'0" x 9'8"

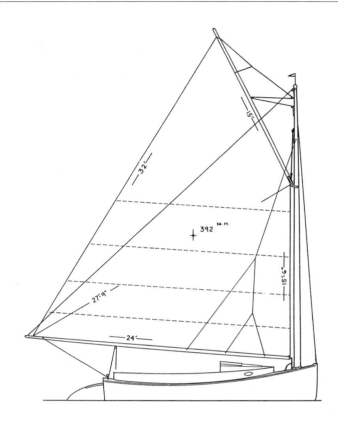

There are complete museum-prepared plans for the boat that spends each summer taking Seaport visitors sailing on the river as one of a fleet of livery boats. She's modeled and constructed to duplicate the catboats produced by the Crosbys of Osterville, Massachusetts, the family most responsible for this popular and variously useful type of craft. The *Marshall* was built from scratch here at the museum—sponsored by the Catboat Association as a memorial to Breck Marshall, the man who made traditional catboating in new fiberglass boats possible for so many of the Association's members. She's handsome, even to the most casual eye, and her cockpit is plenty large enough for the six passengers (the maximum allowed by Coast Guard regulations) to enjoy their sail in comfort. For anyone wanting to follow in the footsteps of Barry Thomas, Clark Poston, and Bret Laurent, the museum staffers who built the *Marshall*, Barry wrote a fine little book (published by the museum) called *Building the Crosby Catboat* that explains the Crosbys' unique construction methods. The book is $9.95, available from Mystic Seaport's Publications Department.   Catalog No. 7.125

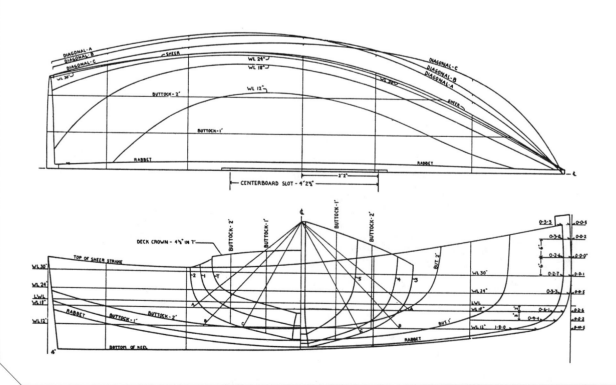

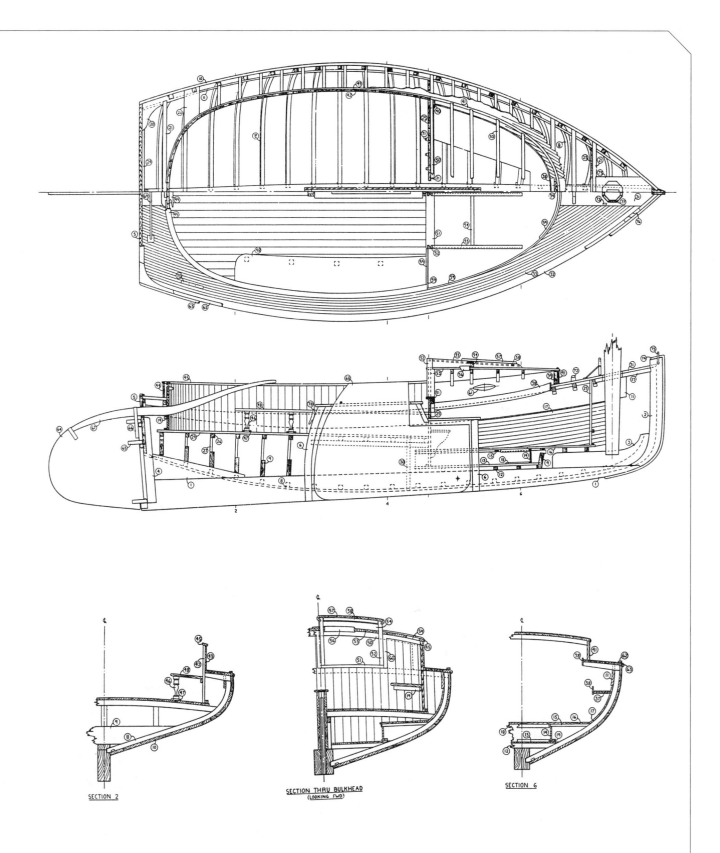

SECTION 2

SECTION THRU BULKHEAD
(LOOKING FWD)

SECTION 6

TRIO, A TURN-OF-THE-CENTURY CAPE COD CATBOAT
14'10" x 6'8"

If the *Breck Marshall* is too big for your needs and a Beetle Cat is too much the other way, you might consider building to this design. For her length, she's really quite a boat, with generous freeboard, especially near the bow, and a reasonably roomy cockpit with seats. And, being familiar with the boat from which these plans were made—a boat that has been in the museum's collection for years—I can assure you that she's lovely to look at.

Catalog No. 7.53

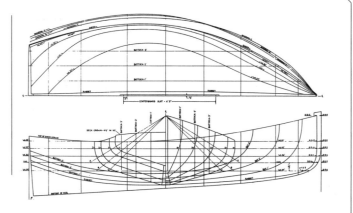

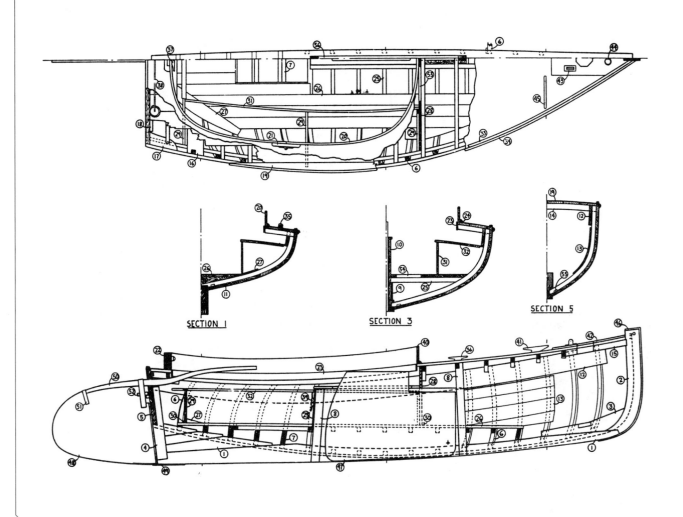

A PAIR OF WOODS HOLE SPRITSAIL BOATS OF ABOUT 1900
13'6" x 6'0"

When E.E. Swift built these beauties, one of which is named *Susie*, spritsail boat racing was at its height, and Swift's craftsmanship was at that level as well. Swift was a cabinetmaker by trade, and took to boatbuilding only occasionally as a change in pace—too bad there were so few Swift-built boats, for this pair are among the very best in terms of form, proportions, and fits. These drawings are of the same high caliber, having been exquisitely drafted by Dave Dillion from his usual precise measurements. They show the few differences between the boats, one of the most obvious being the full-length battens that back up *Susie's* plank seams. In some respects I prefer these spritsail boats to conventional catboats of the Cape Cod model in that they are undecked so can be rowed from either of two thwarts, and their rig is far easier to put up and take down, having only two instead of three spars to deal with.

Catalog Nos. 7.121 and 7.122

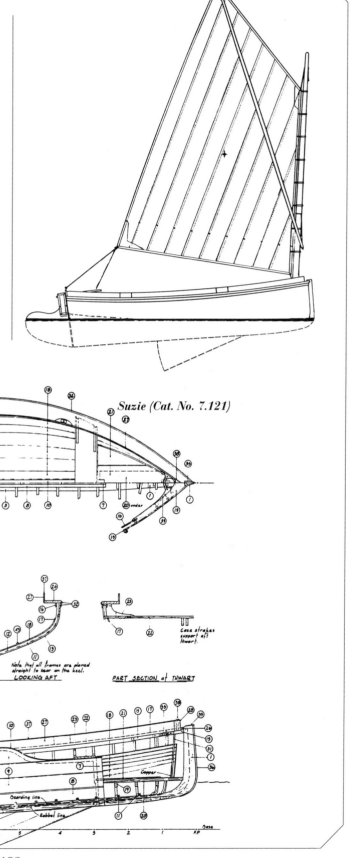

Suzie (Cat. No. 7.121)

JOINT - POST to KEEL

LOOKING AFT

LOOKING AFT

PART SECTION at THWART

193

ESTELLA A, A MAINE SLOOP-BOAT OF 1904
34'5" x 11'9"

Originally built for lobstering from the island of Matinicus at the mouth of Penobscot Bay in Maine, *Estella A*, like many others of her type, was soon made obsolete by rapidly evolving power-driven craft, and was sold "up to the westward" for conversion to a yacht. *Estella* went to Narragansett Bay in Rhode Island, where she was fitted with cruising accommodations, a larger cabin, and a marconi rig. Luckily for those who would later restore her, the original hull and deck structure was pretty much untouched. Rob McLain, her builder, was a fisherman/boatbuilder who would produce one new boat each winter in his Bremen Long Island shop, sometimes fish her, sometimes sell her, and repeat the cycle next season. McLain, partly because of his isolation and partly on account of his relatively low rate of production, never was as well known as nearby Friendship's Wilbur Morse, considered by many to be the father of this type of clipper-bowed, gaff-rigged, inside-ballasted craft popularly called the Friendship Sloop. McLain was a far more careful builder, however, and what was left of *Estella A* before she was restored clearly bore this out. The proportions as well as the fits

were as good as one could ask for, reflecting the passion for perfection that went into all of McLain's work. Although a bit on the large side for ease of handling by one person with the original rig, *Estella*'s model is a fine one, with balanced ends and a handsome appearance from any vantage point.   Catalog No. 7.22

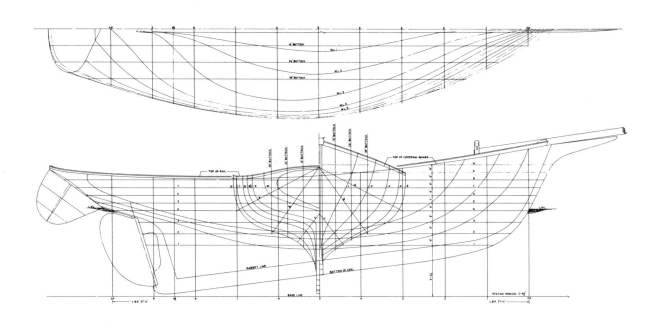

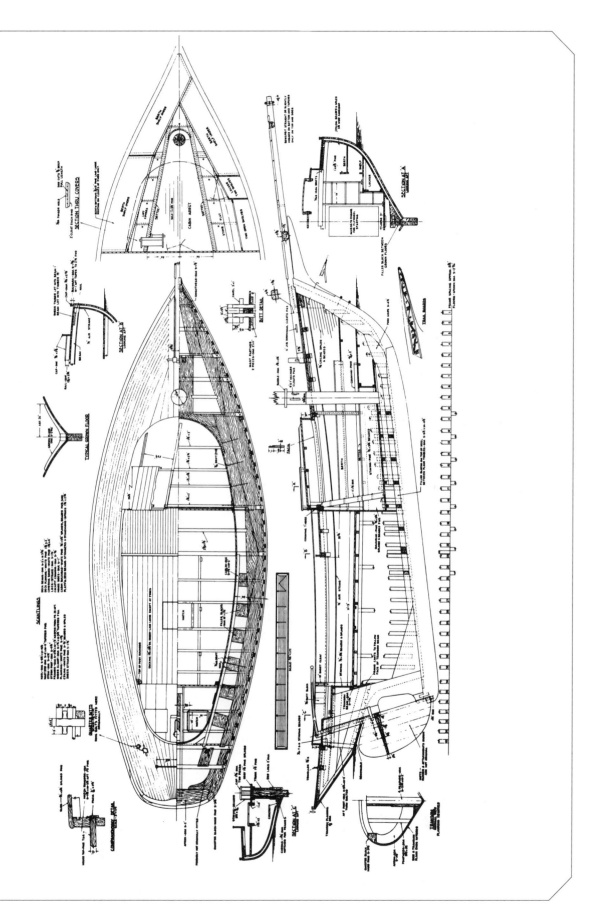

A LIGHTWEIGHT GUNNING DORY
18'0" x 4'6"

Because of their narrow waterplane, dories have proven tippy, and the smaller they are, the more this is evident. Here is a dory that is large enough to overcome this disadvantage and make a very useful boat for taking large loads of people, gear, or whatever else needs to be transported and still row easily. The seats all are removable, as they are in most dories, so the boats could be stacked one inside the other—one of the dory's great advantages. And by taking out some of the seats, there are more options for what can be carried. While this dory was obviously built for rowing, there is a mast step enabling a small spritsail to be set when the wind favors. For ease of construction and overall utility, this design merits some consideration.

Catalog No. Misc. 3.

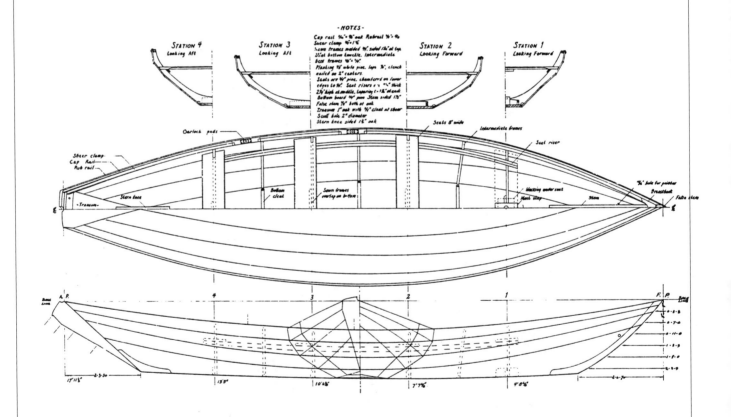

A SKIFF BY ASA THOMSON OF ABOUT 1927
11'2" x 4'3"

Skiffs like these were products of Asa Thomson's New Bedford, Massachusetts, shop. Thomson, a consummate craftsman, built them as yacht tenders as well as for independent use, and his work was so good that many of his boats were varnished all over rather than painted. Mistakes or shoddy workmanship cannot easily be hidden in a boat with a transparent finish. Generous freeboard gives this little boat good carrying capacity. She'll not dry out, open her seams, and leak the way many skiffs do when left out of the water for long periods of time, because Thomson, perhaps realizing that some of his skiffs would be left out in the drying sunshine, gave her a double-planked bottom with a layer of light sheeting between the inner and outer layer as a water barrier. Another feature unique to this skiff is the storage compartment located under the middle seat—used as a water-filled fish well in this particular boat. In effect, this forms a box and serves to stiffen the hull to such an extent that the usual seat knees can be dispensed with. In all, a neat little boat.

Catalog No. 7.95

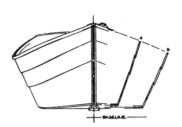

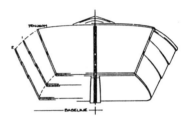

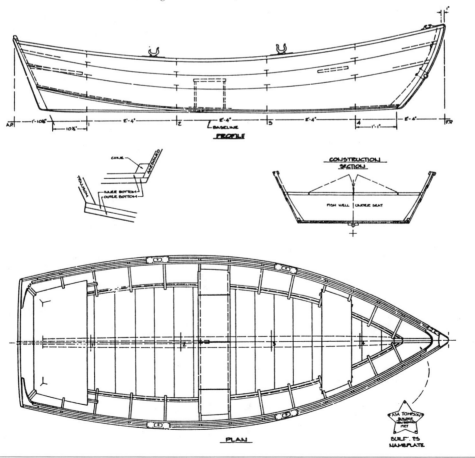

A PLANKED PIROGUE FROM THE SOUTH
13'9" x 2'7"

For simplicity, it would be hard to find a better example than the Louisiana planked pirogue. Only three boards, one of them extra wide to form the bottom, are needed for the planking. And the frames are simple three-piece affairs that can be set up as the first step in the building process or fitted later after the planking is completed. Planked pirogues like this came into being as replacements for earlier pirogues that were hollowed out of single logs, both craft conceived as paddle-propelled boats for use in the narrow, twisting bayous where the water is calm. Pirogues are special-purpose craft with distinct limitations—kind of like a Native American single-paddle canoe. Planked pirogues are infinitely easier to build, however, and might make a lot of sense for rough service and short runs where ease of paddling is not a major concern.

Catalog No. 7.29

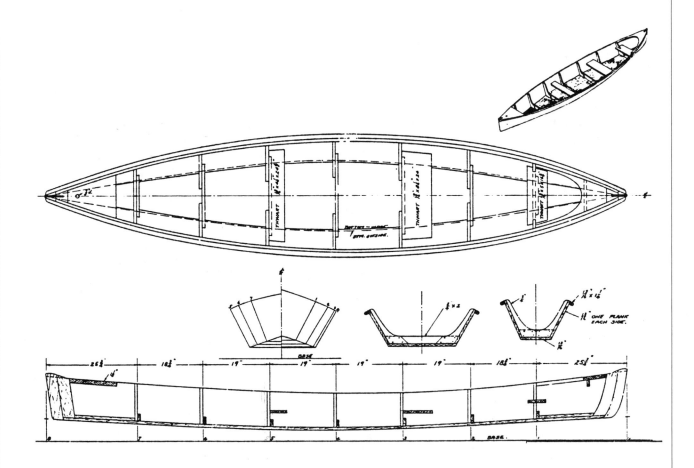

A.L. ROTCH, A DOUBLE-ENDED PULLING BOAT OF ABOUT 1888
14'1" x 3'3"

J. Henry Rushton's Canton, New York boatshop, where this boat was built, mass-produced small boats in a factory environment, offering a wide variety of standard models (this one is simply "model 109"). From a production shop one might expect less than top quality, but quite the reverse is true: Rushton's boats were widely known for their impeccable workmanship and fine materials as well as for their proliferation. A close study of any one of Rushton's boats reveals how a truly elegant creation can incorporate features that promote rapid assembly. Much was learned in the museum's boatshop when several of these Rushton model 109s were built here a few years ago. The steam-bent elm frames, for example, are simply dowels slit lengthwise on the diameter, and the stem is in two pieces—both steam-bent to shape—so the hull could be easily planked over the inner stem, then the planking trimmed back and the outer stem attached afterwards. The fastenings were mostly brass and copper nails whose heads were simply left flush with the surface. In all, an easy-to-build boat if you take the time to understand Rushton's production methods.　　Catalog No. 7.115

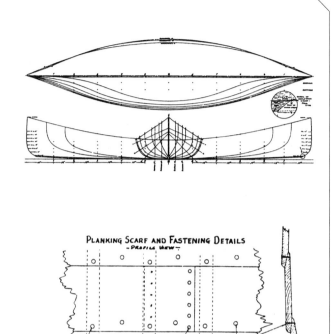

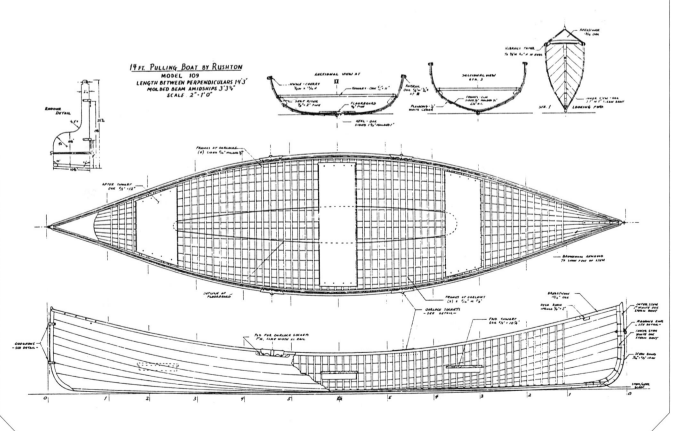

A DELAWARE DUCKER OF ABOUT 1900
15'0" x 4'0"

In 1969, Mystic Seaport was fortunate in receiving this fully equipped Delaware ducker for its small-craft collection. Its equipment even included an awning and a boom tent for lounging and sleeping. The ducker, as its name implies, was basically used for shooting waterfowl. Railbirds, which inhabited the tall marsh grass bordering the Delaware River south of Philadelphia, were a favorite quarry. The boats were many, and racing them became as much of a sport as waterfowling. Cruising in duckers was not as common, but it was obviously possible to go off by oneself in perfect comfort for one or several nights in a ducker fitted for camp-cruising, as this one was. Duckers are fine-lined, making them slippery under either oars or sail, and a deck eliminates having to worry about survival in rough water, compensating as it does for the unusually low freeboard. There can be little argument that a Delaware ducker makes one of the finest all-around small craft going. If you're interested in building one, however, do as these drawings suggest and order the *Greenbrier* drawings from Philadelphia's Independence Seaport Museum in addition to these. And for background, read the article about this boat in *WoodenBoat* No. 48.   Catalog No. 7.123

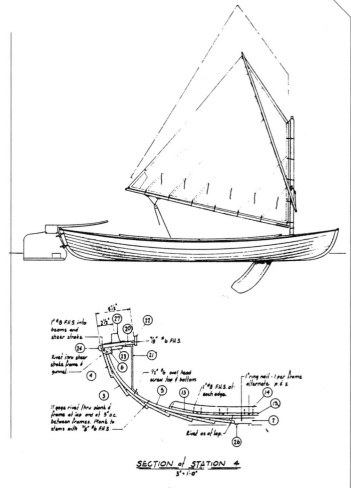

SECTION of STATION 4

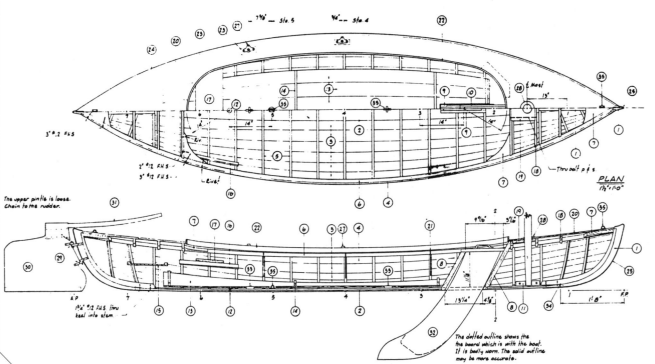

PLAN

WB, A SAILING PLEASURE SHARPIE OF 1888
15'9"x 5'1"

WB is a kind of toy, modeled after the working sharpies of nearly twice her length that were once used for oyster tonging in and around New Haven on the Connecticut coast. She was built strictly for pleasure using the style and construction of her big sisters. A replica of the original, built at the Seaport some years ago, has proven to be a wonderful little boat for sailing in sheltered water—easy to handle and well behaved under sail as well as having room in her cockpit for several passengers. People sit on the floorboards in this boat (cushions are optional), and the advantage of this down-low position is that one's view is then unencumbered by the sails. You can see all around—to leeward as well as to windward. Sprit-booms, besides being the authentic working-sharpie rig, keep the clews of both mainsail and mizzen high for good visibility as well as being high enough themselves to not be head-knockers. Construction is simple—just like a basic flat-bottomed skiff. The centerboard trunk is the only complication, and building it is really quite straightforward. I suppose this boat's hang-down rudder could be a disadvantage (although the one shown is deeper than necessary), and for her size she's fairly heavy. But all boats are a compromise.   Catalog No. 7.65

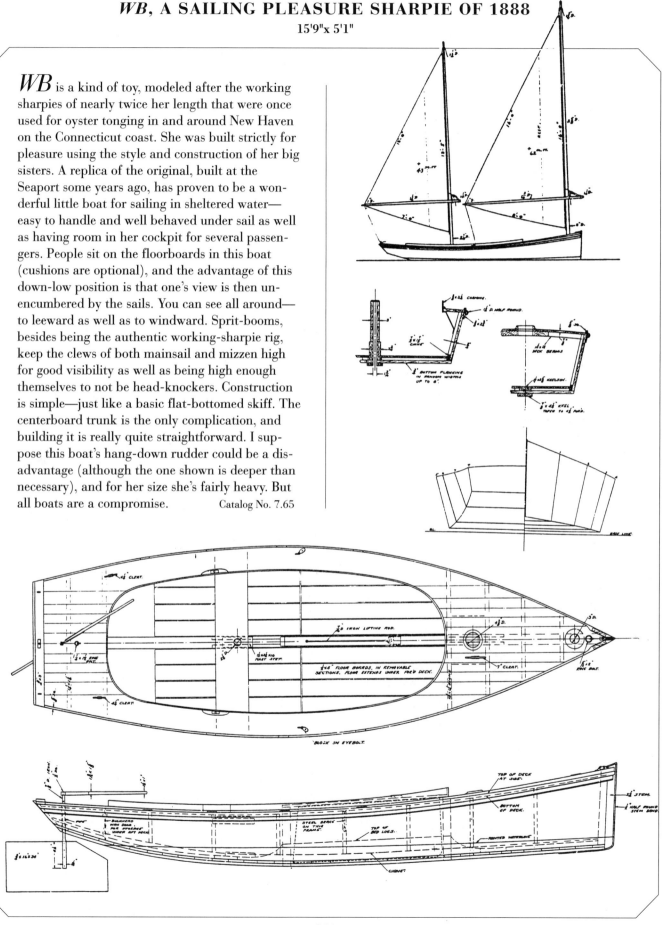

CAPT. HOOK, A WHITEHALL-TYPE TENDER OF ABOUT 1920
11'11" x 3'10"

Capt. Hook was the name this boat somehow ended up with after being donated for waterfront use some years ago. Painted black with a green bottom, a deep red sheerstrake, varnished rails and seats, and a cream interior with tan floorboards, *Capt. Hook* has been much admired and frequently used, in recent years being available for public use as one of the Seaport's livery boat offerings.

Catalog No. 7.102

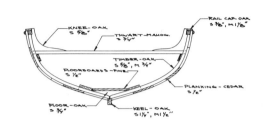

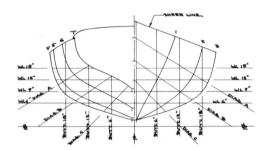

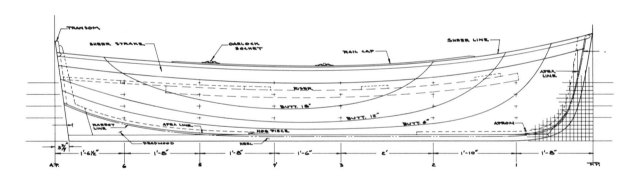

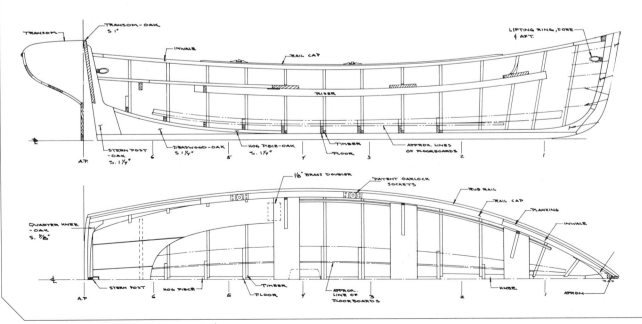

A WHITEHALL PULLING BOAT OF 1870
16'9" x 3'3"

Larger and more sophisticated than *Capt. Hook* is this Whitehall with sliding seat and a daggerboard trunk. She's set up to row with 8' spoon-blade oars and rail-mounted oarlocks, but I'd be inclined to use short folding outriggers for the oarlocks, and oars that were a foot or two longer. The rudder and yoke that came with the boat and which show on the drawings are for use in rowing. At one time, before the Seaport acquired the boat, there must have been a sailing rudder—perhaps tiller-steered—and a rig. If you're partial to the Whitehall shape, this may be what you're looking for, as she is a very handsome model.

Catalog No. 7.21

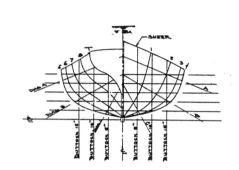

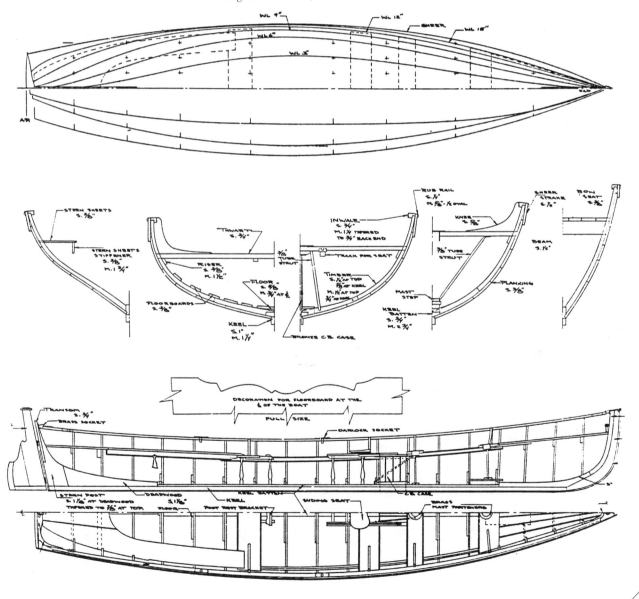

ROWING GIG FROM THE STEAM YACHT *NOMA* OF 1890
24'10" x 5'1"

Steam yachts and the gigs that went with them are long gone, and the waterfronts are poorer for their absence. The choreographed precision with which owners and their guests were rowed to and from their big yachts by a practiced crew in uniform has no contemporary equivalent. I imagine there would have been at least four and maybe five sailors in this boat, four at each of the four oars (she is set up one man to an oar like a whaleboat) and maybe a coxswain to steer and give orders. The dockline aft was kept in a coil on the grating to be picked up by boathook since the stern sheets were exclusively for owners and guests. Landing at the yacht would always be at the starboard-side boarding platform, and once the gig had served (and before the yacht got underway) it would be hoisted well clear of the water on davits, for which purpose the gig has ringbolts forward and aft.

Catalog No. 7.40

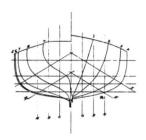

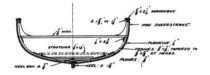

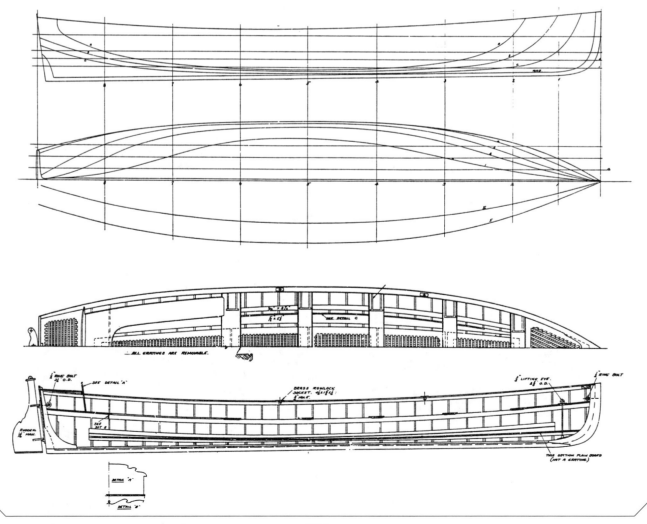

LIFEBOAT OF 1980 FROM THE SHIP *JOSEPH CONRAD*

21'4" x 6'6"

When serving as a training ship for Danish cadets, the *Joseph Conrad*, then named *Georg Stage*, had lifeboats of this design hanging from davits ready for use. Mostly they saw use as shore boats, however. Two were built by the museum for outfitting the *Conrad*. They are of lapstrake construction—the best type of planking for boats that are stored out of the water for long periods. (Lapped planking doesn't open its seams when it dries out, and leak when first launched the way carvel planking does.) Lifeboats are burdensome and heavily built, as they're expected to carry a crowd when necessary and, if there's a sea running, to withstand repeated impacts against the side of the mother vessel during the process of launching and getting clear.   Catalog No. 7.101

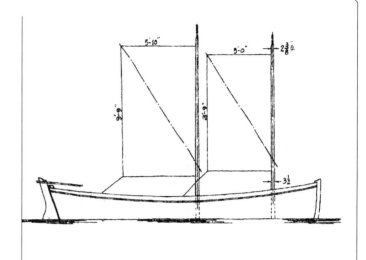

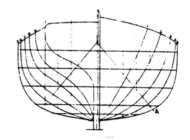

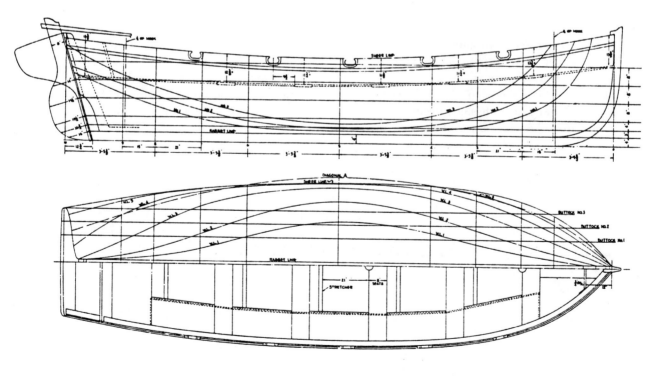

SABINO, A PASSENGER STEAMER OF 1908
57'1" x 23'0"

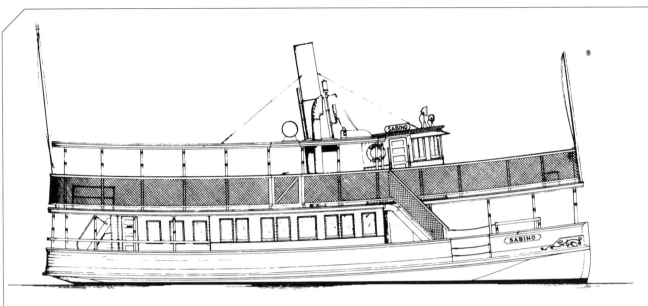

Nowadays, as the only coal-fired steam-driven wooden vessel still in operation in the country, *Sabino* plays host to several thousand Seaport visitors each year, steaming on an hourly schedule along the museum's waterfront and demonstrating her almost silent power plant. Her Paine compound steam engine is the one she was launched with and its operation, as well as everything the licensed engineer does to make it run, can be observed directly, since the machinery space is completely exposed and surrounded by an open rail. The engineer answers to signal bells (One bell for forward when *Sabino* is stopped. If she's underway one bell signals stop. Two bells means reverse.) since the skipper has no direct control of the engine from the pilothouse. *Sabino* is certified by the Coast Guard to carry 100 passengers, and in high season she's usually sold out. But if you miss the boat, you haven't lost out, because viewed from shore as she ghosts noiselessly past, *Sabino* is a sight to be remembered. When W. Irving Adams of East Boothbay, Maine, launched this vessel, then named *Tourist*, she was so much narrower and lower as to be unrecognizable as the *Sabino* of today. After service on the Damariscotta River, she was sold to the Popham Beach Steamboat Company and her name became *Sabino*. She was rebuilt several times as both *Tourist* and *Sabino*. One of her most significant modifications was the addition of sponsons to increase her beam and her stability for service on Casco Bay in the late 1920s.

Catalog No. 7.85

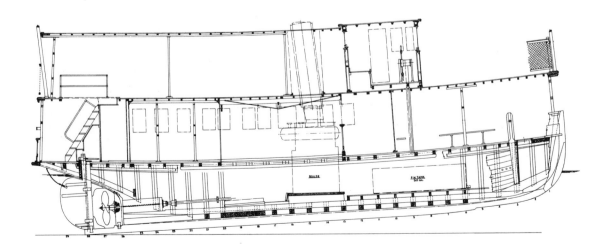

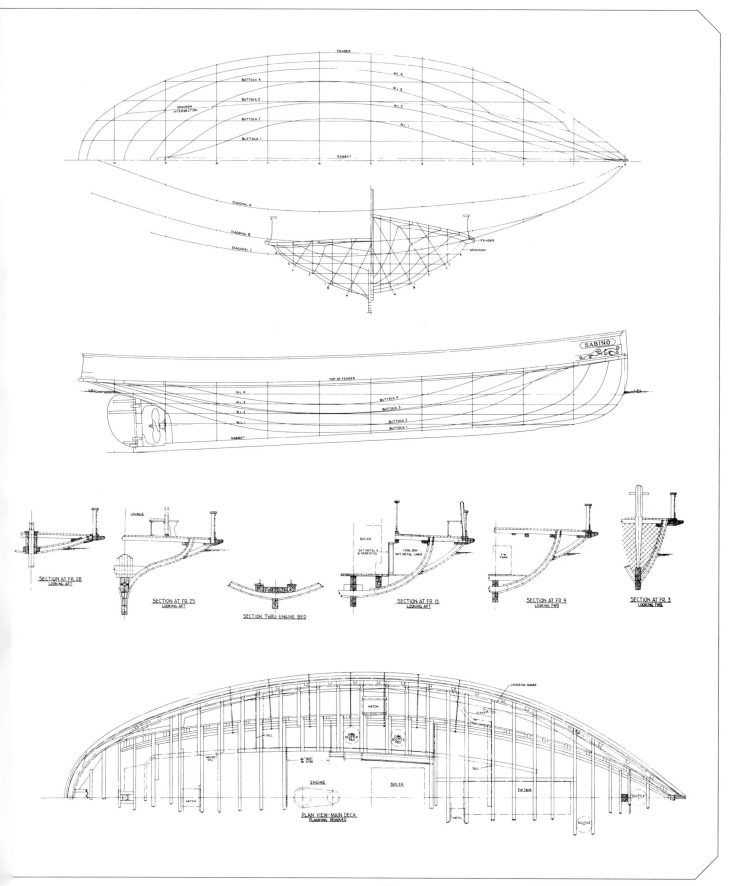

SECTION AT FR. 28
LOOKING AFT

SECTION AT FR. 25
LOOKING AFT

SECTION THRU ENGINE BED

SECTION AT FR. 15
LOOKING AFT

SECTION AT FR. 9
LOOKING FWD

SECTION AT FR. 3
LOOKING FWD

PLAN VIEW-MAIN DECK
PLANKING REMOVED